KU-524-834

WITHDRAWN
FROM
MIC-S

St Patrick's College
Thurles
11946

21, 6

WITHDRAWN
FROM
MIC-SPCT

Ernst Bäumler

A Century of Chemistry

with two contributions by
Prof. Dr. Gustav Ehrhart
and Dr. Volkmar Muthesius

ECON VERLAG · DÜSSELDORF

Coláiste Mhuire Gan Smál Luimneach	
Class	5 L D
Suff	BAu
MI	

Copyright © 1968: Econ Verlag GmbH, Düsseldorf
Cover and outlay: Wolf D. Zimmermann
Colour photos: Rudi Angenendt, Dortmund
English version by David Goodman
  (with exception of the two contributions
  by Prof. Dr. Ehrhart and Dr. Muthesius)
Printed by Brönners Druckerei, Frankfurt/Main

Printed in Germany

Winnacker

Chairman of the board of management of Farbwerke Hoechst AG.

This is the first foreign-language edition of the history of Farbwerke Hoechst AG. Originally, this cross-section of one hundred years of German chemistry was intended for our employees and business friends. But it was soon found that the book also attracted the interest of a much wider circle of people. Indeed, the number of requests received from universities, schools and individuals from all walks of life was so great that a second and finally even a third edition, this time as a pocketbook, had to be published making a total of more than 250 000 copies.

There was also an increasing number of requests from abroad for foreign-language editions. This is the reason why we are now presenting — as a first step — an English version of this book to be followed in due time by editions in other languages.

This has not been done only for the many business friends who for many years have maintained close contacts with Hoechst all over the world. The book will doubtlessly also be of value to many other readers interested in technical and economic problems.

As a result of technological progress economic selfsufficiency is definitely a thing of the past. Especially in the chemical industry, international cooperation has always been of supreme importance. Nowadays, production of many chemical products is economic only in quantities that simply surpass the needs of some of the national markets. Equally important is the exchange of licences and know-how making the fruits of technological and scientific progress available to the people of all nations and continents. All this leads to growing international cooperation within the chemical industry, manifesting itself in the increasing number of joint projects.

The industrialization of the developing countries can also be solved only by joint efforts and close cooperation of the industrialised nations. Government aid will not be enough. It will be up to private business initiative to supply the economies of the young nations with the impulses necessary to secure growing wealth and to level out existing discrepancies in the standard of living.

This will require an ever closer partnership not only between nations and economic communities, but also between private companies and, finally, people themselves. To make cooperation successful, the partners must get to know each other. That is the purpose of this book, and I hope that it can make a modest contribution to the understanding of economic factors and problems which have become so extremely important to all of us.

Frankfurt (M)-Höchst
January 1968

Winnacker

Chairman of the board of management of Farbwerke Hoechst AG.

Hoechst's century of chemistry is closely linked to the general scientific and technical advances during this period.

Throughout its history, the company has always been in touch with the intellectual, economic and political events of these 100 years. It has used the discoveries and advances of this era in order to accelerate its own progress. Conversely, the company's achievements have not been without impact upon the world around it. From small beginnings therefore, an important chapter of chemical and economic history has been written in the last 100 years by all the people that devoted their working life to Hoechst. In laboratory, factory and workshop and in administration and sales the joint effort of many thousands of people helped to forge a single community. Its history mirrors the grave events of that time. In the first 50 years it prospered with the rise of the German Reich. Its second 50 years were overshadowed by the consequences of two catastrophic wars. History has left its traces in the chronicles of Farbwerke Hoechst.

This book «A century of chemistry» is intended to give our staff and our friends an insight into this history.

We wish to thank all those who have made this book possible, particularly the authors. Special thanks are due to Dr. Otto Hirschel, Dr. Ernst Fischer and the many people in our company who contributed through numerous documents and personal recollection to this retelling of Hoechst's history. We are also indebted to the publishers for their excellent production.

The book does not pretend to be complete or to follow any systematic concept. Rather, it is intended as a kaleidoscope of the major events and their consequences. Somewhere in this book everyone of our people will come across his job, its origins and its significance within the intricate Hoechst organism. Our friends will be able to glean from these pages an understanding of the ramifications within the company and the principles that govern its development.

A spirit of discovery and enterprise partnered by unswerving loyalty have moulded the company. Its people have been rewarded by economic security and a humanitarian climate. Love for the job and the satisfaction of working towards an important goal have more than made up for many — albeit unavoidable — disappointments.

Hoechst's history will not stand still on its centenary. The requirements of mankind and the scientific and industrial needs of satisfying them will continue to grow, extending to ever larger areas of our earth.

With these developements, we must keep step — taking care to maintain a balance between man's needs and his capacity to meet them. In this way, Hoechst is playing its part in solving the problems of our age. Not as a state within a state but as an element of the national community.

Jaehne †

Chairman of the supervisory board of Farbwerke Hoechst AG.

The 100 years since the foundation of our company have been marked by almost impetuous scientific progress and the translation of new scientific knowledge into terms of large-scale production. A company that not only survived but in fact continuously expanded during this period, punctuated as it was by political upheavals, must be based on sound foundations indeed.

«It is the spirit that moulds the substance». This is very true of the spirit that has shaped the character and the work of our company, the spirit in which it was born, in which it grew, in which it continues to act today. This realisation of scientific spirit contained the force that drew within its orbit a community of people whose number has grown tremendously from decade to decade. Here lie the roots of our company. So long as the spirit that dominated the past century of Hoechst's history remains alive, so long as the company's management and its people continue to be imbued with it, we need not fear for our future.

Ernst Bäumler

A CENTURY OF CHEMISTRY

mycin Hoechst — *Modern prospectors* — *The golden actinomyces* — *Tetracyclin in capsules* — *A new problem for the Hoechst chemists* — *Reverin* — *the universal broad-spectrum antibiotic* — *As sterile as an operating theatre* — *Antidiabetics* — *How does Rastinon act?* — *Microorganisms as steroid architects* — *Hormones* — *still a large field for research* — *Radiochemists* — *important aides to research* — *A laboratory with special protective devices* — *Life: thousands of years* — *The mysterious realm of the viruses* — *Blood diagnostics and substitutes* — *An agent against thrombosis* — *Blood substitute from Marburg* — *The genesis of a new medicament* — *A new range of test preparations* — *Experiments in Hoechst* — *No. 12512* — *ten years of research* — *The final word* — *the pharmaceutical commission*

A start with investment certificates — *Share law amendment as starting signal* — *Voting rights for employee shareholders* — *Annual bonus and profit sharing* — *Success and risk* — *From the barracks to the owner-occupied home* — *Shortage of houses during the early period* — *Reminiscences from the good old days* — *Co-partnership in the canteen* — *Wages* — *Aid for the aged and the sick* — *Frankfurt physician as works doctor* — *Sickness was the exception* — *Profit-sharing a la 1871* — *The state and its social conscience* — *The Republic and its unhappy debut* — *They get their cards* — *The first social director in Hoechst* — *Social policy in the I.G. era* — *No more appointments in the I.G.* — *Strength through joy* — *a short-lived dream* — *The big attraction: baked potatoes in the canteen* — *The social background of the group* — *Old age pensions* — *Excursion into social statistics* — *«New blood is vital»* — *Remuneration and working hours* — *The Hoechst cultural programme* — *Quo vadis?*

REGISTER

Ernst Bäumler

A Century of Chemistry

One company — two birthdays

Let us turn back to the Germany of 1945; a country without government, with destroyed cities, bombed factories, empty shop windows; camps for prisoners of war, for refugees, for displaced persons, for political prisoners. Germany 1945 — a country of hunger, chaos and desperation.

The hour of settlement for the Allies had come. It affected both guilty and innocent alike, it affected both large and small, it affected individuals and whole organisations. In the economy it hit the smallest undertaking as much as the management of world-wide companies which, only a few weeks previously, had employed tens of thousands of workers.

It was particularly the companies of this size against which the measures of the Allies were directed. These measures were implemented in accordance with a well-defined conception. At the top of the Allied requisitioning lists were the large works of the German chemical industry. They were to be destroyed, dismantled or at any rate dismembered into numerous small groups.

Even history will have a job to elucidate what motivated the Allies in this policy. There can be little doubt that a genuine fear of allegedly omnipotent economic con-stellations played a large part in their attitude. The victors asked themselves whether without these great economic complexes the war machine of the Third Reich could have continued to run at full speed for almost six years. But in a dictatorship, economic power is not always equivalent to political power. This is one of the lessons we have learned since 1945.

When the front line reached the area of Mannheim and the first American tanks broke through to the North, the management, on Friday, 23rd March 1945, ordered the closing down of all the plants. This could, of course, not be achieved by simply pushing a button. Each one of the 200 plants required a special, and frequently complicated system. While the shut-down of workshops, filling and packaging plants was relatively simple, the continuous plant which used toxic, inflammable or explosive materials needed to be carefully handled. Two factors were all-important. The safety of the people in the plant had to be safeguarded and steps had to be taken to make sure that the plant remained operational in the future. It was a depressing moment as though a giant had suddenly ceased to breathe. After a waiting period full of anxiety and uncertainty, Hoechst was occupied a few days later. Many experienced these moments without fully realising what was going on. Everyone was concerned with his own problems. The merciless machinery of the war was still proceeding on its inexorable course. Flats were requisitioned. And although the plant and the town of Hoechst had remained almost untouched by bombs or other acts of war, both now learned what it meant to be in occupied territory. Numerous American special units and interrogation officers poured into the works.

The formal requisition was put into effect only three months later. It was only a formal procedure which took place at Hoechst on the afternoon of 5th July 1945. It took no longer than 20 minutes. The works management was ordered into a conference room at whose entrance army sentries were stationed. In the centre of the room, which was decorated with the American flag, there was a colonel. When the works management had assembled, the officer rose and read a document. This was, in fact, the law for the requisitioning of the I.G. Farbenindustrie. The management was relieved of its post and the works confiscated. Confiscated on the basis of the general regulation No. 2 for the execution of law no. 52 of the American military government. This regulation decreed amongst other things that the entire management of the I.G. Farbenindustrie A.G. was subject to the control of the military government.

Subsequently, the surrender of the works was enacted with all due pomp and circumstance. American troops marched once more into the factory. It was like a movie, but with the background of the war and the unconditional surrender. A few months afterwards, on 30th November 1945, law no. 9 of the Four-Power Control Council was published. Its preamble indicated what the victor powers were after. "In order to render impossible any future threat to Germany's neighbours or to world peace", the Allies decreed the dismemberment of the I.G. Farbenindustrie into dozens of small units and also the dispossession, without compensation, of the I.G. shareholders. At the same time, this law provided the basis for the correlation of all the measures against the I.G. Farbenindustrie in the four zones. Specifically it called for:

1. Providing industrial plants and property for reparations.
2. Destruction of those industrial plants which were used exclusively for war purposes.
3. Splitting up of the property rights in the remaining industrial plants and possessions.
4. Liquidation of all cartel relationships.
5. Control of all research work.
6. Control of production activities

In practice, however, each of the occupying powers followed a different policy in the works which they had taken over. As usual, the USSR cared little about the agreement to which it had been a signatory. It operated the large I.G. works at Leuna, Schkopau, Bitterfeld and Wolfen initially as Russian corporations. Later, the Russians handed over these works, which had been dismantled to a large extent, to the government of the Soviet Zone. In the French Zone, the Ludwigshafen works were placed under French management. Two further works, Rheinfelden and Rottweil, were leased to companies that were controlled by French shareholding majorities. In the British Zone, the competent control officer for the works of the I.G. and of the subsidiary companies appointed trustees. He did, however, permit uniform management for Leverkusen and its adjacent works, Dormagen, Uerdingen and Elberfeld because of their economic interdependence. As a result, the close co-operation of these works remained unaffected. The American occupation forces, on the other hand, rapidly proceeded with dismemberment in their zone. For this purpose, the Americans created in Frankfurt an authority under the name I.G. Farben Control Office. This Control Office immediately proclaimed all works belonging to the I.G. in the US Zone to be independent undertakings.

At the head of these independent units was a trustee appointed by the military government. Later the German Länder governments had a say in the appointment of these trustees. For the Hoechst works, which seemed too large to the US authorities, the American dismemberment policy had planned a special treatment. For the time being, the plan was to split up the works into four or five independent companies. Each one of these was to have economic independence. Fortunately, these plans were destined to a briefer existence than their authors had imagined. The American surgeons in the Control

Office were extremely thorough in their dismemberment of the I.G. body. The works in the US Zone were not only cut off from their traditional links with adjoining works in the other zones but every one of the new economic units had to create its own administrative organisation almost out of nothing. Above all, each plant had to build up an independent finance, purchasing and sales department. Naturally, there was also no longer a joint foreign department. This latter aspect was of no immediate consequence since the Allied decrees prohibited all business correspondence with foreign countries for the time being. All exports and imports were transacted through the occupation authorities.

Only a few believed that these artificially created I.G. derivatives would remain viable. Any hope of arriving at a reasonable solution seemed remote. Prejudice and understandable anger following this bitter war were too intense for rational thinking. But one thing was certain: the era of the I.G. Farbenindustrie had come to an end. This huge undertaking had existed for approximately twenty years, since the day when, under the economic pressure after the first world war, the large old dyestuffs companies joined forces. Each one of them looked back on a history of more than eighty years and each one had assumed a special character which appeared to have been buried and forgotten in the I.G. fusion but which now, at the moment of enforced separation, again came to the surface.

In the I.G. building in Frankfurt am Main, the nerve centre of the company, care had always been taken to avoid smothering the initiative of the individual works. The various works therefore had managed to retain their characteristic nature during the twenty years that they belonged to the I.G. The outsider would not normally have noticed how much these differences had been accentuated and how well they had been preserved. But now, at the moment of dismemberment, this proved to be a welcome advantage which greatly facilitated the new start.

The new masters in the I.G. building

In 1945, the American flag flew over the I.G. building in Frankfurt am Main. It had become the headquarters of General Eisenhower. German visitors were not very welcome in these days of non-fraternisation. But even so, a modest German/American co-operation could not be entirely avoided. The people of the country, hungry and lacking most hygienic facilities, were exposed to epidemics. Accordingly, they also presented a danger to the occupation forces. Chlorine was needed urgently for disinfection. This meant that the electrolysis plant in Hoechst had to be started up again. A modest chlorine

production was permitted in Gersthofen for the supply of the South German water-works. In Griesheim, originally scheduled for complete dismantling, benzidine manufacture was taken up again on the instructions of the Allies. This product was urgently required at the time for the manufacture of a black dyestuff needed for redyeing the former German uniforms. German field grey was no longer in fashion. Yet, even this insignificant manufacture faced almost insuperable obstacles. Everything was in short supply.

Nevertheless, in the villages around the works, there were enough volunteers prepared to work even for a valueless Reichsmark. For many of them, the factory was a haven of refuge after the extinction of all civil order. But there were no raw materials and no sources of power. There was also no kind of organisation to aid in the distribution of the finished products.

Thaw and freeze

Although there were still many barriers between the occupying forces and the Germans, several examples, albeit unintended, of German-American collaboration soon became apparent. To be sure, these thaws in the relationship between the occupying forces and the Germans were frequently interrupted by renewed freeze-ups. Reparation measures that had apparently been cancelled were suddenly resumed. At the same time, however unnoticeable at first, the notions that had formed part of the ideological equipment of the Americans during their 'crusade in Europe' began to crumble away. The progressive break-up of the 'Grand Alliance,' the Soviet-instigated inactivation of four-power control and the forced incorporation of East and South-East Europe into the Soviet satellite zone played their part in forcing this development. After the 'bizone' had been created, the Americans and British, on 3rd August 1948, jointly ordered the final dismemberment of the I.G. But for the first time, the Control Office decided to listen to German opinion on this matter and possibly to take it into account. In November 1948 a German committee was set up to deal with this question. This five-member group began its activities during the last weeks of 1948. Its name was FARDIP, derived from I.G. Farben Dispersal Panel, which soon enjoyed an excellent reputation under its chairman Hermann Bücher.

The work of FARDIP

FARDIP called upon chemists and engineers to work out technical and economical assessments of the I.G. works situated in the British and American zones. In addition, independent private auditing firms were asked to work out detailed reports. This work, of course, took time. And this was precisely the intention of FARDIP. They realised that any delay in the dismemberment of the I.G. was in the German interest for there was bound to come about a better climate, particularly since the Allies for many years had no precise idea at all about how to effect dismemberment.

This was FARDIP's big chance. Many valuable ideas were submitted to the Americans by FARDIP and even the most fanatical supporters of decartelisation could not ignore them in the long run.

Hoechst and the Main group

FARDIP had to submit its proposals to the appropriate Allied control authority BIFCO (bipartite I.G. Farben Control Office). Later, BIFCO, through the addition of a French representative, was expanded into TRIFCO (tripartite I.G. Farben Control Office). This Allied control office used an American-British-French committee (Tripartite Investigation Team) to check recommendations of FARDIP. Mainly on the basis of a recommendation by FARDIP in June 1950, this committee arrived at the conclusion that three large units should be formed, the so-called Main group, Bayer and BASF. This called for long and complicated negotiations.

At the conference table were the Allies, the members of the I.G. Liquidation Committee (which had meanwhile been set up), representatives of the Federal Ministry of Economics and German experts. One of the most difficult problems was to find a solution for the American zone of occupation. Finally, the proposal of the tripartite committee was adopted. It was expected that the three large companies in Leverkusen, Ludwigshafen and Hoechst would soon be able to regain international standards in research, production and sales. For Hoechst, which thanks to generous help under the Marshall Plan and as a result of an agreement with Merck had meanwhile taken up penicillin manufacture, a kind of federation was envisaged. After many fights, this mainly comprised the original Hoechst companies including the Knapsack works in the British Zone.

The only important exception was the former Mainkur works of the I.G. In spite of the intervention of the Federal Republic and of the government of Hesse, Cassella became an independent limited company. However, at a later date, many of the Cassella shareholders sold their shares to one of the three large I.G. successor companies. Today, Hoechst, Bayer and BASF hold some 25.1 per cent each of the share capital of Cassella Farbwerke Mainkur AG.

A cold shower

The decision to create three economically viable successor companies presented considerable progress in the protracted tug of war between Germany and America over the
fate of the I.G. inheritance. But in another sphere, practically no progress at all had been
made. Five years after the end of the war and the subsequent requisition, the entire
share rights of the new I.G. units were still in the hands of Allied control officers. In
August 1950, law no. 35 of the Allied High Commission even seemed to perpetuate this
state of affairs. Article 2 of this law stated expressly: "until the Council of the Allied
High Commission decrees otherwise, the British, French and American Control Officers
appointed for I.G. Farbenindustrie AG affairs will continue to exercise their rights,
derived from the law of occupation, with respect to the property forming the subject
of this law. The rights and powers of the board of management, the directors,
the supervisory board and the annual general meeting of the I.G. Farbenindustrie AG
and its subsidiaries as well as all the powers of attorney conferred by them, are cancelled herewith."
Nevertheless, at the time of publication of this law, which was regarded as a cold
shower in Germany, the Allies began to draw up board of management lists for the
new companies.

The leaders of Hoechst AG.

While at Bayer-Leverkusen and at BASF the members of the board of management
appointed during the I.G. period were simply confirmed in their posts by the British
and French forces of occupation, matters at Hoechst were rather more complicated. The
works that now formed part of the Hoechst complex had become very much accustomed
to their role of independent units. This made it more difficult to constitute a unified
management for the entire group, even by taking the trustees and experts from the
control office.
The absence of an effective board of management for a long time retarded the constitution of the Maingau works as a unified entity. Two factors had to play their parts
before this finally happened, namely the weight of German public opinion and the
increasing reasonableness on the part of the Americans and their realisation that
the future management of Hoechst could not function properly without the appointment of a number of former Hoechst managers. Shortly prior to the final formation

FARBWERKE HOECHST AG
including associated companies

	1966
Total turnover	5,830 million DM
Balance sheet total	5,210 million DM
Number of employees approx.	67,000
Expenditure on personnel	1,109 million DM
Share capital	1,054 million DM
Capital resources	2,280 million DM
Number of shareholders	260,000
Dividend declared for 1966	20 %
Dividend paid out	211 million DM
Investments	946 million DM
Expenditure on research	248 million DM

The Hoechst site
extends over an area of four square kilometres
along both sides of the Main

Works
and important associated companies
of the Farbwerke Hoechst AG
group in Germany

	Location	Share capital in DM	Participation in per cent
Werk Hoechst			
Werk Griesheim			
Werk Offenbach			
Werk Gersthofen			
Werk Bobingen			
Werk Gendorf			
Werk Hersfeld			
Knapsack AG	Knapsack near Cologne	20,000,000	100
Kalle AG	Wiesbaden-Biebrich	20,000,000	100
Behringwerke AG	Marburg (Lahn)	15,000,000	100
Chemische Werke Albert	Wiesbaden-Biebrich	28,840,000	100
Friedrich Uhde GmbH	Dortmund	20,000,000	77.5
Spinnstofffabrik Zehlendorf AG	Berlin-Zehlendorf	14,500,000	72.5
Messer Griesheim GmbH	Frankfurt (M)	30,000,000	66.6
Ticona Polymerwerke GmbH	Kelsterbach near Frankfurt	20,000,000	59
Wacker-Chemie GmbH	Munich	80,000,000	50
Sigri Elektrographit GmbH	Meitingen near Augsburg	24,000,000	50
Ruhrchemie AG	Oberhausen-Holten	60,000,000	33.3
Synthesekautschuk-Beteiligungsges. mbH	Frankfurt (M)	21,000,000	33.3
Duisburger Kupferhütte	Duisburg	42,000,000	30
Cassella Farbwerke Mainkur AG	Frankfurt (M)	34,100,000	25
Chemie-Verwaltungs-AG	Frankfurt (M)	159,120,000	25

of Hoechst, a board of management was nominated that adequately reflected the special conditions at Hoechst.

The list included people who had proved that they had the necessary qualifications either during recent activities or in the I.G. The board of management was not a homogeneous body. Most of its members did not know each other. None of them knew the capabilities and limitations of the others. Such an unusual approach was of course born of unusual times. It required a great deal of determination and objectivity to ensure that the work of the management would not be lost in trivialities and misunderstandings.

The men who had to face this task saw the danger clearly. In any case, the public again and again drew their attention to it. And in spite of all the difficulties that loomed on the horizon, none of the people appointed to the board refused to serve. They knew the job that had to be done and they had the courage to overlook small differences and to subordinate individual ideas.

In confidential meetings, frequently permeated by an aura of conspiracy, — after all, they took place without the express agreement of the Allies, — the future members of the board got together. They discussed distribution of functions, they conceived standing orders for the new management, they discussed company policy — in short they began to work. Energetically they turned towards the day-to-day problems which urgently called for solutions.

The "One hundred thousand mark Company"

The new Farbwerke Hoechst was born at the end of 1951. Strictly in accordance with the ceremony agreed upon with the Allies, five gentlemen appeared on 7th December 1951 before a Frankfurt notary public in order to register the founding of Farbwerke Hoechst AG, official seat Frankfurt am Main.

On 19th December 1951, the same procedure was enacted by Farbenfabriken Bayer AG and on 30th January 1952 by Badische Anilin- & Soda-Fabrik AG. The number of founders was the same in all three cases, as was the starting capital, namely 100,000 Deutsche Mark, an incredibly small sum, particularly when compared to the capital of the I.G. Farbenindustrie.

But in any case the formation of the one hundred thousand mark company was only regarded as a first step. It enabled Hoechst to become once more an independent company in the eyes of the law. Hoechst ceased to be a ward of the court.

The new arrangement meant that companies had been formed which would be able one day to take over the former work from the I.G. complex. And although at this particular time, the shareholders of the one hundred thousand mark company were identical with the founders who appeared before the Frankfurt notary public, there was every hope that after a clarification of the share position, long overdue, and a final release from occupation power control, the former shareholders would regain their old rights.

On the day that Farbwerke Hoechst was reborn, the five founders, each of whom had provided 20,000 marks to form the share capital, appointed the supervisory board of the new company. Two of them, the Frankfurt bank director Dr. Hugo Zinsser and the Berlin company director Carl Mueller, by agreement with the Allies, simply shifted from the circle of founders onto the supervisory board.

As in the case of the board of management, the Allies had also provided a long list of desirable names for the supervisory board. Here, too, a compromise was reached after protracted discussions. After the supervisory board had been constituted and Dr. Zinsser had been elected chairman, the first board of management of the newly founded company was appointed. But the Allies did not let go of the reins entirely. The new articles of association and the distribution of functions within the board of management had to be thoroughly agreed upon with the American control office. The Americans did not agree at all to the appointment of a chairman of the board of management, indeed, there was a proviso in the articles of association that no such chairman was to be appointed for nine months.

Rebirth of Farbwerke Hoechst AG

The American control office desired a board of management whose chairman would be appointed successively in alphabetical order. Both the board of management and the supervisory board solved this problem after a few months without any objection from the US Chief Controller.

In view of these continuing restrictions, the supervisory board raised the question whether the new board of management carried any responsibility at all, because under the prevailing company law it was not properly in charge of the business. For the trustees, although they were members of the board of management, retained the functions that had been imposed upon them by the occupation forces.

The "as though" management

The minutes of the first meeting clearly indicate the decision that was taken in this respect: "After a short address by Dr. Zinsser concerning the uniqueness of the case

Re-constitution of Farbwerke Hoechst AG. —
Extract from historical document of
7. December 1951 —

Die Erschienenen erklärten alsdann:

Wir errichten hiermit eine Aktiengesellschaft unter der Firma

Farbwerke Hoechst Aktiengesellschaft
vormals Meister Lucius & Brüning
----

mit dem Sitz in Frankfurt am Main, der wir die dem No-
tar überreichte und dieser Niederschrift in der A n -
l a g e 2 beigefügte Satzung zugrunde legen.

Auf das Grundkapital von DM. 100.000.- (ein-
hunderttausend Deutsche Mark) übernimmt jeder der Gruen-
der, also jeder der Herren:

1. Dr. Ernst BOESEBECK,
2. Dr. Werner KOETTGEN,
3. Dr. Albert MEIER,
4. Direktor Carl MUELLER,
5. Dr. rer. pol. h.c. Hugo ZINSSER,

20 (zwanzig) Aktien im Nennbetrage von DM. 1.000.-
(eintausend Deutsche Mark). Die Aktien werden zum Nenn-
betrag ausgegeben und sind in bar einzuzahlen.

*Supervisory Board
and Board of Management in joint session
after the lifting of allied control*

and the resulting necessities, the supervisory board and the board of management agree that although the trustees had to retain their function for a certain transition period, the board of management would behave as though it were already formally responsible for the company". It was indeed a unique situation, one that the creators of the German company law had hardly foreseen.

The rights of the 150,000 shareholders of the I.G. had also been suspended following the end of the war. Similarly, any dealings in I.G. shares had been prohibited under penalty. Anyone who wished nevertheless to sell shares could do so only by way of risky transactions and even then could hope to gain no more than a fraction of the former nominal value.

Happy ending

The question marks that were placed behind the rebirth of Hoechst were not so unjustified as they appear today. That the sceptics were wrong, that the thing 'came off' and even better than any of the board of management who entered their new offices on 7th January 1952 would ever have dared to hope, is perhaps no less remarkable a story than the rise of the small company with a few kettles to a concern of world renown.

Farbwerke Hoechst therefore can actually celebrate two birthdays. The first one in 1863 was celebrated for the hundredth time in 1963. The second was in 1951 — the rebirth following total collapse. It was a happy ending, too, for the former occupation officers who started their work as busy decartelisation agents and finished it as understanding godparents to the large, new companies.

It started with tar

The demolition gangs stand ready with their pneumatic hammers and pick-axes: a part of the original Hoechst site is to be demolished — a grey workshop with antiquated dye vats, narrow windows and the figures 1880 above the low entrance. Soon, only the company's archives will preserve what reminder there is of the days when bearded men in blue shirts and heavy leather aprons produced fuchsine, aldehyde green or even brilliant blue indigo which, for centuries, enjoyed the title «king of the dyestuffs». These dyestuffs were no longer obtained from plants, valuable woods or animal products. They owed their existence to chemical syntheses — permutations of the elements of nature which yielded up dyestuffs that were faster than the natural products and that were available in almost unlimited amounts to satisfy the enormous demand of the textile industry. The invention of the steam engine had brought a tremendous upsurge to this industry which, in turn, greatly accelerated the stormy development of the chemical industry which, for its part, had concentrated from its early begin-

The Hoechst site in 1865

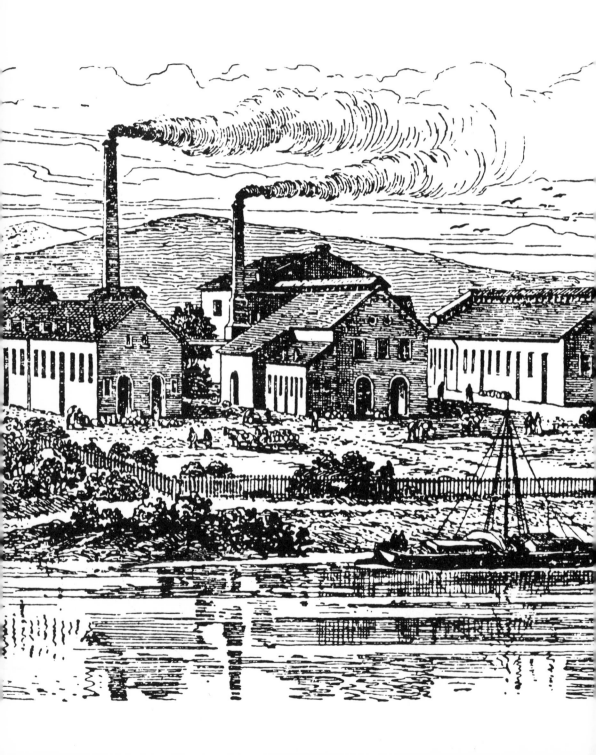

Lake dyestuffs are prepared for drying

nings, on research into dyes and their production. Initially, dyestuffs manufacture was essentially an English domain and it was not surprising that the London World Fair in 1862 became something of a victory parade for the English dyestuffs industry.

Seven Pioneers

It is 1880—almost seventeen long years after the four founders had erected their first "etablissement" on the banks of the Main at Hoechst, "using a small boiler and a three horse-power steam engine," as the first company chronicle faithfully records. Five workmen, an accountant and a chemist formed the first Hoechst crew. What this avant-garde of the present army of more than 50,000 people produced was soon apparent to the world outside: their shoes and their overalls were covered with tell-tale traces of red from Hoechst's first dyestuff production. It was perhaps not surprising, though politically insignificant, that they soon acquired the nickname of the «reds from Hoechst». In the first few years, the daily production of fuchsine was ten to fourteen pounds. The dyestuff was made according to a very simple formula: 25 pounds aniline oil and approximately 50 pounds arsenic acid were heated to 200 °C. From the melt formed in this way, fuchsine was obtained by boiling. At a later date, the toxic arsenic acid was replaced by nitrobenzene.

The quartet of the company founders was well balanced; there were two chemists — Dr. *Eugen Lucius* and Dr. *Adolf Brüning* — and two salesmen — *Wilhelm Meister* and *August Müller*. It was Lucius who had drummed together this band of enterprising men: Brüning was an old student friend of his, Meister was his cousin and Müller his wife's uncle. He, however, left the business in 1864 when the first sanguine hopes of inventions and easy profits were not realized. His role, as a historian once remarked, was that of a catalyst during the formation of a compound.

The company chronicle complains that in the early days fortune did not exactly smile on the firm's affairs. But this did not dim either the enthusiasm or the enterprise of the three remaining founders of the company.

Only a few years after the erection of the first factory, the builders were called in again. Less than a mile downstream, an aniline factory was constructed, — quite a size-able plant for dyestuffs production. This was followed by an acid factory in order to save purchasing and transport costs and to establish an independent raw material base. At that period, people had even less time than today for sentimental atavism or other forms of misguided veneration. By 1874, the original plant, the very first beginnings of the present company, had been demolished down to the very last brick.

More room for technical progress — this impatient motto of the times was not encumbered by the civilized scruples that sometimes seem to overawe the present day heirs to a century that really believed in science. At that time, the discoveries and inventions of research fairly gushed forth in a cascade of sparkling ingenuity. Ever since *William Henry Perkin*, pupil of *August Wilhelm Hofmann*, had conjured up a brilliant dyestuff from black, unpromising coal tar, the growth of dyestuffs chemistry had proceeded with dramatic speed. *Heinrich Caro, Carl Graebe* and *Carl Liebermann*, famous chemists all, played a decisive part in this mercurial development. Graebe, who joined Hoechst in 1864, was the second chemist to join the young company. His intention was to collect practical experience but unfortunately, Graebe did not stay for long because he could not stand the aniline and iodine vapours. He therefore went to Heidelberg as a scientific assistant and later to Berlin. During his work there he succeeded in determining the exact chemical composition of natural madder. This dyestuff was at that time primarily being produced in French fields and had a wide market because of its radiant red colour. In 1868 alone, turnover was 60 million marks.

Analysis was followed by hard-won synthesis. And not as the result of a lucky chance but as the reward for painstaking, sustained research. It was not long from the day when Graebe and Liebermann marvelled at the first few grams of alizarin in the test tube until the day when the French peasantry was obliged to turn its madder plantations into mundane potato fields. Madder growing had become unprofitable, for chemistry was able to supply this dyestuff at a fraction of its former price. While, for example, in 1870 a kilogram of natural madder still cost 90 German marks, in 1888 a kilogram of 20 pc alizarin, the synthetic product, could be bought for less than two marks. In terms of the 100 pc product, this was the equivalent of eight marks. And, of course, to the dyers in the Orient, the main madder users, it was quite immaterial where the colour came from that rendered their garments and fezzes in such pure brilliant red. In 1869, ALIZARIN manufacture using greatly improved processes was taken up simultaneously by BASF and Hoechst. The preparatory work at Hoechst had been done by *Ferdinand Riese.*

Following Perkin's mauvein and Graebe's alizarin, literally hundreds and hundreds of brilliant colours were synthesized in the retorts of the world's chemical laboratories. But even in the cases where their industrial production was an economic proposition — and not all those test tube babies were viable — they remained the domain of their discoverer or producer for only a short time. For in those days, there was no uniform patent law but instead only ruthless, bitter competition between the various chemical complexes that were then shooting up. There was total price war and as soon as large scale production of these dyes was taken up by a number of companies their price fell to intolerable levels. For example, the chronicles of Farbwerke Hoechst record that at the time when the first factory was founded, one pound of fuchsine cost twenty Thalers. Only a few months later, when Hoechst made out the first invoice for a pound of this dyestuff, the price had already dropped to eight Thalers. At the same time, the raw materials became more and more expensive. Anthracene, in particular, was at that time available in adequate amounts only in England. There it had not yet been realized that what was regarded as a useless waste product from the tar factories was an indispensable raw material for the dyestuffs industry. And before it was realized, *August de Ridder*, the commercial chief at Hoechst at the time, inveigled an English company into selling him its entire annual anthracene production. But this outstanding piece of salesmanship could not be repeated. The bewildering amount of interest shown by other buyers soon opened the eyes of English manufacturers to the profitable business that was theirs for the asking.

At that time, the panacea to prevent prices from collapsing and to avoid bankruptcy was the formation of conventions. They controlled, on behalf of their members, buying and selling prices and frequently also the production quotes. The hangover that followed a period of entirely unrestrained industrialization, gave rise to innumerable conventions. There were conventions of the steel industry and of the ball-bearing industry, of the bicycle industry and of innumerable other industrial branches. Not surprisingly, there was also an alizarin convention which Hoechst joined.

Although this fairly rigid cartel calmed the market and resulted in remarkable price stability, it had to suffer the fate of all the other conventions. The strongest members of the convention soon found the chains too much of a drag and as soon as they left the convention, the whole edifice collapsed.

Whenever there was talk at Hoechst about prices and competition, or of great chemical achievements, the names of *Friedrich Bayer* and *Heinrich Caro* could always be heard. Bayer had founded Bayerwerke in Elberfeld and Caro was scientific director of BASF in Ludwigshafen. Both companies had developed from the same small beginnings and at the same breathtaking speed as Hoechst. Both had taken up dyestuffs production and both had approximately the same number of qualified chemists who had learned all they knew from *A. W. Hofmann*, the pioneer of the aniline dyes, and from *August Kékulé*, both of them pupils of the great *Justus Liebig*. Even as a 29-year old, Kékulé had made sure of his place in the history of chemistry. His formulae were

*Representation of the benzene ring
in the reports of the
« thirsty chemical society » in 1886*

fascinating symbolic representations of the smallest parts of benzene and other hydro-carbons, and of their reactions with other chemical compounds. Kékulé's work had made it possible to identify the building bricks of dyestuffs, to take them apart and to reassemble them into new structures with different properties.

Chemists, too, need luck

As yet, it was individual workers rather than research teams directed by scientific high commands that were penetrating the secrets of the atomic and molecular realm. And often enough, it was pure coincidence and the accidental detail rather than precise scientific planning that caused them to stumble on the truth. For not only generals, but chemists, too, need a little bit of luck. Perkins, for example, was not even thinking of dyestuffs when he was concocting his potions in the laboratory. He was trying to synthesize quinine — to discover the first coal-tar dyestuff.

Fortune also smiled on Lucius in the form of a leather merchant who visited him a few years after the foundation of Hoechst. This go-ahead trader was looking for a simpler dyeing method for a green aniline dyestuff. Lucius innocently asked him for a piece of tanned hide and placed it into the dyeing solution. Lucius thought he was seeing things: instead of dyeing the leather, the dyestuff was precipitated and settled out as a paste.

Brüning was sent for immediately. Soon the two chemists realized what had happened. The tannin in the leather had precipitated the dye. Lucius and Brüning were not men to miss the implication of such a discovery. Lucius worked out a new manufacturing method by which the very popular green, which up till then had had to be despatched as a solution, could be processed into a ready-for-use paste whose transport was far simpler and cheaper.

Opening up a new market was an equally original and dramatic business in those days. Sales chief de Ridder got on a train to Lyon, the town of the French silk-dyers. In his luggage were ten pounds of ALDEHYDE GREEN. As soon as he set foot in Lyons, de Ridder immediately made tracks for Renard & Villet, the largest and best known silk-dyers in Lyons. *Renard* found the green from Germany superb. With the half kilo of paste de Ridder had given him, he carried out an experiment that very evening. The result must have been outstanding. De Ridder recounted the story many years later. "Next morning, Renard was very very early in my hotel and asked to have the remaining cans of green as well. I refused and explained to him that it was my intention to offer the material also to other dyers in Lyon. This upset the man visibly. He became

tremendously excited. After a short discussion with his partner, he made a firm proposal to buy from Hoechst over the period of the next twelve months all the aldehyde
green that we could supply. The price was to be our price of the day. We for our part
were to undertake to supply this green only to him in France." After a certain amount
of argument, de Ridder concluded the agreement. Renard made one other condition —
de Ridder had to leave Lyons at once without visiting the other companies. In order
to make absolutely certain of this, Renard came to the platform to supervise de Ridder's
prompt departure personally.

The green dress of the Empress

After de Ridder had gone, Renard immediately dyed a batch of silk with the new green
from Hoechst, had it woven and took it to the tailoress of the Empress Eugenie who was
engaged in creating a new evening dress for Her Majesty. A few days later, the empress
appeared at the Opera wearing a stunning robe. The men and women in the audience
craned their necks. Hitherto, the light of the gas lamp had mercilessly changed any
green into a blue. But the green dress of the empress stayed green. The reverberations
of this opera visit by the French empress were considerable. Soon fashionable ladies
everywhere clamoured for the empress' green. De Ridder was able to close his report
with the somewhat laconic, but apt sentence «Renard did good business and so did we».

Unfortunately, not every new dyestuff from Hoechst had the good fortune of imperial
sales promotion.
However inventive chemical research may have been in those years, the enthusiasm
of the scientists was not in every case matched by that of the salesmen. The long road
from laboratory invention to large-scale industrial production involved a considerable
amount of expenditure even at that time. And yet, any day, a new formula could render
useless the investment of many thousands of pounds if it resulted in a better, cheaper
and faster dye. Costing and pre-planning had always to be carried out against the
background of this incalculable risk.
Aldehyde green, too, did not remain a selling favourite for very long. IODINE GREEN
appeared on the horizon only to give way a few years later to METHYL GREEN which,
in turn, was displaced by MALACHITE GREEN, although this too survived for only a little
time. As a result of all this, the dyestuffs range of the company increased by leaps
and bounds and at the Paris World Exhibition of 1867, Messrs. Meister Lucius and
Brüning were able to present thirty different dyestuffs.

The temptation of indigo

Such a production volume and the continuous need for new developments and modifications meant that new manufacturing plants had to be continually erected in Hoechst. The number of employees increased to 1660 workers, 40 supervisors, 25 chemists, 10 technicians and 45 salesmen. Not surprisingly, the structure of the company proved inadequate for such a vigorous undertaking. In 1880, seventeen years after its foundation, the company was therefore converted into a joint stock company. The capital was 8.5 million marks. Quite a lump of money for a company devoted to normal dyestuffs production, but not nearly enough for a company whose declared aim was the dethronement of the king of dyestuffs — indigo. For many centuries, this greatly desired dyestuff had been produced mainly from Indian plants with the help of cheap Hindu labour. The value of the annual output of indigo at the end of the nineteenth century was roughly 100 million marks. If indigo had not been superseded by better synthetic dyestuffs, and if it were still produced by the original methods, half of India would have to consist of indigo plantations to meet the present vast demand.

The first laboratory syntheses

Indigo could not for long keep secret its chemical building bricks. Plants contain indigo in the form of a glucoside. Under certain conditions, this glucoside decomposes during hydrolysis as a result of the absorption of water, indoxyl being formed. Two molecules of this immediately combine, under the influence of atmospheric oxygen, to form the dyestuff indigotin — indigo.

Intensive research soon yielded up even more striking results. This time the scene of the success was Munich. Professor *Adolf Baeyer*, Liebig's successor to the chemical chair of Munich university, succeeded in the first laboratory synthesis of indigo.

Baeyer and his pupils then developed a whole bunch of different indigo syntheses. The press justly hailed his work as a great triumph of science. A few years later Baeyer was awarded the Nobel prize.

For many people, this was the end of the indigo saga. Science had had the last word. All that remained to do was for the chemical engineers to translate the test-tube synthesis into terms of industrial production. The result would be, so they thought, tons and tons of synthetic indigo. This popular view was shared by many salesmen and speculators and the price for natural indigo rapidly fell on the world's stock exchanges. Naturally, industry quickly secured Baeyer's patents which were taken over jointly

Berlin. 14/4. 81.

Lieber Doctor Greiff!

Mit ziemlicher Sicherheit habe
ich erfahren dass das von
B. hier angemeldete Patent
die künstliche Darstellung
des Indigo zum Gegenstand
hat. Die Ausführung sei
einfach und schön nur
der Preis des Ausgangs
Materials vor der Hand
zu hoch. Unter diesen
Umständen müssen wir
Alles aufbieten mit dabei
zu sein. Zu dem Zweck
werde ich wahrscheinlich
Montag oder Dienstag nach
München kommen auf
die Gefahr hin das B

nicht sehr von meinem
Besuche entzückt sein wird. Theil
en Sie mir Ihr Ansicht da-
rüber mit. Im Übrigen
behandeln Sie die ganze
Sache sehr diskret und
engagiren Sie sich nur
und nicht mehr mir
nöthig. Briefe und Tele-
gramme richten Sie ge-
fälligst nach Frankfurt th
wo ich Samstag oder Sonntag
eintreffen werde. Mit
freundschaftlichem Gruß Ihr

L. Brüning

Coláiste Mhuire Gan Smál
Luimneach

11946

by BASF and Hoechst. But these two were soon to find that natural indigo had by no means been conquered. While it was quite true that the Baeyer formula yielded perfect indigo both in Hoechst and Ludwigshafen, the starting material proved so expensive that the price of any dyestuffs produced from it were astronomical.

Nonetheless, BASF tried to market its synthetic indigo. It was an abysmal failure. Ludwigshafen and Hoechst were not slow to draw the consequences. The two companies concluded an agreement for a joint assault on the problem of indigo. For this, they were well equipped. Together, they disposed over something like 4000 employees and several hundred trained chemists and highly qualified technicians. Their laboratories were amongst the most modern in the world. Millions of marks were made available for relentless trials and experiments. But whenever chemists and engineers came up with a new process, the salesmen threw it out. Their pencils offered no hope. 'Uneconomic became a fatal word in Hoechst and Ludwigshafen.

The difficult way to large-scale production

In 1882, the indefatigable Adolf Baeyer developed yet another indigo synthesis. Once again the anxious question was "can it be carried out an industrial scale?" For eight years experiment followed experiment. All in vain, until *Karl Heumann* of the Swiss Federal Polytechnic in Zurich appeared on the scene with his discovery of two indigo syntheses. Hoechst and Ludwigshafen acquired the patents.

In the first of the two new processes, the starting material did not offer any difficulties. The phenylglycine required could be readily prepared from aniline and chloroacetic acid. But conversion of phenylglycine into the dyestuff led into a blind alley: the yield was too low.

The second method offered a better yield but the production of its starting material — phenylglycine-o-carboxylic acid — presented a considerable problem. It involved the oxidation of naphthalene to phthalic anhydride and so long as this process could be effected only with expensive nitric acid, the entire process was hopelessly uneconomic. Therefore, all efforts concentrated on a search for a cheap way of oxidising naphthalene into phthalic acid. Hoechst tried chromic acid and chromates. Once again, there was the usual dilemma: the method was technically practicable but economically untenable Unless a cheap way could be found of reconverting the chromium lyes into chromic acid and returning the regenerated acid to the manufacturing process. Only fresh experiments using electrolysis could answer this question. But everybody knew that the success of electro-chemical processes depended on the supply of cheap current.

A welcome accident

While Hoechst was thus busy building an experimental electro-chemical plant, Ludwigshafen investigated oxidation with fuming sulphuric acid. Once again the first results were disappointing. And then coincidence — one of the most famous in chemical history — joined in the nerve-wracking game. A thermometer broke during one of the experiments. Mercury flowed into the reaction vessel. The chemists looked in dismay at their apparently spoiled experiment. Only to find, to their amazement, that the mercury was proving an ideal catalyst. The reaction was at once accelerated enormously. BASF had found, overnight, an economically sound method for the oxidation of naphthalene to phthalic acid. And when, for good measure, *Rudolf Knietsch* of BASF developed a cheap new technique for the production of fuming sulphuric acid, the Ludwigshafen chemists had at long last achieved their goal: twenty years of research, twenty million marks of investment and twenty years of hopes had not been in vain.

Vom Rath is full of good advice

But Farbwerke Hoechst had not yet conquered indigo. On the contrary, the method that the company was pursuing became more and more involved. Eventually, since chromic acid regeneration stubbornly remained too expensive, Hoechst fell back on the Baeyer method, first described in 1882. This involved the use of nitrobenzaldehyde which had, however, the disadvantage that it started from toluene. And toluene was rare, very rare, only small amounts being obtained from coal tar.

To place the production of indigo on so narrow a raw material basis was hardly practicable. At any rate, price competition from BASF, which was able to build up its production on a broad naphthalene basis, would have been overwhelming. Even so, Hoechst's INDIGO F was marketed in 1897. Its successor was INDIGO M which appeared a year later, Hoechst having acquired a number of French patents in the meantime. But both products were no more than stop gaps for Hoechst had clearly become rather nervous. There was an almost desperate anxiety to keep up with the smart boys in Ludwigshafen.

So it came about that Hoechst developed three separate indigo processes before the turn of the century. Each represented some measure of progress, none was perfect. And then once again, fate took an entirely unexpected hand. The men in the supervisory boards see and hear a great deal. Frequently, they sit on more than one board. *Walter vom Rath*, at that time the chairman of the supervisory board of Hoechst, was no exception.

He was at the same time chairman of the supervisory board of a Frankfurt electricity company which obtained cheap current from the Lech river in Bavaria. Cheap current meant cheap chromic acid which, in turn, was used for phthalic acid manufacture. Hoechst eagerly seized their chance. It concluded a contract with this electricity company for the supply of current, acquired land at Gersthofen near Augsburg and erected a new works at a cost of approximately 3.5 million marks for the production of indigo and its starting products.

Whole battalions of chemists, technicians and experts moved from Hoechst to Gersthofen. But it was to be another six months before the turbines of the new electricity work started up. The newly-arrived staff in Gersthofen was eagerly waiting for Hoechst to fire the starting pistol. But no pistol was fired. The chequered history of synthetic indigo was not yet at an end.

Even before the mortar for the new Gersthofen works had properly set, new formulae were being tested at Hoechst. They were, in fact, based on the original work carried out in Zurich polytechnic which *Johannes Pfleger* of the Deutsche Gold- und Silber-Scheideanstalt, now known as Degussa, had meanwhile significantly improved with the aid of sodamide. Within a few weeks, Degussa and Hoechst founded the Indigo GmbH to exploit the new process.

But now *Herrmann Reisenegger,* chief of the Gersthofen works, stepped into the ring. He was understandably anxious to secure the production of synthetic indigo for his new factory. Reisenegger set out to prove in innumerable tables and calculations that Gersthofen would be able to produce indigo by the phthalic acid process just as cheaply as by the Pfleger method and that the purity of its indigo would be second to none.

The goal is reached

Experimental production on a large scale was clearly needed to cut through the jungle of contradictory theories and to arrive at a reliable answer. For this reason, four different experimental plants were operated simultaneously in Hoechst. It might have seemed extravagant but it was well worth the money. In 1902, these plants produced 308 tons of indigo and in 1903, their output was 765 tons. Soon it became absolutely clear: Pfleger's method for the production of INDIGO G offered the greatest promise. As soon as this had been finally determined, no more time was lost in Hoechst. Production in Gersthofen was stopped and indigo production in Hoechst expanded. Another 11,000,000 marks were spent on production plants and equipment.

Indisputable figures soon proved that the years of determined effort were at last

bearing fruit. As early as 1903, more than three quarters of a million kg of indigo were shipped from Hoechst. In 1904, it was 1.5 million kg and by 1913, the figure had risen to 4.5 million kg. "The indigo was almost snatched out of our hands," chronicled *Gustav von Brüning*, member of the executive board of Hoechst and son of the co-founder of the company.

By that time, the role of natural indigo in the world markets had become insignificant. In 1895/96, indigo exports from India amounted to 187,000 tons. In 1913/14, they had been reduced to 11,000 tons and the price had dropped from 11 marks per kg to approximately 6.50 marks. And yet, triumphant though synthetic indigo was, its rule was not undisputed. Of the 15,000 coal tar dyestuffs patented by that time — no mean achievement — many remained high in favour with the public. The sales of these dyestuffs were determined not only by colour, price and fastness but also by their dyeing behaviour. The first dyestuffs varied a great deal in this respect. Alizarin and indigo were water-insoluble. They could be applied to the fibre only by roundabout ways or with the aid of auxiliaries. Indigo, for example, was dyed as follows: the dyestuff was reduced and an almost colourless solution was formed. The fibre was impregnated with this solution and exposed to the air. As a result, the indigo white was again able to oxidise, the fibre becoming blue. In the case of madder red, the fibre had first to be treated with a mordant before the actual dyeing process could be carried out.

The vat dyestuffs

A close chemical relative of indigo is thioindigo. In this product, the NH group of the indigo is replaced by sulphur. Thioindigo, which is dyed in the hydrosulphite vat, was discovered in 1905 by *Paul Friedländer*. It was at that time manufactured by Kalle-Biebrich and sold under the name of THIOINDIGO RED. The product caught the attention of the scientists of the dyestuffs factories who undertook further investigations into this field. Numerous derivatives of thioindigo were prepared. At Hoechst, the HELINDON DYESTUFFS were developed as a result. They owe their existence primarily to the work of *Albrecht Schmidt* and *Karl Schirmacher*.

The rise of the azo dyestuffs

By far the greater part of the 15,000 patented dyestuffs that were being produced at the end of the century in Germany's dyestuffs factories were azo dyestuffs. These are formed by the action of nitrous acid on aromatic amines in acid solution. Chemists call this process diazotization. Dyestuff formation is achieved by coupling of the diazotized amine with certain organic compounds. *Peter Grieß*, a pupil of A. W. Hofmann living in England, had first discovered diazotization in 1857. The method led to the large-scale production of the azo dyestuffs. At first, basic dyestuffs were produced with whose help animal fibres, such as wool and silk, could be dyed directly. Cotton had first to be mordanted, i. e. it had to be pretreated with tannin or antimony potassium tartrate, in order to ensure that it accepted the dyestuff.

The first German patent

Hoechst took up the manufacture of azo dyestuffs only in 1878. *Heinrich Baum* produced two disulphonic acids from β-naphthol and these he coupled with diazotized amines. The result was the PONCEAU DYESTUFFS: scarlet red shades of particular intensity which fascinated the industry not only because of their beauty but also because of their low price. With their aid, cochineal dyestuff, obtained from shield lice, was ousted from wool dyeing. This invention provided Hoechst with its first German patent in 1878.

A great step forward in the development of the azo dyestuffs was the discovery of Congo Red by *Paul Böttiger* in 1884. This dyestuff had a remarkable property. It dyed substantively — the dye was taken up directly by the cotton. Full of optimism, Böttiger went to Leverkusen, to Ludwigshafen and finally to Hoechst. But none of the three large companies showed any interest. The dyestuff was not sufficiently resistant to acids. Finally, the Böttiger patent was acquired by Agfa in Berlin. And, to everybody's great surprise, the dyestuff that nobody else wanted, promptly became a great success. Spurred on by this, *Carl Duisberg* of Bayer-Elberfeld searched for a similar product. In contrast to Agfa, he did not start from benzidine but from its homologue, toluidine. But hundreds and hundreds of test-tube preparations proved fruitless and were ignominiously poured away every evening. All that Duisberg could obtain were dark unattractive precipitates. Until one day, when through an oversight, a few test-tubes remained uncleaned. The result was astonishing. A beautiful red precipitate had formed. It was found that the reaction simply took far longer than Duisberg had at first thought and that he had thrown his preparations away before the results could be seen. A new star appeared on the dyestuff firmament: Benzopurpurin.

Hoechst did not take up production of this group of dyestuffs, which was of extraordinary importance for cotton dyeing, until 1896. The reason was the discovery, in 1894, of a black trisazo dyestuff which was based on benzidine. It was marketed under the name DIANIL BLACK R.

Lake dyestuffs from Hoechst

The organic dyestuffs were used for the largest part in the dyeing and printing of wool, silk, cotton and linen. They were, however, also successful in other fields, for example, in leather, fur and paper dyeing. Moreover, they achieved great importance in the preparation of printing inks and paints.

In Hoechst, the foundation stone for this range was LAKE RED P and LAKE RED C. An outstanding success were the HANSA DYES brought out in 1909. These dyestuffs, which belonged to the azo series and which were discovered by *Hermann Wagner* and *Josef Erber,* have extraordinarily high light-and colour-fastness. In the development of lake dyes, physical form and the development of suitable laking methods played a considerable part. Close collaboration between chemists, physicists and technical service experts was, therefore, necessary to achieve products that met practical requirements. Soon, the various dyestuffs and their fanciful terminology filled fat catalogues. The dyestuffs industry knew no rest. Although there was in those days no affluent society whose spending sprees could have alarmed the custodians of the country's economic fortune, large sections of the population were nevertheless rapidly increasing their living standards. And concomitant with this, there developed a demand for new and more beautiful colours. The chemists became architects who erected ever bolder molecular structures. Although the complicated structural and constitutional formulae of the molecules they created remained a form of abstract art for the layman, the products made from them and the places where they were manufactured acquired an aura of historical importance.

Dyestuffs as medicaments

Chemists had produced the synthetic dyestuffs. Process engineers had achieved their production on an industrial scale. Soon, they were joined by the biologists and medical men who also wanted to use dyestuffs. Naturally, the doctors did not normally dye silk or wool. But they did stain living and dead tissue to facilitate penetration of the secrets of the blood with the aid of the microscope. A young country doctor, *Robert Koch,* had made two important discoveries. He had succeeded in isolating the pathogen of anthrax and later, with the aid of methylene blue, the tubercular bacillus. Nobody knew at first whether the tiny stained foreign bodies in the tissue were lifeless structures or living organisms. It fell to Koch to prove beyond all doubt that the most minute organisms were the pathogens of all infectious diseases. He thus became one of the pioneers of bacterial research and the teacher of a whole generation of research workers.

New chlorine/alkali electrolysis in the Hoechst plant

Paul Ehrlich dyes tissue

One of Koch's pupils was *Paul Ehrlich*. Even as a very young student he was fascinated by the technique of tissue staining. For his doctorate thesis he chose as subject the «theory and practice of tissue staining». For years, Ehrlich sat in front of his microscopes at the Robert Koch institute in Berlin. The dye which he used most was once more methylene blue. Ehrlich had observed that this substance had a remarkable affinity for the living nerve cells. It stained them blue. Ehrlich drew from this the conclusion that only certain cells were stained — a revolutionary thought. Would it not be possible that certain dyestuffs would stain only the pathogens, and at the same time destroy them, without affecting the cells of the human body tissue? The search for the answer to this question took a long time. But the question would not leave Ehrlich alone and it led to one of the most fundamental ideas in medical science.

Ehrlich turned to Farbwerke Hoechst who had been producing methylene blue since 1885. «I am convinced», wrote Ehrlich, «that methylene blue will perhaps achieve a small but firm place in therapy».

What would have happened if at that time there had not been a man at Hoechst who, though preoccupied with the daily problems of a large industrial company, was still able to grasp the significance of the visionary work of a genius?

Perhaps it is a superfluous question. No doubt, a man like Ehrlich would have succeeded anyway. But, probably it would have taken longer. Too long for millions of sick people. Ehrlich knew that he was regarded by most people as an individualist whose optimism caused a tired smile among many. After Professor *August Laubenheimer*, a member of the board of management of Farbwerke Hoechst, had promised his support, Ehrlich wrote «the purely chemical approach in medicine is at the present time finding neither understanding nor recognition among a large number of my colleagues. It is, therefore, all the more encouraging for me that you have recognized with great precision the theoretical nucleus of my investigation."

This exchange between Ehrlich and Laubenheimer was the beginning of a long and fruitful period of collaboration between Ehrlich and Hoechst, a collaboration that became even closer after Ehrlich's institute for serum research and serum testing had been moved from Berlin to Frankfurt in 1899. "Ehrlich was now in the direct vicinity of the manufacturing site of his beloved dyes," wrote *Boris Sokoloff* in his "Triumph of the drugs."

Ehrlich investigated the pathogens of malaria, of sleeping sickness and of syphilis. He infected mice with trypanosomae and attempted to cure them with azo dyestuffs. One of the dyestuffs was called Trypan Red. It was, however, not strong enough to achieve a curative effect. Ehrlich looked for new preparations. He came across Atoxyl which contains a benzene ring with arsenic oxide in the nucleus. But this preparation poisoned the human organism. New, non-toxic compounds from azo dyestuffs and arsenic had to be found.

Mice die for progress

The chase after non-toxic arsenic compounds lasted for many years. Each one of the many compounds was carefully numbered and tested by Ehrlich and his assistants who were joined in 1909 by the Japanese *Sahachiro Hata*. Each experiment cost the lives of innumerable mice. Thousands of them died for progress.

After more than 300 compounds had been evaluated, many of Ehrlich's collaborators no longer believed in this progress. The goal had become a phantom for them and they thought it is a waste of time to go on. But Ehrlich was not the man to give up. He drove himself and his few helpers from experiment to experiment. He may have had doubts himself now and again but he let nobody notice them. "If necessary," wrote Ehrlich, "we shall prepare a thousand or even more compounds." And yet Ehrlich was nearer to his goal than he knew. As compound number 592 was entered in the laboratory notebook, the famous silver lining began to show. Substance number 592 was almost non-toxic but all the more effective. The way from compound 592 to 606 was not very far. The promise of early success inspired Ehrlich and his disciples to new efforts. And, although SALVARSAN, the name given to preparation 606, was not suitable for the treatment of sleeping sickness, it effectively fought the world scourge syphilis and the spirochaetae. Thousands of experiments during the next few months proved this.

For the authors of popular medical books, the history of this major medical success usually ends at this point. Perhaps there is the final dramatic note that Ehrlich, in spite of all successes, was not able to realize the dream of his life, namely the magic bullet that would destroy all pathogens in the body without attacking the body cells.

Difficult Salvarsan production

For Farbwerke Hoechst, however, who had faithfully supported Ehrlich during all these long years, the real work had only just begun. For arsenobenzenes like Salvarsan are not uniform substances. Even minor variations in the manufacturing process may lead to considerable dangers. They change the proportion of the various molecule and particle

Paul Ehrlich in his study

sizes and thus the curative value, the toxicity and the solubility of the preparation. The characteristics of the end products are also influenced by the type and amount of the precipitant and by the technique used for separating the solid substances. The oxygen sensivity of the arsenobenzenes, especially if these were slightly contaminated, also faced the production chemists with considerable problems during the first year. New methods and new equipment had to be developed. Only silver-plated kettles and stirrers ensured that the new substance could be smoothly produced. Soon afterwards, Hoechst's Salvarsan was awarded the top mark that the Paul Ehrlich Institute in Frankfurt, with its stringent tests, had to give.

Paul Ehrlich and Farbwerke Hoechst joined forces once more. It was in the development of Neosalvarsan which was given the Ehrlich number 914 and which had been preceded by hundreds of experiments. This preparation started the second offensive against syphilis which was largely eliminated from Europe as a result.

Thanks to Hoechst

Paul Ehrlich, who had been awarded the Nobel Prize for his immunological work in 1908, had become midwife to a new branch of medicine — chemotherapy. Ehrlich never forgot the support that Hoechst had given him. In 1914, he wrote to the company «I should like to give particular expression to my thanks for the great help and for the full understanding of my efforts that I have had from you all the time and that has filled me always with the greatest joy and satisfaction. You have done everything you could to remove the obstacles from the difficult path that I have had to travel». It was his valedictory letter without either sender or recipient knowing it. A year later, Ehrlich was dead.

Salvarsan was, however, not the beginning of pharmaceutical production in Hoechst. The pharmaceutical division had, in fact, been formed many years earlier in 1883, just twenty years after the foundation of the company. As in the case of the coal tar dyestuffs, all the chemists wanted to achieve was the synthesis of quinine, a drug that up to then had always been obtained from natural products. It transpired, however, that science had greatly over-estimated its ability to solve this apparently simple task. It took 50 years for quinine synthesis to be accomplished. During this half-century, research workers attempted ceaselessly to find a substitute for quinine won from the bark of the cinchona tree. Eugen Lucius, one of the four Hoechst founders closely followed every development in this field. Initially the investigations were aimed at establishing whether the entire quinine molecule had an antifebritic and curative action or whether only certain parts were involved. Soon, the quinoline ring was found to be an essential component of quinine. The next question was whether quinoline derivatives also reduced fever. Science was unable to provide the answer to this question for a long time. But eventually it was found that although many of the synthetic products did reduce fever, they were themselves not entirely harmless. A case in point was KAIRIN produced in Hoechst.

The beginnings of Hoechst's pharmaceutical division were therefore not exactly promising. Until Hoechst obtained a substance prepared by a young scientist from Erlangen which was to change the picture completely. His name was *Ludwig Knorr*. Under the influence of his teacher *Emil Fischer*, he was at first by no means inclined to entrust industry with his discovery. In any case, Knorr thought that he had found a quinoline derivative. It was not until much later that he realized that the new substance belonged to the group of the pyrazolones.

There was another difficulty. Pharmacological tests had established that Knorr's substance had a comparatively low degree of efficiency. It was not until certain modifications proposed by the pharmacologist Prof. *Wilhelm Filehne* of Erlangen had been made that it became a promising pharmaceutical. It was christened ANTIPYRIN and soon found its way into chemists' shops and the medicine chests of the doctors. It confirmed the laboratory tests again and again. Antipyrin depressed fever and pain with a reliability completely unknown at that time. And when in 1888, a big influenza epidemic ravaged parts of the world, doctors, thanks to Antipyrin, were no longer helpless. From then on medical science sat up whenever a new Hoechst preparation was launched. And now that a pharmaceutical research laboratory had been added to Hoechst's central research laboratory, this happened with encouraging regularity. But the main emphasis of the company's activities continued to be on dyestuffs production. Indeed when Hoechst celebrated its 25-year jubilee in 1888, the festival brochure dismissed its pharmaceutical production in a single sentence.

The creator of Pyramidon

But by 1893, the company had taken up the production of a pharmaceutical that was to become one of the bestsellers on the prescription pads. The history of this preparation makes fascinating reading. Professor Filehne, who had by now joined the scientific staff of the company, had not been satisfied with Antipyrin. He recommended the preparation of a certain Antipyrin derivative of which he expected an even greater therapeutic action. *Friedrich Stolz*, manager of the Hoechst pharmaceutical laboratory and a terse Bavarian who had only two passions — bicycling and pharmaceutical synthesis — was asked to develop this substance. Stolz promptly obliged. All he had to do was to get it off the shelf for he had prepared it long ago by molecular rearrangement. His modesty and his, perhaps misguided, desire not to cause the company unnecessary expense had prevented him from submitting it for tests. Stolz's preparation was three times as effective against fever as Antipyrin. In addition, it eased pain and suppressed inflammations. The preparation was tried for four years, in laboratories, clinics and in hospitals before Hoechst decided to release it under the trade name PYRAMIDON.

What was public reaction? Initially, there was disappoinment at Hoechst. Certainly Pyramidon had had a favourable reception. Medical journals praised it, pharmacists recommended it. And yet, the company's hopes for Pyramidon did not look like being fulfilled. For the time being, Pyramidon was living in the shadow of its forerunner Antipyrin. It was only after the turn of the century that the victorious advance of Pyramidon begun. It was to last for many years and bring universal fame to Pyramidon.

The road to tuberculin

There can be no doubt that these initial pharmaceutical successes played a considerable part in *Koch's* decision in 1892 to entrust Farbwerke Hoechst with the production of TUBERCULIN. This was the grand slam for Hoechst pharmaceuticals. It was equivalent to an award by the highest medical authority. But elation over this was mixed with concern. Was Hoechst sufficiently prepared for this tremendous task? After all, it was an entirely new field calling for a number of unusual activities. Bacteria had to be grown and suitable nutrient media had to be prepared. Bacteriological departments whose work had little to do with chemical methods and facilities had to be created almost overnight.

Nor was it likely that science would provide much help. Certainly Robert Koch was revered throughout the world. But the science of bacteriology which he had founded had not so far achieved general acceptance. A large number of medical men regarded bacteriology with the greatest scepticism. As yet it was impossible to foresee who was likely to come out on top in this intellectual confrontation. The world watched anxiously every success and every failure in this fight against disease. The name name of the winner is printed in every textbook: bacteriology has long since become one of the most important branches of medical science. And although tuberculin did not in the end become the magic bullet to defeat the dreaded tuberculosis, it was nevertheless indispensable for the early identification of this insidious disease. The Hoechst symbiosis of science and industry induced yet another man to collaborate with the company. He, too, has become one of the immortals in the realm of medicine — *Emil Behring*, another of Robert Koch's pupils. But he chose another method of attack. While his teacher had attempted to treat tuberculosis with preparations won from the pathogens of the disease, Behring concentrated on the antigens which the human and animal body itself produced. Proceeding from the observation that the animal body produces antitoxins for every form of intoxication, Behring, after infinitely painstaking experiments, finally arrived at his serum therapy. But in order to achieve incontestable results he needed whole herds of animals.

Animals as serum donors

Even at that time, there was apparently a considerable shortage in the coffers of the State so far as research was concerned. Farbwerke Hoechst therefore lent a helping hand and soon the works acquired a certain similarity to Noah's Ark. A herd of sheep, a cow and a horse took up residence. They were the avant-garde of a succession of animal serum donors that was soon to assume considerable proportions. The chemical factory had to be transferred into the animal body. Soon afterwards, the serum plant started to operate on a site away from the main factory. A high wall separated it from the other production units. In 1894 serum production on a large scale began. As a result, diphtheria and tetanus were gradually robbed of the terror that they had spread throughout the world.

But there was no time for Hoechst to sit on its laurels. The field grew at an unprecedented rate. No sooner was a new pathogen described in the medical annals, than there followed an account, a few editions later, of an antitoxin to combat it. Apart from Salvarsan, Tuberculin, the Behring sera and Pyramidon, mention must also be made of NOVOCAIN. It was found by Professor *Alfred Einhorn* and first manufactured by Hoechst in 1906 to become the standard preparation for local anasthesia. Almost on the same day that Hoechst was able to announce the release of Novocain, another scientific achievement of far-reaching importance was accomplished: the first synthesis of a hormone.

Once more, scientists ventured forth into virgin territory. The man in charge of this particular expedition was *Friedrich Stolz*, the discoverer of Pyramidon. Stolz's starting point was the fact, known for some time, that the suprarenal gland contains a substance which is transmitted to the blood in the form of a hormone. It promotes cardiac activity and causes constriction of the vascular extremities. The hormone was called Adrenalin. The Japanese research worker *Jokichi Takamine* needed almost 10,000 suprarenal glands from the ox in order to obtain four precious grams of Adrenalin. Scientists in many countries had unsuccessfully attempted to unravel the structural formula of Adrenalin. Stolz unravelled its constitutional formula by producing this regulator through chemical methods. Soon afterwards, Farbwerke Hoechst marketed marketed it as the first chemical hormone preparation and later as a vaso-constrictory auxiliary for local anasthesia. The name given to it by the company was SUPRARENIN. Only few may have formed the word in their mouth, but a good many have had it injected into their gums. Together with Novocain, it can be found in the injections administered by most dentists and serves to make treatment less painful and less bloody.

Electrical current and chemistry

The «Griesheim Alps» rise suddenly out of the ground. More than two hundred metres long and more than thirty metres high they deny the visitor a full view of the imposing silhouette of the great Griesheim works, a Hoechst subsidiary about five kilometres away from the parent site. Griesheim occupies an unusual position in the company's history if only for the fact that, like the Offenbach works, it can boast a rather peculiar paradox: the offspring is seven years older than the parent company.

The «Griesheim Alps» — so christened by the Griesheim workers — are thinly covered by coarse grass and spindly shrubs. They owe their existence not to any geological upheaval but to soda production, one of the first large-scale chemical processes of the last century. The waste products of this process, joined later by the left-overs from chromate and alumina production, gradually grew into this ugly slag heap whose removal today would cost many millions of marks. Since there is no desire at Hoechst, at any rate for the time being, to dip that deeply into the company coffers, this soda monument of the early Griesheim days is being preserved for posterity.

Leblanc harvests soda — and ingratitude

At the end of the 18th century, ordinary soda, together with sulphuric acid, was the universal material for almost every branch of the growing chemical industry. The white gold was used in large amounts for the production of soap needed in the cleaning of cotton textiles which had meanwhile gained great popularity. Glass factories, too, bought soda by the hundredweight or even by the ton. Earlier, Egypt, thanks to its caustic soda lakes, had been the main supplier of this much sought-after product. It had, however, been found that the rapidly increasing requirements for this product could no longer be met from this traditional source. As far back as 1775, the French Academy, with a remarkable degree of foresight, offered a prize of 12,000 livres to the first person to develop a method for producing soda by another route. By rights, this prize should have gone to the French doctor *Nicolas Leblanc* and to the apothecary *Dizé*. Both had hit on a successful method after many years of difficult experiments: sodium sulphate, chalk and carbon were heated together in a reverberatory furnace. «The substance changes into a pulpy flux, foams and is transformed into soda which differs from the commercial product only by being far more concentrated.» This was how Leblanc described these first successful experiments. Physician Leblanc, lately turned chemist, set up his own factory which started production in 1791. But soon after Leblanc had made his first few hundred pounds of soda, the factory was confiscated. Revolution was sweeping France. The Duke of Orleans, his benefactor and financier, was sentenced to death by a revolutionary tribunal and the factory closed. The patent was declared void and Leblanc was refused the academy prize.

Leblanc was eventually driven to suicide in the poorhouse but his process conquered the world. Dozens of soda factories were built, especially in highly industrialized England. They served almost the entire European market and consolidated the dominant position of Britain's technology and industry at that time. But the price for a ton of artificial soda was still high — 800 marks in 1820. It was not until twenty years later, in 1843, that the first German soda factory was constructed at Magdeburg. Sixteen years later still, Griesheim took up production on the basis of Leblanc's process.

Second to none

This was three years after the foundation of the company whose godfathers had been Liebig pupil *Ludwig Baist* and *Friedrich Rössler*. At first, the production programme was confined entirely to sulphuric acid, nitric acid and copper sulphate. These heavy chemicals — another English domain — at that time formed the essential basis of the entire chemical industry. Sulphuric acid, in particular, which was another of the starting materials for the Leblanc process, was regarded as the acid par excellence. Its consumption had always been a barometer for the industrial progress of a country. Textile manufacturers required it for the finishing of their fibres,

The «Griesheim Alps» —
huge accumulations of factory waste
at the edge of the Griesheim works

the metal industry used it as separating agent for ores, and the fertilizer industry employed it in the manufacture of its phosphate fertilizers. The fertilizer industry, too, had developed extremely rapidly. The initial incentive for this had been provided by *Justus Liebig,* the doyen of German chemical science. In 1840, Liebig in his «Application of chemistry in agriculture and physiology» had postulated the theory that the mineral substances that the crops took out of the soil must be returned to it.

But above all, it was the expanding coal tar industry that was clamouring for sulphuric acid. For centuries it was produced in lead chambers. The raw material was pyrites and the catalyst nitric acid.

Bad news for Griesheim

Griesheim, if only because of its favourable geographical position, became the main supplier of acid to Hoechst. At first, only modest quantities were involved. But with the quick growth of dyestuffs production, Griesheim, too, rapidly expanded its output of sulphuric acid. Until that fateful day when a letter from Hoechst arrived in Griesheim giving notice of the termination of all the contracts for the supply of acid. It was 1880 and Hoechst had decided to erect its own acid factory. It was the first, and quite logical, step in the subsequent, almost vertical integration of the company. In contrast to the first almost haphazardly built plants, the acid factory was constructed according to a long-term plan. But even so, demand remained so high that the plants had to be continuously expanded. By 1895, Hoechst had enlarged the lead chamber plant to include ten systems, five refining furnaces, seven fine gravel furnaces und a total of twenty-two concentrating towers. Six years later, 40,000 tons of sulphuric acid were produced and, in addition, 9,300 tons of fuming sulphuric acid which was required mainly for alizarin production.

The manufacture of fuming sulphuric acid was carried out in gold, or even platinum kettles, because other metals are attacked and destroyed by this highly concentrated liquid. In spite of the vast output at Hoechst, it was still necessary from time to time to buy quantities of sulphuric acid. But then *Rudolf Knietsch* of BASF came along with his new contact process which was to make BASF one of the largest sulphuric acid producers of Germany. There were no longer any limits to the amount of sulphuric acid that could be produced.

The fact that the parent company should treat one of its future offspring with so little love did not worry Griesheim for long. Forsaken by their main user of an organic acids, the Griesheim chemists began to search for a new production basis. They set themselves a target that was as attractive as it was difficult to achieve: the decomposition of common salt by means of electric current passed through the salt solution via electrodes so that the various ions are separated. On the negative pole – the cathode – caustic soda solution and hydrogen are formed, and on the positive pole – the anode – chlorine gas.

Werner von Siemens and his dynamo

The potentialities of the electrolytic process had given chemists no rest since the beginning of the nineteenth century, or to be more precise, since 1801. In that year, *P. L. Simon,* professor at the Berlin academy for building, discovered that in a common salt solution, chlorine tended to accumulate on the positive pole of a current source. However interesting the theories that could be built around this – it was a long way from the laboratory observation to the large-scale industrial process. A quarter of a century was to pass before Faraday formulated the law that provided the theoretical basis of electrolysis.

And when *Werner von Siemens* propounded his electrodynamic principle in 1866 – three years after the foundation of Hoechst – and especially after he had constructed his first dynamo, electrochemistry was born. For it was not until the appearance of the dynamo that current became cheap enough for large-scale use in the chemical industry.

Electrolysis not the only way out

At Griesheim, which was threatened by stagnating sales, thoughts did not at first centre only around electrolysis. Indeed, the first counter to Hoechst's moves was the erection of production plants for nitrobenzene and aniline. Griesheim thus became a user of part of its own output of heavy chemicals and also a supplier of intermediates to the dyestuffs industries. As a result, two new plants were erected at Griesheim: an aniline factory and the chemical plant at Mainthal.

Solvay displaces Leblanc

Both these plants were moderately successful. Nevertheless, the loss of the Hoechst market was a hard blow to Griesheim. Nor were these the only clouds to darken the Griesheim skies. For the Belgian *Ernest Solvay,* the Leblanc process was not the last word. He returned to a process, originally discovered in 1811, in which common salt was reacted in aqueous solution with ammonium bicarbonate obtained from ammonia and carbon dioxide. It was, however, highly uneconomic even though the ammonia was recovered. Solvay, working close on the edge of bankruptcy, made heavy financial sacrifices. Finally, he succeeded in perfecting the process in such a manner that it became economically viable. Moreover, his process could be operated at low temperatures so that coal could be saved. Salt consumption was very high but it was not necessary to use solid rock salt but simply a cheap common salt solution which could be pumped directly from the earth in many places.

Solvay erected his first factory in the vicinity of Brussels in 1863. Its success was evidenced by the numerous subsidiary companies that grew up over the next few years in almost every European country and in North America. The Solvay process yielded a purer product than the Leblanc process and was cheaper. Nevertheless, the Leblanc process managed to maintain its position for a comparatively long time, largely because hydrochloric acid is obtained during the production of sodium sulphate, the starting material. The acid, in turn, formed the raw material for the manufacture of chlorine. This was important because there was a market for chlorine, both for bleaching purposes in the textile industry and for the syntheses of organic intermediates for dyestuffs and pharmaceutical production.

Griesheim stuck to Leblanc's formula for as long as it could. Soda manufacture had become the nucleus of the entire Griesheim production. The loss of this production would probably have forced Griesheim to shut down forever. Griesheim therefore had little choice but to concentrate all its efforts on developing a viable electrolysis process. Since the financial resources necessary for this far exceeded the funds available to Griesheim, other companies were approached. The result was the foundation of a syndicate «for the study of alkali and chlorine using electric current».

In doing this, were they really chasing a mirage as Dr. *Herter*, chief chemist of United Alkali in Manchester, derisively described their efforts?

Secret tests

Only a few years later, this English competitor was made to eat his words. The main credit for this must go to *Ignaz Stroof*, the chemical director of Griesheim. Stroof was from the Rhineland, an incurable optimist and a brilliant chemist. But above all Stroof was thorough. Before beginning his work with electrolysis, he studied every scrap of information about electrical engineering on which he could lay his hands. Finally, he went to Professor *Erasmus Kittler* in Darmstadt in order to attend lectures on the subject.

Only then did Stroof undertake the construction of an experimental plant, the erection of decomposition baths for the salt brine and the development of a method for current supply. One of the most difficult problems proved to be the continuous separation of chlorine and caustic soda solution.

No sooner had one of the members of the syndicate succeeded in constructing a current-permeable membrane with the aid of Portland cement, than another problem arose: the retort graphite required for the electrodes could not be supplied by the gasworks in amounts adequate for large plants. After a long, intensive search, artificial carbon electrodes were finally developed. They are still an important part of Griesheim production.

With some pride, the company went to the Frankfurt Electricity Fair in 1891 to show the first products that had been obtained by electrolytic methods. The surprise was all the more complete since, at Stroof's behest, all work in this field had been kept extremely secret. Although in comparison with Hoechst, Bayer or BASF, Griesheim was only small fry so far as the chemical industry was concerned, it had achieved a technical break-through of the utmost importance.

After the First World War, the carbon electrodes produced in Griesheim were burnt into graphite in the electrothermic furnaces of the Bitterfeld works. Graphite not only displaced the carbon electrodes in electrolysis but also found wide application in the construction of chemical apparatus. Following the loss of Bitterfeld at the end of the Second World War, Griesheim and the Siemens-Planiawerke AG collaborated closely in this field. Siemens-Plania owned a graphitization plant in Meitingen near Augsburg but it had lost its crude electrode plants in Berlin-Lichtenberg and Ratibor. The production programmes of the two companies therefore complemented each other and together they founded the Sigri-Kohlefabrikate GmbH in Meitingen for the distribution of their joint manufactures.

Chlorine prices tumble

The Griesheim electrolysis plant, which produced sufficient amounts of chlorine, finally displaced soda manufacture by the Leblanc process. Even as late as 1898, something like 600,000 tons of Leblanc soda were still being produced throughout the world. Only a few years later, output had dropped to a twelfth of this figure. Germany, which had previously imported large amounts of calcium chloride from abroad, now became an exporter. The price for chlorine was slashed by half. In those years, world consumption of chlorine was approximately 250,000 tons, roughly the amount produced today by Farbwerke Hoechst and its subsidiary companies alone.

Hydrogen, one of the by-products of salt electrolysis, could not at first be utilized at all and was simply discharged into the air but a few years later it was to find a somewhat curious, not to say dubious metier. Hydrogen was used to fill the balloons of Jules Verne-like devices which gave a great deal of proud satisfaction, especially to the more patriotic spirits of that time. Hydrogen floated the balloons of research workers and keen sportsmen and later the airships of Count Zeppelin, who was initially greeted with ridicule and finally buried a national hero.

Griesheim had become the pioneer of electrolysis, a process that was to conquer the future — as the famous Zürich technologist, Professor *Georg Lunge,* enthusiastically exclaimed after a visit to the Griesheim plant. The lead that Griesheim had established in the development of electrolysis was duly recognised at the 1893 World Fair in Chicago. Professor *Otto N. Witt,* the representative of the German chemical industry at this exhibition wrote in his report, «The Chemische Fabrik Griesheim can boast of having been the first factory to succeed, after five years of experimentation, in the practical solution of the problem of producing pure caustic soda, chlorine and hydrogen by the electrolytic decomposition of chlorine-potash salts.»

The road to lignite

In 1895, BASF acquired a licence for operating the Stroof process. In France, Spain and Russia, factories operating on the Griesheim principle were set up. Griesheim itself made strenuous efforts to expand this promising new industry in Germany. It erected a new factory in Bitterfeld.

It was soon found that the know-how gained by the Griesheim technicians and chemists during intensive pioneering work was absolutely vital.

Walther Rathenau, the foreign minister of the Weimar Republic but at that time still a director of the AEG, had attempted to launch plants for chlorine alkali electrolysis in both Bitterfeld and Rheinfelden. The AEG, at that time already one of the leading electricity companies, had, understandably, no intention of letting this revolutionary process slip through its fingers. The sites for the projected plants were well chosen. Bitterfeld was in the middle of the central German lignite reservoir and Rheinfelden was located above Basle on the Rhine. Both plants were therefore assured of cheap electric current. The AEG, in collaboration with a number of Swiss industrialists, had erected a continuous power plant in Rheinfelden. This was so modern that it became the prototype for similar plants throughout the world. But in spite of this promising constellation, Rathenau was dogged by ill-luck in his electrolysis projects. The AEG

encountered endless difficulties. For example, in Bitterfeld, the process failed the very first time it was tried. Modification after modification was tried but without success. The plant at Rheinfelden, which was constructed according to an improved design, was also disappointing in its first trial run. Its cells could not cope with the requirements made on them.

New bridgeheads for Griesheim

Faced by all these difficulties, the AEG eventually gave up. Its two plants were leased to Griesheim and equipped with the well-tried Stroof cells. Soon afterwards, they functioned without difficulty. Thus, Griesheim was able to add to its parent site and its own plant in Bitterfeld two new bridgeheads in areas whose power potential was sufficient to satisfy the high current requirements of electrochemistry.

The failure of the AEG, or to be more precise, of its subsidiary, the Elektrochemische Werke GmbH, to realize its ambitious electrolysis project, had another advantage for Griesheim. The Bitterfeld heritage of the AEG also included an experimental plant for the production of magnesium. Griesheim at once attempted to gain a foothold in this field. Light metals had only just made their appearance and had been a tremendous sensation, even though their full potential was hardly realized at that time. *Gustav Pistor*, Stroof's successor, soon found a technically useful method for magnesium production. The amounts produced were however modest. As in the case of aluminium, large-scale production was realized only during the war.

For the time being, Griesheim's main effort was reserved for electrolysis. After all, this was not simply a new production method for a well-known chemical.

Precious stones for only two marks

The Griesheim electrolysis method had created the essential basis for the application of electrochemical processes in the chemical industry. But the method had also resulted in a number of important by-products among them chlorates. In Gersthofen, chromic acid was regenerated from the waste liquors of naphthalene oxidation. Hydrogen found an additional application apart from its role as gas for balloons and airships. It was used as an auxiliary for the realization of mankind's oldest dream, the production of artificial precious stones. Griesheim had taken over this plant from the Elektrochemische Werke GmbH. Purest alumina was fused in a furnace in an oxyhydrogen flame. The alumina was prepared from aluminum ammonium sulfate. The stones were sintered together with metallic oxides.

The first artificial ruby was produced in 1902. This was followed in 1910 by the first sapphire. Thereafter, about six million carats were manufactured every year. The price for these synthetic precious stones was between 2 and 8 marks. Today, vast amounts of these stones are used, mainly for industrial purposes, e.g. watches, balances and precision instruments. A factory in the Bavarian forest, for example, has an annual capacity of 30 million carats.

Wiss develops autogenous welding

Griesheim maintained its strenuous efforts to find an economic use for its hydrogen. This finally led to a new and very important field. In 1901, Griesheim and the Airship Commission concluded an agreement for the delivery of compressed hydrogen. *Ernst Wiss*, an engineer at Griesheim, was put in charge of its manufacture. He succeeded in compressing hydrogen to 150 atm in steel cylinders. But what else could be done with compressed hydrogen? An accidental observation gave Wiss an important clue and he thought this so significant that he followed it up with a great deal of intensity. In the lead soldering workshop in Griesheim, the lead apparatus of the sulphuric acid and calcium chloride chambers were soldered with hydrogen. This hydrogen was produced by a complicated method from zinc and sulphuric acid. Wiss tried the use of compressed hydrogen for which he constructed a suitable hydrogen burner. With its aid, it was possible to solder lead sheets 15 mm thick. The hydrogen was oxidized with air.

Wiss went further still. By replacing the air with oxygen, he was able to melt iron. In this way, the oxyhydrogen welding burner — the first Griesheim autogenous welding implement — was developed.

Following the success achieved with this novel welding unit, the question arose whether it would not be possible to produce a similar implement for the cutting of metals. This, however, involved the exploitation of a patent by Dr. *Ernst Menne* of the Cöln-Müsener Bergwerks-Actien-Verein. But soon, welding and cutting implements were operated without hydrogen, for the French engineer *Edmond Fouché* had succeeded in designing a welding torch that worked on acetylene. This gas has a high calorific value and it can be readily prepared from carbide. As a result, experiments in this field were carried out by Griesheim and these eventually bore fruit in the development of the acetylene torch.

The Wiss equipment was at first produced at the Drägerwerk in Lübeck and later in Griesheim itself. Special plants for the production of oxygen were also set up. The manufacture of autogenous cutting and welding assumed such proportions that in 1916 a separate company — the Griesheim-Autogen works — was formed within the Griesheim-Elektron organization. It is today part of the Messer-Griesheim GmbH.

Noble gases as subsidiary products

The first oxygen plant went on stream in Griesheim in 1908. By 1938, the I.G. Farbenindustrie in Germany had nineteen oxygen plants. Following the dismemberment of the I.G., all those that were located in the Federal Republic were attached to the then Knapsack-Griesheim AG. During the manufacture of oxygen, noble gases are generated as side products. Among these, neon plays a particularly important part. Another noble gas, argon, is used as a protective gas in the welding of stainless steel. Since huge amounts of oxygen are required in steel production, Hoechst, together with the other big German oxygen producer, the Gesellschaft für Linde's Eismaschinen AG., founded the Hüttensauerstoff GmbH. This company is engaged in the erection of large plants for the supply of oxygen to foundries.

A basis for chemical development

Following the development of the chlorine-alkali process, caustic soda solution used by the soap industry became very cheap. Moreover, the coal tar dyestuffs manufacturers were able to obtain a far cheaper chlorine and the textile manufacturers were able to reduce their expenditure on bleaching auxiliaries to one third of the original cost.

Nor was this all. Caustic soda solution, the second product of common salt electrolysis, became an auxiliary for man-made fibres, particularly after ways had been found of producing it in very pure form. Without chlorine-alkali electrolysis, the rise of artificial silk and rayon would hardly have been feasible.

The other product of the electrolysis—chlorine—promoted the development of plastics. Polyvinyl chloride, the prototype of all the thermoplastics, requires large amounts of chlorine in the form of hydrogen chloride. This hydrogen chloride is added to acetylene and the resulting vinyl chloride is polymerized to give polyvinyl chloride.

With its electrolytic processes, Griesheim therefore created the essential pre-requisites for the production of plastics. But it achieved even greater honours. The Mainthal works of Griesheim were the site where polyvinyl chloride and polyvinyl acetate were discovered—two plastics that have conquered the world in a multitude of variations. Their basis—the vinyl compounds—became an inexhaustable reservoir from which entire industries are deriving their products today. Present-day consumption of these plastics amounts to millions of tons. In the Federal Republic alone, production in 1961 was more than a million tons.

Fritz Klatte makes a discovery

One of the earliest names in plastics history was *Fritz Klatte*. Not that Klatte discovered the plastics world all by himself. Earlier chemists and scientists had mapped out the route along which Klatte was to travel. Outstanding among them was *Adolf von Baeyer* who had done so much valuable preliminary work on indigo synthesis.

In 1872, Baeyer, together with his assistant, had observed that formaldehyde and phenol combined to form a resinous product in the presence of acid. Chemists all over the world, and especially in Germany and the United States, pursued this discovery and developed a whole range of different synthetic resins. Most of those were based on formaldehyde and phenol.

Initially, Griesheim had little interest in these products. Nevertheless, a few chemists were asked to investigate the highly reactive acetylene which, as every schoolboy knows, is formed when water is added to carbide. By adding hydrochloric acid gas on to acetylene, vinyl chloride is formed. When acetic acid is added on to acetylene, another compound — vinyl acetate — results.

Molecular metamorphoses

Both vinyl chloride and vinyl acetate are liquids. During polymerization, they are transformed into solid substances. Polymerization is a fundamental process in the production of plastics. Its principle is the addition of numerous molecules to form large molecules or macromolecules. A typical example of such a chemical metamorphosis is ethylene. It is formed in the coking of coal or in the crude oil cracking processes of petrochemistry. Ethylene is content with six atoms in its molecule, two carbon atoms and four hydrogen atoms. It has therefore only a very small molecule and hence a low molecular weight (28). If ethylene is polymerized, however, its miniature molecules grow into macromolecules. Ethylene becomes polyethylene, a solid material with a molecular weight of 60,000 or more.

In nature too, small molecules are continuously being converted into large molecules under the influence of the rays of light, although in their case other chemical processes also play a part.

Fritz Klatte utilized this fact, although rather unwittingly. Following initial observations in the laboratory, he filled dozens of carboys with liquid vinyl ester and exposed them

Fritz Klatte in his laboratory

to sunlight. This resulted in a polymerization process and the contents of the carboys solidified into a solid compound. Klatte then shattered the carboys with a hammer. He obtained thousands of glass splinters as well as a synthetic resin which he christened MOWILITH.

The new resin was distinguished by outstanding versatility. Depending on whether it was heated, cooled or dissolved in a solvent and the solvent evaporated, it could be processed into numerous products: lacquers, films and filaments; clear, transparent, hard and soft compounds. The Mowilith patent granted to Fritz Klatte on 4th July 1913, therefore, had the fairly general title, «Method for the production of technically useful products from organic vinyl esters».

However, if Klatte had hoped that the echo of his hammer blows in the factory yard of Mainthal would herald a plastic epoch, he was in for a rude shock. His scientific and technological performance was duly applauded but that was all. No one showed the least inclination to engage in the large-scale production of Mowilith. The time simply was not ripe for such a development, because the «Ersatz» products of the war period had thoroughly spoilt the market for any new synthetic products. In addition, Griesheim was preoccupied with the expansion of the Bitterfeld works. Finally, there came a very bitter day for Klatte. He was very ill in Arosa when he heard the news that the thrifty Griesheim administration intended to yield up his patents in the polyvinyl acetate field. Klatte's invention aroused no further interest until shortly before his death when Wacker-Werke in Burghausen on Salzach and Farbwerke Hoechst took it up once more. Under their aegis, polyvinyl acetate was marketed at the end of the twenties under a variety of trade names and became a popular commodity.

Griesheim acquires Offenbach

It was at this point that the paths of Hoechst and Griesheim crossed once more, finally merging under the I. G. Farbenindustrie umbrella. Prior to the First World War, Hoechst's interest in the fortune of its neighbour Griesheim was rather limited. The former supplier of acid had in fact become a competitor. This happened in 1905 when Griesheim had acquired the aniline dyestuffs factory of K. Oehler in Offenbach, a small company but full of great traditions. In its laboratories, *A. W. Hofmann*, the founder of the German coal tar dyestuffs industry, had distilled the first quantities of aniline from coal tar. Soon afterwards, Hofmann had emigrated to England, much to the chagrin of the infant dyestuffs industry in Germany. Nevertheless, Offenbach too, eventually joined the ranks of the important German dyestuffs producers.

A new star in the dyestuffs firmament

The marriage between Griesheim and Offenbach was well-matched. Each partner was able to offer a worthwhile dowry. Griesheim had a great deal of experience in the production of heavy chemicals and intermediates. Offenbach, on the other hand, could offer its expertise in the production of aniline dyestuffs. The union was soon blessed with its first offspring — the NAPHTOL as dyestuffs which rapidly became one of the brightest stars in the firmament of the German dyestuffs chemistry. Naphtol AS, or in chemical language, the anilide of 2,3-hydroxynaphthoic acid, has a particular affinity for cotton. If cotton is impregnated with it, fast dyeings can immediately be produced in the coupling bath without need for prior drying.

In the course of time, a veritable rainbow of Naphtol AS shades was developed. In this way, Griesheim and Offenbach had secured for themselves an important outlet that was unassailable, even by the largest competitors. No matter how many shades were produced, no matter how quickly fashions changed — the Naphtol AS products remained firm favourites with the public.

Hoechst generously acknowledged this Offenbach success without envy. The German dyestuffs industry, in these last years before the First World War, absolutely dominated the world market. In 1863 — when Hoechst was founded — England and France were still able to share the production of aniline dyestuffs between them. But by 1877, the position had already changed. Germany now accounted for half of world dyestuff production. During the next decade, this German share rose to more than 80 pc. This did not give rise to rejoicing in every land. An English daily newspaper wrote in 1913: «Although England was the cradle of the coal tar dyestuffs industry, it no longer has any say in the upbringing of this offspring of chemistry. The dyestuffs industry», it continued, «has become a purely German affair. This is the result of a unique degree of collaboration between fanatic scientists, inventors and indefatigable organizers. They have proved stronger than any financial or raw material strength».

Even if this lament contained certain political overtones, it was not far from the truth. German dyestuffs producers had no need to engage in pitiless competition. The cake was large enough not only for the big three — Hoechst, Elberfeld and Ludwigshafen — but also for the vigorous medium-sized companies such as Offenbach and Kalle in Wiesbaden-Biebrich. In any case, Hoechst was no longer dependent on dyestuffs only. It had gained a leading position in the pharmaceutical sector which it had expanded carefully. Only one important obstacle remained — the absence of a sound energy and

raw materials base. The plans for expansion that Hoechst harboured were therefore concerned with areas other than Frankfurt. Similar considerations had already led to the birth of the Gersthofen works which were to make one of the most important contributions to indigo synthesis.

Electrolysis in Gersthofen and Hoechst

Following the debut of the Griesheim chlorine-alkali electrolysis, Hoechst erected a common salt electrolysis plant in Gersthofen in 1903. This was designed to produce chlorine for the manufacture of monochloracetic acid, an important indigo starting product. The investment costs amounted to almost two million Marks. But in return, Gersthofen was able to produce, as early as 1905, almost 2000 tons of chlorine and even larger amounts of caustic soda solution. The Gersthofen method differed from the Griesheim process in only one point. The latter employed a diaphragm while the former operated without a diaphragm using a method that had been developed independently by the American *Hamilton Young Castner* and the Austrian *K. Kellner* in 1892. They used mercury as cathode.

The Castner-Kellner cells had, however, one serious weakness. Since hydrogen occasionally got into the chlorine, chlorine-oxyhydrogen gas was formed which gave rise to explosions. This was a risk that Hoechst did not want to run. When in 1909 a chlorine/ caustic soda electrolysis plant became indispensable to the Hoechst works, diaphragm cells were used. They had been developed jointly by the Vienna Professor *Jean Billiter* and Siemens & Halske. The Billiter cells had two advantages: there was a better current yield and they had a longer life.

Hoechst looks to the Rhineland lignite areas

At the turn of the century, Hoechst was expanding southwards but ten years later it began to look northwards or, to be more precise, to the lignite areas near Cologne. In 1906, the Deutsche Carbid-Aktien-Gesellschaft had erected a plant in this area. It was a modest undertaking compared with Hoechst who at that time employed some 5790 people. The carbide furnaces of the Deutsche Carbid-Aktien-Gesellschaft were operated by some fifty hands. In any case, the company was not very sound. There was insufficient capital, there were selling difficulties and transport problems, and even at a time when full employment was still a distant Utopia, it had difficulty in getting sufficient labour. Tempting awards were offered to itinerant workers that passed along the road flanking the works. Dutchmen and Croats, Bavarians and Italians formed an early European community whose activities, alas, were confined to the operation of the Knapsack carbide furnaces. The furnaces were tapped with 6 m long rods as the carbide was discharged from the furnaces at a temperature of more than 2000 °C. It was exhausting work that only few could do for any length of time, in spite of the high wages offered. In those Knapsack pioneer years, the company looked more like a camp of desperadoes than a factory. And it was fitting that wages should be paid in the manner almost of the Wild West. Every Friday, two employees arrived in high boots one carrying a list and a pencil and the other producing gold and other coins from his trouser pocket. No doubt, the guns were not far away.

Why, we may well ask ourselves, should Hoechst have had any desire to acquire this factory. The answer to this question encompasses one of the most dramatic chapters of German chemical history — the fight for nitrogen and nitric acid. This acid was indispensable in the manufacture of intermediates for dyestuffs and pharmaceuticals and it was equally vital as oxidation and nitrating agent in the munitions industry. Nitric acid was produced from Chile nitrate. As late as 1859, the entire Chile export of nitrate was only 75,000 tons. But with the rise of the chemical industry, these figures rose steeply. In 1900, Chile exported a million tons of nitrate of which a third went to Germany. A few years later it had reached two and a half times this amount. It was a tremendous business for the Chilean mine owners, especially since they were able to dictate prices.

But the consumption of such vast quantities of nitrate raised serious questions. The Chilean reserves were not unlimited. Warnings by the experts about the early exhaustion of the Chilean saltpetre reserves became more and more urgent. Thorough investigations showed that the total remaining amount of Chile nitrate was no more than 200 million tons.

Threatening famine

This alarming news proved premature. But when it was first announced, it caused tremendous excitement and even panic. After all, nitric acid was used not only for industry but also for the production of vital fertilizers for agriculture. *Sir William Crookes* of the British Association for the Advancement of Science made a now famous speech which was described in the newspaper headlines as a cry of despair. Crookes declared: «The wheat crop of the world depends on Chile's nitrate reserves. A world famine is unavoidable unless a way can be found of overcoming the nitrogen problem». Chemists had been engaged for some time in finding a method of taming nitrogen. The easiest way seemed to be the oxidation of ammonia to nitric acid. But where was the required ammonia to come from? One of the few sources was once again coal, or to be precise, the ammoniacal water of the coking plants and gasworks. Before the purification of ammonium sulphate was mastered, this valuable by-product had simply been discharged.

Nitric acid from ammonia

In Hoechst, *Gustav von Brüning,* son of the co-founder of Farbwerke Hoechst, was devoting his whole attention to this subject. He ensured that the company had a good starting position in the coming race for ammonia. Thanks to his initiative, a small team was formed in Gersthofen, under the direction of *Martin Rohmer,* a chemist whose instructions were to carry out research on the production of ammonia and nitric acid and to conduct practical trials. First of all, a method for the oxidation of ammonia to nitric acid was developed. At the same time, experiments were conducted in the production of ammonia. Eventually, three viable possibilities crystallized. One employed aluminium nitrite, another calcium cyanamide and the third the Haber process. This latter method, developed by Professor *Fritz Haber* and perfected by *Carl Bosch* and BASF, without doubt represented the boldest approach. It was based on the synthesis of ammonia from its elements. The nitrogen of the air was forced into union with hydrogen with the aid of catalysts — of which thousands had been tested — and very high temperatures. Liquid ammonia was produced in the final phase in an externally-heated pressure furnace for which highly resistant steel alloys had to be developed.

Hoechst, however, did not adopt this initially expensive method but concentrated on the construction of a plant in which ammonia was oxidized to nitric acid. The necessary ammonia was obtained from calcium cyanamide, a grey compound produced if nitrogen is passed over carbide at a temperature of 700—800 °C in the presence of a certain amount of granulated calcium chloride.

The Bayerische Stickstoff-Werke AG in Germany had also pursued the manufacture of calcium cyanamide. This company had been founded in 1908 and had constructed two plants in Upper Bavaria, a carbide factory in Hart and a calcium cyanamide factory in Trostberg. During the First World War, it erected a calcium cyanamide and nitric acid plant at Piesteritz on the Elbe. The State owned and financed this plant and the Bayerische Stickstoff-Werke were entrusted with its management.

In 1921, the shares of BStW were acquired by BASF and Merseburg. Subsequently, BStW acquired the Piesteritz works. The upper Bavarian works were formed into a new

company — the Süddeutsche Kalkstickstoff-Werke AG (SKW). Seventy percent of the financing for the SKW was provided by the State and the remaining thirty percent by the I.G. Farbenindustrie. Following the dismemberment of the I.G., half the interest was awarded to BASF and the other half to Hoechst.

A newcomer to the family

Knapsack had caught the attention of Hoechst even before World War I started. In contrast to Griesheim, Knapsack with its carbide was concerned not with electrolytic but with electrothermic processes. In these processes, the current is not used to decompose compounds but as a heat source producing tremendously high temperatures. This is illustrated by the fact that Knapsack today uses more current than the Federal Railways and twice as much current as the city of Cologne with its 800,000 inhabitants. One tenth of the total current consumption of the German chemical industry is accounted for by Knapsack alone. In tall furnaces fed with a mixture of lime and coal, Knapsack produces more than 1000 tons of carbide every day. But at the time when Hoechst quietly planned the acquisition of this subsidiary, the daily output from the Knapsack carbide furnaces was no more than a few tons.

This acquisition, in which the earlier foster parents of Knapsack readily acquiesced, was not accomplished in one move. In November 1914, Hoechst took over shares to the value of 550,000 DM from the Berliner Handelsgesellschaft and a month later another block of shares worth 950,000 DM from the Metallbank and the Metallurgische Gesellschaft in Frankfurt. This meant that Hoechst had gained control of precisely half of the Knapsack capital. At the same time, it entered into contractual obligation to promote the interests of Knapsack to the best of its ability. In return, Hoechst was given an option on the entire ammonia output of Knapsack.

This clause in the contract was particularly important. It was the whole purpose of the transaction, for it secured for Hoechst the raw material basis for nitric acid manufacture.

But an even more important result of the take-over was that the Knapsack carbide provided Hoechst with a jumping-off ground for its advance into acetylene chemistry. For without this versatile raw material, further expansion of the German chemical industry would hardly have been possible.

If one talks at Hoechst about acetylene, the name *Paul Duden* will inevitably crop up. Son of the famous creator of the Duden lexikon, Paul Duden was more interested in chemistry than in grammar or dry orthographic problems. Paul Duden was one of that

Tapping a carbide furnace in Knapsack

species of chemist to whom Germany's industry owes so much because it represented such a happy mixture of scientist and practical man. Duden had been a professor at Jena university before he came to Hoechst in 1905 where, barely five years later, he created the famous stepladder whose rungs led from carbide to acetylene, thence to acetaldehyde and finally right at the top to acetic acid and acetone.

From carbon and lime, Duden created an industry of organic key products which had previously been prepared by a far more complicated and far more expensive method.

Duden's stepladder

The first rung of Duden's chemical ladder did not present any difficulties so long as you knew your chemical ABC: carbide and a little water — and instantly acetylene bubbled to the surface. If water was added on to this gas, a new compound — ACETAL-DEHYDE — was formed, a colourless liquid of pungent odour. During oxidation with oxygen, this intermediate acetaldehyde is transformed into acetic acid. The route from carbide to acetaldehyde and acetic acid was, of course, known before Duden — Gries-heim had played a significant part in its development — but it appeared much too dangerous to most companies. For when working with such inflammable liquids as acetaldehyde and oxygen the danger of explosion is never far away, especially if large volumes are involved. And, of course, the chemical industry was interested only in such large volumes.

Once Duden had worked out a reliable production method for acetic acid from the cheap and inexhaustible carbide, Hoechst at once realized its importance. The company, which even in its early history had required acetic acid, for example for indigo syntheses and Pyramidon manufacture, immediately set about the construction of an experimental plant.

The outbreak of World War I dealt a heavy blow to Hoechst's production programme and most of its plans. The munition factories developed an insatiable demand for acetone. They required it by the ton as a gelling agent for bullets and explosives. Very soon, the work of the Hoechst central laboratory was classified as vital to the war effort and a similar distinction was conferred upon Knapsack and its carbide. The German High Command suddenly recognised that in modern war, it wasn't only divisions and the guns that counted but that other factors, such as industrial capacity, were equally important, for on them depended the vital supplies, without which no army could hope to fight successfully.

Chemistry classes for the military

Although Europe had moved from crisis to crisis for many years, neither Government nor army had paid much attention to the significance of adequate industrial capacity. Not that the self-confidence of the army was in any way jolted by this. *Walther Rathenau* and the highly-respected Professor Emil Fischer were sternly rebuffed when, after the start of the war, they drew attention to the bottleneck in the nitrate supplies. This, the High Command declared brusquely, represented intolerable interference in military affairs.

The conferences in the ministry of war revealed clearly just how ignorant most military men were even in matters of elementary chemistry. When the chiefs of the large chemical companies pointed out on such occasions that Germany would be finished once the supplies of Chile nitrate came to an end, they were asked, in all innocence: «But what about our huge potash deposits?» The fine difference between nitrate and potash had not impressed itself on the brains of the ministry of war.

It was not until the autumn of 1914 that the general staff in Berlin had caught up with its homework in chemistry and economics. But then the pace became military. The raw materials department of the ministry of war imposed its requirements on the chemical industry. In the case of Knapsack, this meant an increase in capacity up to the practicable limit. The number of workers increased from 60 to 400 in a short period of time. The forest around the factory site was felled and building material arrived in such quantities that suburban railway stations in Cologne were choked for several days. New and larger carbide factories were installed at a hectic pace.

Field grey — the most important dyestuff

The war also made its mark on Hoechst. With the exception of field grey, dyestuffs were no longer in demand. Instead, the army was clamouring for drugs. As the fighting increased in severity, so the pharmaceutical department expanded by leaps and bounds. Wagonloads of analgesics such as Novocain, of vaccines against typhoid and cholera and of sera against the fatal gangrene and tetanus poured into the hospitals, field hospitals and dressing stations. They saved the lives of hundreds of thousands.

Next to the expansion of the pharmaceutical department, ammonia oxidation was given high priority. Highly concentrated nitric acid was manufactured from dilute nitric acid via solid sodium nitrate. In 1916, a Pauling plant was installed which did away with the detour via sodium nitrate. For now it was possible to produce highly concentrated

nitric acid directly from dilute nitric acid with the aid of concentrated sulphuric acid. But this plant, too, had its drawbacks for it used comparatively high amounts of sulphuric acid. In addition, its output was only small. Hoechst therefore constructed a completely new plant which became a tremendous success.

At the end of 1916, Hoechst was directed by the ministry of war to take up large-scale production of highly concentrated nitric acid. In July 1918, the new factory set up for this was visited by a delegation from the ministry of war which subsequently reported: «June production of concentrated acid at Hoechst was 3,380 tons. This shows that in its efforts to manufacture concentrated acid Hoechst has been more succesful than any other company. Hoechst has solved the problem of the nitric acid and sulphuric acid concentration in a manner that indicates that the required production output will be achieved also in future.»

Rubber from the test tube

The expansion of the acetic acid plants was a race against time right from the start of the war. For acetone was vital not only for grenades. It also formed the starting material for methyl rubber. This synthetic rubber was the answer of the German chemical industry to the excessively high price of natural rubber and to the danger of being cut off from natural rubber supplies.

The methyl rubber invented by the Elberfeld chemist *Fritz Hofmann* was, of course, inferior in some respects to the natural product. But the war and the consequent raw material shortage placed synthetic rubber high on the army list of priorities. For meanwhile the motor vehicle had become a decisive factor in many operations — as a lorry, first-aid car, artillery tractor, mobile kitchen or tank. Many of these vehicles were soon to run only on methyl rubber tyres but this required volumes of acetone that had never before been produced.

Berlin becomes unpleasant

Thanks to Paul Duden and his collaborator *Otto Ernst*, acetic acid and acetone had become the domain of Hoechst. Production went on stream at the beginning of 1917 but considerable difficulties in manufacture arose because Hoechst had cut out all intermediate stages and had jumped straight into large-scale production. There was friction between Hoechst and the war office. When only 175 tons of acetone were supplied by Hoechst in December 1917, the mood in Berlin became distinctly unpleasant: «Production continues to lag behind schedule. A delay like that experienced during recent months can no longer be tolerated in view of the serious consequences that it will have.» In the meantime, however, Hoechst had already decided to install a second acetic acid factory in Knapsack. In view of this, it seemed advisable to consolidate the tenuous Hoechst share majority in the Knapsack undertaking. After some hard bargaining, and only after Farbwerke Hoechst had agreed to a rate of 160, was it possible to acquire a block of shares from the Metallbank and the Metallurgische Gesellschaft, that made it possible to integrate Knapsack completely in the Hoechst group.

The shadows of impending defeat were already falling over the Kaiser's Reich when the new acetic acid factory in Knapsack got under way. It was September 1918. Two months later, fulfilment of war office quotas was no longer a problem. There was no war office any more. Defeated Germany had become a Republic that was being convulsed by internal and external pressures. The extremists had gained the field while the victors were preparing the Peace of Versailles.

Joining the IG Farben

The result of the war was no longer in doubt once America joined England and France. In any case, the German leaders of industry had a very precise idea of the reserves of economic power available to the Allies. The many Hoechst factories abroad and the world-wide sales network had provided a comprehensive idea of the economic state of the major industrial countries. This proved to be a highly effective antidote to any form of national over-confidence. The raw material and industrial potential of America was especially well-known. For, almost earlier than anyone else, the US economy had produced trusts and super-companies against whose dynamism Germany could compete only with difficulty, in spite of its scientific efforts.

The American example, more than anything else, had exercised a decisive influence on the organisation of the German dyestuffs industry. There is a good deal of truth in the claim that America had twice intervened in the fortunes of the chemical industry of Germany: the first time during the birth of the IG Farbenindustrie; the second time during its destruction.

Promising Duisberg journey

On the first occasion, of course, the United States played only a passive role — forty years later it was another matter. The idea for the integration of the leading German chemical companies, though conceived on American soil, sprung from the head of *Carl Duisberg*, «the great man» of Farbenfabriken Bayer. He made a trip to America in 1903 in order to assess the possibilities of intensifying the activities of his company on the American continent. Duisberg had been to the United States a few years earlier and had returned greatly impressed. But this time his judgement was more sober and more critical. He noted many weaknesses that only a country with unlimited resources could indulge in. There was no equivalent in the USA to the close link between science and industry that had grown out of the German raw material shortages. But Duisberg also noted the tremendous achievements of America which had resulted in a thoroughly mechanized, rationalized and closely integrated economy. He realized the dimensions of the industrial power that was emerging in the States and how ill-equipped Germany was to meet it.

Trusts — born out of need?

It was because of this that Duisberg became beguiled by a tempting vision — the concentration of the most important German dyestuffs manufacturers. This vision was not fed by economic power designs or a desire for a price dictatorship. Nor were Duisberg's fusion plans children of necessity as the many cartels which were being formed at that time were described by a leading economist.

The large German dyestuffs manufacturers were not in distress. They only suffered growing pains because they had developed at a breathtaking speed from minor companies into world concerns. In the case of Hoechst, as in the case of Bayer and BASF, this unique process had been accomplished in less than forty years. During this period, the number of employees had grown almost a thousandfold; a shabby shed had become a factory town with hundreds of buildings and kilometres of roads and rails. The daily output of inorganic products and dyestuffs was now being measured by the ton and the railway wagon.

Happy times for shareholders

Naturally, the companies' capital had grown to the same extent. In 1863, the year of foundation, Lucius, Meister and Mueller had provided 66,450 guilders as a starting capital. In 1880, when the company was converted into a limited company, the capital was 8.5 million marks. And in 1904, the Hoechst balance sheet showed a share capital of 25.5 million marks. The ordinary reserves stood at more than 11 million marks, turnover was 40 million marks and the net profits 6.7 million marks. These were proud figures which were reflected in equally proud dividends. Since 1896, dividend payments had varied between 20 and 30 per cent.

Happy times for shareholders. In but a few years, they had been able to double the capital that they had invested.

On the other hand, these successes had involved an unusual amount of hard work. The chemical industry, more than any other, was subject to unusual risks. The potential of a chemical invention or discovery could not be calculated, not even by the cleverest systems. If a new invention offered any kind of promise, millions of marks had to be invested before it could be finally established whether a successful product had been found. This applied particularly to pharmaceuticals. It required clinical trials extending over many years to determine whether a new preparation was likely to gain a permanent place in the pharmaceutical arsenal of the company. And even in this favourable case, the financial returns were usually very limited. After it had taken up manufacture of pharmaceuticals, Hoechst had tested thousands upon thousands of chemical compounds for their curative action. The result: a few hundred effective preparations of which up to 1909 only three showed any financial succes — ANTIPYRIN, PYRAMIDON and DIPHTHERIA SERUM. It was some years later before these three were joined by SALVARSAN.

Ten thousand different dyestuffs

The turnover in dyestuffs was almost ten times that of pharmaceuticals. But in this case, the wide range available and public caprice presented a real threat to the economic structure of the industry. In 1880, Hoechst disposed over a range of approximately 1,100 dyestuffs. It was thought at that time that this was an adequate selection for the public. But only seven years later, Hoechst was producing ten thousand different dyestuffs. This was not the result of uninhibited joy in experimentation on the part of Hoechst's chemists. It was simply the consequence of extremely keen competition among the leading German dyestuffs manufacturers. This sharp competition no doubt also had its positive side: dyestuffs were continuously improved, new production methods were developed, manufacturing costs were reduced. But the financial strain all this placed on the companies concerned was extremely great.

Dyestuffs laboratory at Hoechst
at the turn of the century

However, restraint — wrongly interpreted — might have been suicide. At any rate, it would seriously have shaken the market position of the company. What, for example, would have happened if Hoechst had not joined the INDIGO race early enough, or not at all? It would have been hopelessly left behind by BASF and probably also by Bayer. And a reduction in dyestuffs sales would have had similar results in other branches of the company. Output and profitability of the inorganic raw materials and intermediates, which formed the basis both of dyestuffs and pharmaceutical products, would have been seriously reduced.

Price competition and conventions

But at that time, competition was no longer governed by free enterprise alone. As early as 1881, after a period of intense price cutting in the ALIZARIN field, conventions had been established which had been joined by seven German dyestuffs manufacturers and one English company. Output and turnover of the individual companies were agreed and minimum prices were laid down. Within the convention, a leading group — the «big three» of the dyestuffs industry — emerged publicly for the first time. Fifty-two convention shares had been issued. Of these, Hoechst, BASF and Bayer obtained ten each.

Although this agreement was only short-lived, it was soon followed by many new agreements between the dyestuffs manufacturers. Conventions were concluded not only for Alizarin but for whole series of dyestuffs. There was no other choice. The crisis into which the dyestuffs manufacturers had been drawn between 1885 and 1900 as a result of the rapid drop in prices made such solutions inevitable. Some companies disappeared from the scene altogether. Others had to give up Alizarin production at least and move into other fields.

Dividend reduction at Hoechst

Hoechst, too, had got caught up in this depression. A year after the foundation of the limited company in 1881, it was possible to distribute a net profit of 2.3 million marks amongst the new shareholders. The year after, this figure rose to 2.7 million marks net profit and a dividend of 16%. But then, the honeymoon was over and regressive trends affected the Hoechst balance sheet. By 1885, net profit had dropped to 0.7 million marks and the dividend to 5%. Hoechst was, however, able to derive some comfort from the fortunes of Farbenfabriken Bayer in Elberfeld who were unable to distribute any dividend at all that year. These warning notes alarmed the various companies and increased their readiness to seek agreement between themselves.

However, there was as yet no general predisposition to enter into an official exchange of know-how, although Hoechst and the Swiss firm of Johann Rudolf Geigy did so in 1882. Both companies had agreed «to support each other by the regular exchange of news concerning the progress of business and the level of raw materials so as to arrange both their buying and selling correspondingly».

Although the German companies were unable to reach a similar agreement, good relations nevertheless existed between them in spite of the competitive conditions. There was collaboration in the various dyestuff conventions; between Hoechst and BASF, extensive agreements had been reached in the indigo field. Relationships between Hoechst and Bayer were also satisfactory. This manifested itself in 1891 when Bayer was planning an acid plant in order to make itself independent of the Rhenish/West-phalian sulphuric acid syndicate. Hoechst had had such plants in operation for a long time. *Duisberg* became friendly with *Philipp Pauli*, the manager of the Hoechst acid plant and received an invitation to inspect the Hoechst works. As a result, Bayer was able to take up manufacture of the three most important inorganic acids in 1895.

Shop window of the chemical industry

It was, however, mainly the «Verein zur Wahrung der Interessen der chemischen Industrie Deutschlands» (Society for the maintenance of the interests of the chemical industry in Germany), founded in 1887, that enabled the leading men of the large chemical companies to make contact with each other. The society discussed common problems in the fields of economic and social policy and in patent, fiscal and customs matters. It proved to be the ideal medium through which the chemical industry could project its problems to the public at large.

It was at one of the meetings of this society that *Carl Duisberg*, just returned from

Duisberg meets Brüning

America, sat next to the general manager of Hoechst, *Gustav von Brüning*. There was another fortuitous circumstance. Brüning, too, had just been in America to inspect the contact plants for sulphuric acid production and the American selling organization there. He, too, had taken a close look at the great American trusts.

Duisberg thus found Brüning very sympathetic to his project of writing a memorandum concerning the amalgamation of the German dyestuffs factories. Brüning was able to tell Duisberg that BASF, too, would not be unreceptive to such ideas. More than that, on the initiative of Agfa Berlin, a discussion had been agreed between Agfa, Farbwerke Hoechst and BASF to take place in the hotel Kaiserhof Berlin in January 1904. Brüning suggested to Duisberg that he should complete his memorandum by that date. All this spurred Duisberg on to proceed with his ideas. By the middle of January 1904, the memorandum was written. Duisberg's theory was that a dyestuff company could succeed against competition only if it had a certain minimum size. The expenditure on scientific research, on plant experiments, on experimental dyeings, had climbed astronomically in recent years. The selling organizations, the stores in many countries throughout the world and the chain of agencies and representatives would consume increasing amounts of money. To this would be added the over-production of dyestuffs resulting from the competition between the individual companies.

Page for page, Duisberg exposed the weaknesses of the dyestuffs industry. But he did not confine himself to the diagnosis; he specified the cure, too. It was a radical, once-and-for-all cure. Duisberg called for complete fusion, the foundation of a limited company, perhaps under the title «Vereinigte deutsche Farbenfabriken» with a capital of 200 to 300 million marks.

The Vereinigte deutsche Farbenfabriken were not to be a monolithic structure. Although Duisberg intended to standardise production and to centralize the buying and above all the expensive selling organization, he proposed retention of the competitive principle. His plan was that in the new company every important product should be manufactured by two plants so that production and price comparisons could still be carried out. As an incentive to the workers, Duisberg proposed bonuses and profit sharing. The management of the new organization was also to be set up according to democratic principles.

The conference in the Kaiserhof

It was doubtless a seductive picture that Duisberg painted in the Berlin Kaiserhof in the presence of the directors of Agfa, BASF and Farbwerke Hoechst. The first reaction was positive and even enthusiastic. In the weeks following, however, the enthusiasm that had seized the conference rapidly evaporated. After the directors had returned to their respective companies, they assessed the situation far more soberly.

This applied particularly to Hoechst where the Duisberg memorandum had been examined in great detail at a number of board meetings. There was general agreement that most of the deficiencies that Duisberg had listed did, indeed, exist and that it would be more than desirable to find a remedy. A memorandum by Brüning stated: «There is a great deal to be said for the proposals that have been made to reduce production and selling expenses, to mitigate the ruinous competition, to lower costs generally and to cut out undesirable selling methods. At first sight, they appear quite capable of practical realization. On closer inspection, however, they give rise to the gravest doubts for the future.»

A step in the dark?

It was particularly the example of existing trusts that failed to convince Hoechst. Duisberg had referred to the coal and coke syndicate. On this issue, Hoechst stated: «In the case of these huge undertakings, conditions are quite different from those in the chemical industry. In the first place, the products merged in these trusts are of a far more uniform nature; secondly, the conditions of these trusts are such, especially in the case of the coal and coke syndicate, that if the economic advantages expected should not be realized, these giant mergers could be dissolved tomorrow without any of the constituent companies losing its viability.» No such possibility was, however, envisaged in the Duisberg plan which clearly stated that «in the fusion of the large chemical factories, the prime purpose is to stop production of materials that can be made more economically in another plant. Also it is planned to reduce the number of personnel and to centralize commercial direction».

What would happen, however, asked Hoechst, if the expectations placed on the formation of such a chemical combine were not fulfilled? Would it then not be impossible to give back to the constituent companies their former independence since they would in the meantime have changed to such an extent that their reconstitution in the earlier form would be entirely impracticable? «Duisberg's proposal», Hoechst said, «means a step in the dark from which there is no return.»

«Everybody knows», so the Hoechst memorandum continued, «that present conditions in the dyestuffs industry and the extraordinarily keen competition is becoming more and more intolerable. But in spite of this, or perhaps because of it, we have today a strong and prosperous dyestuffs industry which is powerful and which does not have to fear competition from abroad. There are grave doubts as to whether it will be possible to maintain these stimulating and fertilizing competitive factors in a trust, however much that may be the intention. It is only natural that where one works under reasonably comfortable conditions, keenness will slacken and people will rely on others; artificial means cannot spur on employees to the same extent as the pressures of competition.»

Hoechst also felt that the provision of adequate management talent was not secured in the planned trust. «The directors of the individual departments will not be able to

make their judgement with the free, independent outlook that the management of the individual companies have today, especially with regard to personnel questions. Being comparatively disposable personalities, their main concern will be the maintenance of their own position. This would especially affect the next management generation. At present, anyone who does not feel he is getting proper recognition in his job can always give notice and thus enforce any improvement to which he is entitled. Failing this, he can seek employment under more favourable conditions in another company. Such remedies would not exist under the provisions in a trust since the field outside the trust will be very narrow indeed.»

In view of all these considerations, Hoechst came to the conclusion that the merger could not be carried out under present conditions on the proposed basis. The company felt that it would be irresponsible to endanger by precipitate action organizations and companies that had required many years to grow, that had involved a tremendous amount of work, intelligence and capital and that had always been the pride of German industry. Brüning communicated these thoughts to Duisberg in a very frank letter. He also drew attention to the special situation in which Hoechst found itself.

This special situation concerned indigo. In 1904, the Hoechst order books showed a most satisfactory return for the millions that the company had invested in the preceding years in the development of indigo production. At long last, the king of the dyestuffs could be produced at a price that allowed Hoechst to look forward to a considerable expansion of the market. This was all the more important because in the preceding years, Hoechst's great efforts in the pharmaceutical field had rather tended to slow down dyestuffs development.

With so many stars rising brightly on the horizon, Hoechst was not in a mood to enter into commitments that might have clouded their prospects.

For all these reasons, Hoechst decided not to go along with Duisberg's plan. The company regarded a phased, organic fusion as more useful than the dive at the deep end that Duisberg had proposed.

A first step

It seemed a very favourable time for such a phased fusion. In April, Leopold Cassella & Co. of Frankfurt had turned to Hoechst in order to probe the prospects of a merger between the two companies. In his private notes, Gustav von Brüning wrote at the time: «By February this year, Duisberg's plans had failed. Cassella had not been a party to these discussions and was only told about them afterwards. This snub had made

Deutsche

1902.	Actien-Kapital M.	Obli-gationen M.	Reserve-Fonds M.	Hypo-theken M.	Gesamt-betriebs-Kapital M.	Grund-stücke
I. Theerfarbstoffe.						
a. Actiengesellschaften.						
(Geordnet nach der Grösse des Betriebskapitals.)						
Badische Anilin- u. Sodafabrik, Ludwigshafen a/Rh.	21,000,000	10,000,000	20,811,687	—	51,811,687	Geht aus ●
Farbwerke vorm. Meister, Lucius und Brüning, Höchst a/M.	17,000,000	10,000,000	8,752,875	—	35,752,875	1,502,398
Farbenfabriken vorm. Friedr. Bayer u. C°, Elberfeld	14,000,000	7,644,000	6,415,884	—	28,059,884	2,585,010
Actiengesellschaft für Anilinfabrikation, Berlin	9,000,000	4,721,600	3,711,905	500,000	17,933,505	2,507,140
Chemische Fabriken vorm. Weiler ter Meer, Uerdingen a/Rh.	4,000,000	2,981,000	500,000	—	7,481,000	2,002,555
Farbwerk Mühlheim vorm. A. Leonhardt u. C°, Mühlheim a/M.	1,700,000	1,500,000 (Darlehen)	19,202	300,000	3,519,202	103,217
Total	66,700,000	36,846,600	40,211,353	800,000	144,558,153	●

b. Privat-Firmen.

Leopold Cassella u. C°, Frankfurt a/M.
L. Oehler, Offenbach a/M.
Kalle u. C°, Biebrich a/Rh.
Dahl u. C°, Barmen.
Beyer u. Kegel, Fürstenberg
Lembach u. Schleicher, Biebrich a/Rh.
Chemikalienwerk, G. m. b. H., Griesheim.
Gr. Remy u. C°, Weissenthurm.

Fabriken.

Tabelle I.

Gebäude	Maschinen und Geräthe	Total Grundstücke Gebäude Maschinen u. Geräthe	Bestände an Waaren und Materialien M.	Dividende					Durchschnitt der letzten	
				1898 %	1899 %	1900 %	1901 %	1902 %	3 Jahre %	5 Jahre %
der Bilanz nicht hervor		*) 25,485,191	23,030,000	24	24	24	24	26	24^{67}	24^{4}
5,349,262	8,809,291	15,660,951	15,360,000	26	26	20	20	20	20^{0}	22^{4}
3,389,811	2,752,305	8,727,126	12,419,070	18	18	18	20	22	20^{0}	19^{2}
1,500,180	2,058,921	6,066,241	6,740,543	15	15	15	15	16	15^{34}	15^{2}
955,337	1,365,619	4,323,511	2,060,155	14	14	9	9	10	9^{34}	11^{2}
767,673	888,511	1,759,401	1,796,536	3	5	0	0	4	1^{34}	2^{4}
		62,022,421	61,906,304	16^{67}	17	14^{33}	14^{67}	16^{33}	15^{11}	15^{2}

them rather suspicious and had given them the idea that it might be useful to join with another company since the foundation of a trust as outlined by Duisberg's views did not apparently seem opportune to them».

Cassella was one of the best-known dyestuffs factories. It had been founded in 1789 but for many years had confined itself solely to the import and selling of coloured woods and natural dyestuffs. Cassella took up dyestuffs manufacture only in 1870. The company bought many intermediates from Hoechst so that in any case there was already a close relationship between the two companies.

The merger between Cassella and Hoechst was completed fairly smoothly. Cassella was converted into a limited company 50 pc of whose shares were acquired by Hoechst. The association quickly bore fruit. In its report for 1905, Farbwerke Hoechst emphasised: «The conditions that caused us to enter this merger have been fulfilled». On the occasion of the fiftieth anniversary of Farbwerke Cassella, their chief, *Arthur von Weinberg* wrote: «There can be few instances in which the problems of collaboration between two companies have been so happily resolved and with such beneficial results to both sides.»

Surprise for Duisberg

The association between Hoechst and Cassella had been secretly prepared behind closed doors. Carl Duisberg learnt about it from the Frankfurter Zeitung while he was on holiday in Italy. He wrote in his memoirs: «Suddenly, like a flash of lightning from a blue sky, we got the news in Bellagio that Farbwerke Hoechst and Leopold Cassella & Co. had entered into an association.»

On his own admission, Duisberg spent a sleepless night. Next morning he had made up his mind: «I was going to attempt to come to a similar agreement with Ludwigshafen if, as appeared certain to me, a merger between Hoechst and ourselves was impracticable at the present time.»

With the intensity so characteristic of him Duisberg began to woo BASF. He did not have to wait long for his reward — an association with Bayer was soon formed. It was joined shortly afterwards by Agfa Berlin.

The two camps

Hoechst's move had thus been countered. Both camps eyed each other suspiciously. Would there be war, a bitter contest with no quarter given? Would Hoechst be boycotted, as Brüning sometimes feared?

Dr. vom Rath and Geheimrat Duisberg

In fact, neither side was anxious to fight. In its report for 1904, Hoechst restated its views: «We believe that the formation of groups is to be preferred to an immediate general trust since in this way the advantages of such a trust, though achieved more slowly, can be better thought out and accomplished less violently.» And then followed a few sentences of relief: «Always assuming, of course, that, as seems to be the intention of the Bayer camp, there is no proposal to fight out the various questions but, on the contrary, to come to an agreement about them. The formation of conventions, which cover ever-increasing areas of our field of activity, will facilitate mutual collaboration and will pave the way to a fusion of our industry by a process of natural evolution». Although this did not mean the end of Duisberg's memorandum altogether, it did not, in fact, achieve any great significance in the course of the next few years. The BASF, Bayer and Agfa group were finding it increasingly difficult to adapt themselves to each other. The products and the activities of the three companies overlapped at many points. Self-interest frequently upset joint planning. Again and again, there were differences of opinion in the management committee that was set up to steer the affairs of the group. Occasionally, there were even anxious questions as to whether it might not be advisable to dissolve the association. Certainly, no one in the group thought for one moment of increasing its number.

At Hoechst, the position was more favourable. The association was far looser and, what is even more important, the two companies were far more complementary than competitive. The Hoechst report for 1904 states: «There is only limited competition between our two companies so that collisions of interest are far less frequent than within the other group».

Nevertheless, friction could not be avoided altogether. The report for 1905 made particular mention of this. At the same time, it emphasised that agreement was reached quickly in all cases. «Joint purchasing was particularly successful because many items could be bought at far lower prices». Relations with the Bayer group were described as satisfactory: «Joint participation in conventions has provided a number of contact points which have placed our mutual relationships on a very friendly basis. Happily, we have succeeded in being accepted for the two black conventions (Dianil and sulphur black)».

Kalle — the third member

The Hoechst-Cassella association had thus paid off and there was, therefore, no reason for Hoechst to close the door to anyone else who might wish to join. The third member of the group was to be Kalle & Co. in Wiesbaden-Biebrich. This company had been formed eight months after the foundation of Farbwerke Hoechst. Its founder was an enterprising young man, barely twenty-five years old — *Paul Wilhelm Kalle.*

His father had provided him with a capital of 100,000 Guilders. Kalle junior knew how to use this money. In 1900, the company already owned more than 98 patents and some 160 trademarks. Biebrich Scarlet became world-famous. Kalle had gained a successful foothold in the pharmaceutical field, too. Still, in spite of these successes, there was one hurdle that Kalle could not surmount. It had to buy the inorganic chemicals and intermediates needed for its pharmaceutical and dyestuffs production, for the construction of its own acid factory would have been too expensive. In any case, Kalle had found that the continuously increasing and constantly more complex tasks of the chemical industry favoured the large and financially powerful companies. For this reason, Wiesbaden-Biebrich looked around for the possibility of a merger. Duisberg suggested that Kalle should form a separate group with a number of other small chemical companies and that this group should join the Bayer camp at some later date. Negotiations to this end had already taken place when Hoechst intervened. Hoechst, naturally enough, did not view this enlargement of the other camp with any particular degree of enthusiasm. And when Kalle let it be known that it would prefer to join the Hoechst-Cassella association, both in view of the geographical position of the two companies and also because of the confidence which it had in Farbwerke Hoechst, the marriage was soon arranged.

Fifty years of Hoechst

It was 1913 — half a century had passed since the foundation of Farbwerke Hoechst. None of the founders was alive any longer. But their work had assumed dimensions that far exceeded even their wildest dreams. Along the banks of the Main, workshop followed upon workshop, chimney upon chimney. More than 8,000 people were working in these plants and more than 300 chemists in the laboratories. The site had grown in the last 25 years from 95,000 to almost 400,000 square metres. More than fifty kilometers of narrow-gauge railway wound through the works, dotted with the skeleton structure of new plant. The company had its own gas plant which produced more gas than the gasworks of a town with 80,000 inhabitants. Water usage was exceeded only by that of Berlin, Munich and Hamburg. Hoechst used as much electric power as Krupp in Essen, Germany's largest industrial undertaking. The balance sheet showed a net profit of 16 million marks.

Only a single shadow lay over the Jubilee celebration of 1913. One of the men that had played such a large part in this tremendous progress could not participate. General-direktor *Gustav von Brüning* was seriously ill and, like his father, died shortly before his fiftieth birthday. His collaborator, *Herbert von Meister*, who joined the company in 1898, survived him by only six years.

This was the end of the company's tradition of founder families, a tradition that *Eugen Lucius*, who died in 1903, had done so much to foster.

Not that Lucius had conducted a narrow, feudal policy. His motto, which was doubtlessly shared by his co-founders was «The outstanding members of the three founder families at the head of the company, the others for the more honorary posts.»

The «little I.G.»

In 1916 — three years before his death — Herbert von Meister left the board of management of Farbwerke Hoechst. In the same year, the company joined the association of German coal tar dyestuffs producers set up by Duisberg. The two events were, of course, entirely unrelated.

Whoever was leading Hoechst could not dismiss one overriding fact: the war had seriously hit the German dyestuff factories. It had destroyed their international monopoly. All the signs were that it would never be re-established in its old form or on its former scale. The fact that the former dyestuffs plants were idle or had gone over to armament production was the least of their worries. This could easily be put right after the war.

Far more threatening was the establishment of many new dyestuff factories abroad, both in enemy and neutral countries. There was no doubt that these factories would make every effort in future to maintain their position, especially in view of the tremendous propaganda campaign to render the world independent of the German chemical industry. Even little-industrialized countries like Italy and Spain had erected their own dyestuff plants with considerable support from their governments.

In spite of the curtains of war, Hoechst, Leverkusen and Ludwigshafen were closely informed about this alarming development. For an industry that at one time sold three quarters of its output in countries abroad, this was news of a most serious nature. Again, it was Duisberg who seized the initiative. He wrote new memoranda; he drummed together the leading men of the large companie, he implored that there was only one way out — fusion.

The threat to the foreign markets silenced the former scruples, particularly since Duisberg no longer propagated total fusion whose irrevocability Brüning had so greatly feared. As a result, on 18th August 1916, the two groups that had been formed in 1904 joined forces, reinforced by Chemische Fabrik Griesheim-Elektron and Chemische Fabriken Weiler-ter Meer in Uerdingen. The initial agreement was for a term of fifty years.

They can withdraw

The «little I.G.» was not a closely integrated concern but only a loosely-linked association. Each member company was entitled to withdraw whenever it wished. It maintained its complete independence and retained sole liability in respect of third parties. But one essential aim was achieved. The various companies no longer seriously competed with each other. Instead, they exchanged know-how and information, rationalized and centralized their buying and selling.

All the takings went into the common I.G. till after the individual companies had drawn up their balance sheet and had calculated the preliminary profit. A final profit was then awarded to the various companies in accordance with the extent of their participation. Hoechst, which shortly before the merger had increased its share capital from 50 to 54 million in order to be level with BASF and Bayer, had a quota of 24.82 per cent. Special fields in which no significant profits had yet been achieved and whose future development could not yet be foreseen, were expressly excepted from this profit sharing and treated separately. Such special fields were, in the case of Ludwigshafen, the manufacture and selling of synthetic ammonia and the nitrogenous products and mixed fertilizers prepared from them, and in the case of Hoechst including Knapsack: carbide and the acetaldehyde products obtained from it, as well as calcium cyanamide. The highest authority of the association was its council. It decided on new plants, increases or reductions in share capital, the acquisition of other companies, the conclusion of cartels and conventions. Above all, however, the council decided on the rundown or curtailment of certain plants or the selling organization of any company within the association.

The association had retained the principle expressly laid down by Duisberg in his first memorandum, namely that every important product should, wherever possible, be manufactured by two companies. But this also caused the greatest area of conflict. For the merger had not obliterated the specific interests of the various firms. Even when the greater I.G. was formed, the former identities of the constituent companies survived underneath the new facade.

The council veto

For this reason, the founders of the 1916 I.G. had made a far-reaching provision. Every decision that interfered with the essential organism of its constituent companies required unanimous approval. Any such decision could therefore be vetoed.

Hoechst was represented on this council by Geheimrat *Adolf Haeuser*. In the nine years of the association, he was the dominating personality at Hoechst. He was a lawyer, however, — albeit an extremely capable one — and not a chemist like *Carl Bosch* and *Carl Duisberg*, the chairmen of BASF and Bayer respectively. This did not always prove of advantage for Hoechst, especially in organizational respects and where production matters were involved. Haeuser had joined Hoechst in 1889, the company's first resident lawyer. He assumed the chairmanship of Farbwerke Hoechst in 1916 in succession to Herbert Meister. Haeuser commanded ample authority and knew how to use it. For in the first post-war years, firm management was more important than ever.

The balance sheet of the lost war exceeded the worst fears. The chemical industry of Germany, which had lost most of its export markets, was charged with taxes by the victor states that brought it close to complete collapse. They culminated in the continuing acquisition of the foreign works, the forfeiture of many thousands of patents and a number of special reparation payments. For example, the companies were required to deliver 50 pc of their stocks and 25 pc of their production until the end of 1925 as part of the reparation debt. «To secure productive pawns», an interallied military control commission was set up in the various companies. A customs frontier was drawn along the Rhine. Finally, there came the unhappy separatist Ruhr affair and, as a consequence, the imposition of numerous sanctions. In March 1923, the Hoechst factory was surrounded by French troops. Machine guns were installed. Further discordant notes in all this were strikes, a catastrophic shortage of coal and transport, and continuous inflation. Recovery did not come until the Mark had been stabilised. It proceeded slowly enough. But, even so, in May 1924, the Hoechst management was able to chalk up a significant success: expenditure had not exceeded income to any significant extent. Nevertheless, more workers had to be dismissed.

Union with Wacker

One question in particular presented a great headache: what was to be done with the excess acetic acid capacity established during the war. For the requirements of vinegar were strictly limited — times were sour enough.

Not only Hoechst and Knapsack faced this problem. The Wacker-Gesellschaft, too, was producing acetic acid and acetone at Burghausen, having taken up this branch of manufacture at the same time as Hoechst. Farbwerke Hoechst was very interested in retaining the acetic acid market in peacetime. The consequence was intense competition with the wood-carbonisers and the fermentation vinegar producers. This required a great deal of effort and an additional trial of strength with Wacker-Gesellschaft could hardly be in the interest of Hoechst, particularly since Burghausen employed the same production process. An understanding with Wacker appeared advisable also for another reason. During the war, chlorine capacities had been considerably expanded, especially in Gersthofen. There was a danger that it would be difficult to sell the Gersthofen chlorine after the war, particularly if Wacker was going to offer its excess chlorine in South Germany. For all these reasons, the first contact between the two potential competitors was established as early as 1917. Initially, it led to close collaboration and then, in 1920, to a fifty-fifty partnership. The agreement also provided for an exchange of know-how in identical products.

A new product group: solvents

Gradually, a solution became apparent in the acetic acid field also. The Americans had started to turn the motor car from a luxury item into a utilitarian item whose acquisition was no longer the privilege of millionaires. As early as 1921, turnover of the Ford works alone had increased to more than a thousand million dollars and the five-millionth Ford car had been produced on the endless belt. Each one of these was lacquered black for *Henry Ford's* motto was «You can have your car in any colour you like, provided it's black».

Black or coloured, mass production of the motor car had become possible only through the development of nitrocellulose lacquers and these, in turn, had called for a vast solvent capacity. In the USA, amyl acetate was used at that time. It was obtained from amyl alcohol which was supplied in large amounts by the American fermentation industry. Hoechst chemists, however, found that a mixture of butyl acetate and butanol was at least equal to amyl acetate. The two solvents were produced from acetaldehyde.

In this way, at any rate part of the market difficulties were overcome as a result of the growth of the car industry. The little-used Hoechst acetic acid plants again came into their own. In time, many novel solvents were developed for a great variety of applications. The solvent range extended from low to high boiling compounds.

Amongst the dyestuffs, the prospects were less rosy. In 1924, there was no longer any doubt: approximately 40–50 pc of the peacetime business had irrevocably been lost to foreign competition. The I.G. Council had to draw the necessary consequences. As early as 1920, the I.G. formed a manufacturing commission. It was the predecessor of a large number of such commissions with whose aid the entire I.G. complex was eventually run.

This manufacturing commission selected the plants that were to be reduced, merged or dismantled altogether. Its recommendations, supported by data concerning the individual companies obtained through an exchange of costing figures, enabled the council to make the final decisions.

Kalle produces films

Some of these decisions hit Hoechst hard. As early as 1921, Hoechst's Alizarin production had been liquidated. In exchange, Hoechst was given the azo dyestuff production of Kalle which had become uneconomic because of an inadequate production volume. But, being properly concerned with the progress of its subsidiaries, Hoechst provided Kalle with a new outlet by assigning to it the rights to a promising foreign licence for the manufacture of CELLOPHANE.

Cellophane had been invented before the First World War by the Swiss chemist *Jacques Edwin Brandenberger*. Brandenberger had attempted to provide cotton fabrics with a dirt-repellent finish. He used for this purpose a viscose solution of the type employed for the manufacture of artificial silk.

Initially, the experiment proved a failure. Brandenberger was unable to achieve a finish that was closely combined with the fibre. All he got was a transparent skin that could be easily removed. But after numerous further experiments, Brandenberger made a major breakthrough. He produced a film that was only two hundredths of a millimeter thick. An ideal, completely transparent packaging material had been discovered.

Although Kalle had not the least experience in this type of production, it was able to take up the manufacture of film without difficulty in 1925. It proved much more difficult to find a market for the new cellophane because the packaging industry was exceedingly slow in recognising the potential of this novelty. Products wrapped in cellophane not only proved more attractive to the customer but they also protected the goods inside against moisture and heat. And when in 1930 CELLOPHANE WEATHERFAST appeared on the market, dry products such as biscuits could at last be kept dry, and moist products such as tobacco could be kept moist. Even today, cellophane weatherfast accounts for the largest share of Kalle's film production.

This complete change in Kalle's manufacturing activities had been achieved practically without hitch. In most other cases, however, the individual companies defended every inch of their terrain, even if only cuts in production were envisaged. It became daily clearer that the relatively loose structure of the association did not ensure the necessary reforms of the individual works. At the same time, foreign competition was daily gaining a greater share of the traditional markets of the German dyestuffs industry. And yet, the rationalisation of the I.G. companies had already borne the first fruits. It would have been a cause for great satisfaction if sales had risen correspondingly. But, in fact, they had considerably decreased so that large amounts of material began to accumulate in the company's stores. Dyestuffs stocks alone amounted to 87,000 tons or the requirements for one and a half years.

New fusion negotiations

In view of this situation, renewed merger talks took place at the turn of 1923/24. *Duisberg* of Bayer was now no longer alone in pressing for full fusion. *Bosch* of BASF, who had been in America only a few months previously, also advocated it. And although Duisberg would, in fact, have been satisfied with the formation of a group of independent companies, the majority of the I.G. members no longer wanted half-measures. If sacrifices had to be made, they felt, then the association should be so close that no one should be able to withdraw from it at will. «No management of any of the constituent companies», wrote *Fritz ter Meer* in his memorandum concerning the I.G. Farbenindustrie, «would be discharging its responsibilities to shareholders if it allowed production and selling to be curtailed at the risk that if the company had to withdraw at a later date for any important reason, its viability would be impaired.»

In contrast to 1904, Hoechst, too, was now ready to accept complete fusion. *Haeuser* and *Walter vom Rath*, the chairman of the Hoechst supervisory board, acted as go-betweens whenever differences of opinion between Duisberg and Bosch seemed to endanger realization of the I.G. project. And so, between the 13th and 14th November 1924, the great moment at last arrived. From the conference room of Bayer Leverkusen where the I.G. council was meeting, the white smoke was rising. Fusion had been decided upon. 'The little I.G. is dead, long live the big I.G.'

While agreement in principle was difficult enough, practical execution of the merger was almost a nightmare. The Frankfurter Zeitung wrote: «In a merger of such dimensions, unknown in financial history, this is hardly surprising.» A veritable jungle of legal, commercial and fiscal problems had to be resolved. On the 21st November 1925, how-

The joint council of the small I.G. in session

ever, matters had progressed far enough for the first stage of the merger to be put into effect. Farbwerke Hoechst, vormals Meister Lucius & Brüning, made over to BASF their entire assets, without liquidation, in exchange for BASF shares, nominal value for nominal value. The merger agreement was signed on 2nd December 1925. The other companies of the I.G. — Bayer-Leverkusen, Agfa-Berlin, Chemische Fabrik Griesheim-Elektron and Chemische Fabriken Weiler-ter Meer, Uerdingen — also assumed the BASF mantle. Now the second phase could begin. BASF changed its name to I.G. Farbenindustrie Aktiengesellschaft, moved its headquarters to Frankfurt and increased its capital by that of the newly-absorbed companies. The I.G. giant was about to move forward.

The management organization of the I.G. consisted of 83 people. All the members of the boards of management of the constituent companies belonged to it, a wise step which no doubt greatly helped to facilitate unification. Chairman was Karl Bosch, and the supervisory board, nearly as big, was headed by Carl Duisberg. Since these two bodies were clearly too large, an executive committee was appointed by each.

On the whole, the public did not react unfavourably to the I.G. fusion. It was widely recognised that this unique concentration of scientific, technical, financial and economic power was not an attempt to establish an omnipotent dictatorship but was simply designed to achieve the greatest degree of competitiveness.

The Frankfurter Zeitung wrote: «The first industrial trust in Germany has been realized as the result of a merger between the large chemical factories. A giant undertaking has been formed whose capital of 641.6 million ordinary shares and 4.4 million preference shares represents a present-day value of 750 million marks; a giant undertaking that has drawn together the entire German dyestuffs industry with its auxiliary branches and has the absolute power of a private monopoly that is quite unshakeable even if only because of its tremendous capital resources. This sounds like a tremendous event in the history of German industrial capitalism but in reality it is only the final recognition of a state of affairs that has long existed ... rationalisation of production and selling, uniformly concentrated mass production — that is the aim.»

The Vossische Zeitung commented: «If these various industrial companies are now becoming joined under one flag, then this is once more due to our present conditions which dictate cheaper production costs and simplification or improvement of the various organizations. That the new group will succeed can be confidently assumed because of the outstanding people that are to head it.»

The organs of the left not unnaturally expressed their displeasure over this new economic power which might easily become a state within a state. The social-democratic

«Vorwärts» was particularly critical of the new I.G. Its editors discussed the event in strictly ideological terms. «To proclaim Marxism dead is the vain endeavour of private capitalism. That Marxism is as alive as ever is shown by the large chemical industry of Germany. The transition that has now taken place from the aniline association to a fully merged complex is historical proof of the basic theory of Marxism — the concentration of capital. The reason for the fusion is not any inner weakness of the various constituents, as in the case of the Rheinisch-Westfälische Montan trust, but the inner strength favoured by technical development and promoted over many years by the constituent companies of the I.G.»

England's reply to the I.G.

Abroad, too, the I.G. merger was followed with close attention. After the Dupont group in America had achieved a dominant position, Imperial Chemical Industries was formed in England, a chemical complex of comparable proportions. As one of the founders of ICI declared at the time, this British chemical dominion was to secure the chemical independence of the Empire.

I.G. Farbenindustrie Aktiengesellschaft, Werk Farbwerke Hoechst, was the name on the Hoechst nameplate. Apart from the parent site, the Hoechst works also managed the I.G. Mittelrhein region which included Gersthofen, Knapsack and Kalle. Other regions were Oberrhein, Niederrhein, central Germany and Berlin. Later on, the Mittelrhein region was renamed Maingau and now included the Mainkur, Griesheim and Offenbach works but not Kalle. In addition to this regional arrangement, the entire I.G. production was split into three divisions. Of particular importance for Hoechst was division II, which comprised inorganic and organic chemicals as well as metals, dyestuffs, dyeing auxiliaries, pharmaceuticals and pesticides. The first chief of this group was *Paul Duden*. He was succeeded in 1933 by *Ludwig Hermann* who had given sterling service in Gersthofen. Gersthofen camphor and wax production, still among Hoechst's best-sellers, was in the main built up by him.

The first years of the I.G. were inseparably linked with Carl Bosch. He directed the entire energy potential of the I.G. to large-scale chemical syntheses which BASF had already so successfully undertaken in the field of ammonia. Bosch's citadel of technology, the huge Leunawerk, was constructed first of all in Oppau and later at Merseburg, under the aegis of the 1916 association. Oppau and Leuna supplied 1.5 million tons of nitrogenous fertilizer per year. But Bosch had even greater ambitions. «You cannot afford to rest on your laurels or to be satisfied with the information that has been gained», he wrote in the Frankfurter Zeitung. And his future targets were ambitious indeed: rubber synthesis, hydrogenation of coal, man-made fibres. These plans brought the I.G. deeper and deeper into central Germany. For it was here, in the midst of large lignite deposits, that there was sufficient cheap power for undertakings of this size.

Surgery for the dyestuffs range

In order to concentrate all available forces on these projects, it was necessary to economize elsewhere and to apply the brakes in certain fields. An obvious victim was the inflated dyestuffs range.

As late as 1926, the I.G. works were still producing some 32,000 commercial dyestuff grades although the colorist commission had already deleted 60 pc from the original selection. Dyestuffs like Patent Blue were produced by eight different works within the I.G. No less than eleven dyestuffs sub-commissions were painstakingly weeding out this overgrown field. Thousands of figures had to be produced to be able to make comparisons and to determine where production was most economic. Once these reports were available — the I.G. spirit so frequently cited by Duisberg must at that time have been residing in but a few of its members — a truly titanic struggle began. A report «Hoechst and the I.G.» stated: «Since every works was concerned with gaining the maximum benefit from the fusion of dyestuffs production and without suffering any weakening of its own position, some of the meetings were very acrimonious indeed. There was a tough fight for every product.»

In the commission meetings, the figures provided by the various works concerning costing, capacities etc. were critically examined. Everything depended on these figures For Hoechst had been selected to suffer the major part of the intended surgery in the dyestuff field. This was due to two reasons. Firstly, it was doubtlessly true that, technically, the Hoechst dyestuffs plants were not entirely equal to those of the other two major merger partners. Secondly, the Hoechst works had been extensively decentralized during the period of independence. This meant that dyestuffs were manufactured in completely different departments. This applied even to dyestuffs of the same class, for example, the vat dyestuffs. Each of these departments was the responsibility of another member of the board of management. It was not until 1934 that the four dyestuffs departments were joined into one factory, as part of the reorganisation of the Hoechst works started by Dr. *Ludwig Hermann* when he assumed the post of works manager in 1933.

Bloodletting for Hoechst

As a result of the first major re-organisation within the I.G., Hoechst lost some 2.5 pc of its dyestuff production. The Leverkusen production on the other hand increased by 27.4 pc and that of Ludwigshafen by 6.2 pc. The biggest bloodletting operation was in respect of the Hoechst-Azo department. Its production was reduced by 20 pc. Large parts of intermediates production were also pared off.

For the first time, therefore, the equilibrium of the former big three was upset. Until then, all three were of approximately equal strength in the dyestuffs field. But now, after the great sacrifices on the I.G. altar, Hoechst was reduced to third place.

The end of duplication

In 1930, production was once more re-grouped. The basis for this was the following decision by the technical committee: «Following the first concentration three years ago, the time has come to carry out further rationalisation. The immediate aim will be the elimination of any duplicate production that may still exist. A reduction in the number of manufacturing units for certain product classes will also be investigated». This meant the abandonment of Duisberg's maxim that every important product should be manufactured in two different plants so that internal competition was not entirely eliminated. Once more, there was a tremendous tug-of-war between the individual companies. The incipient international economic crisis increased the pressure for rationalisation. In addition, American chemical undertakings were trying desperately to break into the European dyestuffs market. Only chemicals and pharmaceuticals managed to maintain their position.

Hoechst now had to do without large parts of its dyestuff and intermediate production. Even the residual production of azo dyestuffs had to be partly shared with other works. The only exception were the paint and pyrazolone dyestuffs.

But in other fields, Hoechst was strengthened. It became the sole producer of PATENT BLUE, METHYLENE BLUE, SAFRANIN and ROSANILIN BLUE. As a result of the curtailment of production, the number of employees in Hoechst was reduced from 8,981 in 1929 to 5,615 in 1930. This meant a reduction of 60 pc in twelve months. The solvent department, too, was threatened by a plant shutdown. In this case, however, Hoechst refused to budge. After all, it was Hoechst who, together with Wacker, had created industrial acetylene chemistry. At one time, even Griesheim and Offenbach were to be shut down.

The renaissance of the alizarin department

The alizarin department had been weakened most by the rationalisation measures. A large part of its former output was now being made elsewhere. There was, however, little disposition in Hoechst to accept this state of affairs without a fight. Henceforth, the motto was: «intensification of research.» This was pursued with considerable energy under the management of *Georg Kränzlein* who had become manager of the alizarin department at the end of 1922. The result was a range of valuable dyestuffs which were in part developed from entirely new bases. Most of them qualified for the Indanthren trade mark which had been created by the I.G. and which was a guarantee of outstanding light and washing fastness. To propagate the Indanthren label, the I.G. established several Indanthren houses throughout Germany. These sold nothing but Indanthren-dyed or printed textiles. Since the dismemberment of the I.G., the Indanthren House Munich GmbH has been owned by Hoechst. The INDIGOSOLS, now known as ANTHRASOLS, were another entirely new class of dyestuffs to be included in the production programme. The credit for this must go to two Alsatian chemists, *Marcel Bader* and *Charles Sunder* who sought to simplify the use of water-soluble vat dyestuffs. They discovered that sulphuric esters of leuko-vat dyestuffs are water-soluble compounds which are absorbed by the fibre and then developed, the ester group being split off.

The Swiss company of Durand & Huguenin, Basle, acquired this process and concluded a contract with Leverkusen, Ludwigshafen and Hoechst for its industrial exploitation. The Hoechst alizarin department looked after this new field. Together with the coloristic department, the process was perfected from the point of view of both manufacture and application. By 1929, a dyestuffs range comprising some 29 different grades had been developed.

Modest dividends

However drastic some of the rationalisation measures might have been, the credit side of the picture was improving steadily although the days were past when the shareholders of Hoechst, Ludwigshafen and Leverkusen collected dividends of 20 or even 25 pc. The I.G. was a thrifty dividend payer because of the changed world situation and the subsequent dividend stop imposed by war conditions. In the first years, a dividend of 12 pc was paid, between 1931 and 1936 it was 7 pc and thereafter, 8 pc. The bulk of the profits went into new investments, associates and research and experimental plants.

Among the large number of «indirect associates», as Bosch called them, the Riebeck'sche Montanwerke at Halle assumed particular importance. Together with a number of other mines, they formed the coal basis for the Leunawerke. The coal basis for the works in Western Germany was provided by the Gewerkschaft Auguste Victoria, which was wholly-owned by the I.G., and the Rheinische Stahlwerke in which I.G. had a holding of approximately 47.5 pc.

The man-made fibre field

Many other companies came within the orbit of the I.G. Among these, the former explosives factories of the Nobel concern were of particular importance. The Köln-Rottweil AG, with the artificial silk factories of Rottweil on Neckar, Bobingen near Augsburg and Premnitz in Mark Brandenburg, merged with the I.G. in 1926. This meant that the artificial silk production of the I.G. was greatly enlarged. In the Wolfen-Film works near Bitterfeld, artificial silk based on viscose had been manufactured since 1921. Dormagen took up the production of cuprammonium continuous filament in 1926, followed in 1927 by Aceta GmbH in Lichtenberg which engaged in the manufacture of artificial silk from acetate. In 1930, all the shares of this company were acquired by the I.G. During the Second World War, the Landsberg works on the Warthe river were constructed as a pioneer plant for the large-scale production of Perlon staple and continuous filament. In 1926, the I.G. had again included rubber synthesis in its manufacturing programme and after the first production plant had been built at Schkopau near Halle in 1936, decisive progress could at last be recorded. In 1938, the I.G. set up its second Buna plant in Hüls near Recklinghausen. Schkopau, Hüls and a smaller company at Ludwigshafen supplied no less than 120,000 tons of Buna in 1943. «This Buna synthesis was an outstanding co-operative effort by the I.G. works at Leverkusen, Ludwigshafen, Oppau and Hoechst» wrote *Fritz ter Meer*. In Oppau, an important starting position for formaldehyde-based plastics had additionally been created with the aid of methanol high-pressure synthesis.

Although the nationalistic noises in Germany were becoming louder and louder, new flags continued to be placed in the maps of the world in the I.G. headquarters in Frankfurt. More and more foreign companies came to an understanding with the I.G. There was a particularly close connection between the I.G. and the American Standard Oil Co. which culminated in the Standard I.G. Co. which was intended to exploit the patents for the liquefaction of naphtha. Through the American Chemical Corporation, the I.G. also had an interest in half a dozen other American companies.

International connections

Similar functions were fulfilled in Western Europe by I.G. Chemie Basle and Internationale Gesellschaft für Chemische Unternehmungen A.G. The I.G. also had relations with Norsk Hydro in Oslo. In addition, there was a nitrogen syndicate and a large number of trusts, including the European dyestuffs trust in whose formation the manager of the I.G. dyestuffs sales department, *Georg von Schnitzler,* played a decisive part. The trust was originally formed from the French and Swiss groups and the I.G. Later on, the ICI also joined. From this point of view, the I.G. can rightly be described as an internationally-orientated trust, a complex and very independent trust which, for this very reason, never quite gained the full confidence of the new rulers of Germany.

Abroad, however, the company enjoyed almost boundless admiration. Apart from the major syntheses, it was probably the I.G. pharmaceuticals that earned most of the goodwill and admiration. It was in this field particularly that the anachronism of nationalism showed up most clearly. The fight against illness and disease was world-wide and frequently the same successes were achieved in various parts of the world at the same time.

A typical example is the history of INSULIN. Since the development of SUPRARENIN, the labyrinth of the hormonal principles had been thoroughly investigated by Hoechst. German scientists had been on the trail of the hormone of the pancreatic gland even before the First World War. This hormone reduced the blood sugar level, a prime condition for successful treatment of diabetes, a disease suffered by hundreds of thousands without any prospect of help from the medical world. However, there were, as yet, no accurate analytical methods to determine blood sugar precisely. For years, Hoechst laboratory workers edged their way forward in this field without however making more than minimum progress. It was not until after 1918 that the right way was found. But this time it did not involve chemical syntheses as in the case of Adrenalin but the conversion of animal glands into a useful antidiabetic. Hoechst concluded agreements with the slaughterhouses of Frankfurt and Karlsruhe concerning the supply of pancreatic glands from calves and cattle.

While Hoechst was still waiting for the test results, a piece of news of the utmost medical importance hit the headlines of the world. In the physiological laboratory of Toronto University, Canada, the preparation of the pure active ingredient of the pancreatic gland had been successfully accomplished. Even before precise details became available, Farbwerke Hoechst produced two new pancreatic extracts. They were tested by Professor *Carl von Noorden* in Frankfurt. His verdict: in principle, just as effective as Insulin. In Canada, too, Hoechst's pioneering work was acknowledged unreservedly. Farbwerke Hoechst was granted the first licence for insulin manufacture by the Toronto process.

Greater expectation of life — thanks to insulin

Thus, with the aid of insulin, another widespread scourge of mankind had been brought under control. Insulin increased the expectation of life of a ten-year-old diabetic more than twenty times and that of a thirty-year-old six times; it doubled that of a fifty-year-old. Hundreds of thousands who had been made semi-invalids by this disease and who had not been able to follow a normal occupation, were able to do so once again. It will not be difficult to guess just how great a blessing this was to all concerned — in physical, psychological and material respects.

Fifteen years after the first insulin ampoules had been filled in Hoechst, the company was able to score another major triumph in this field. It became the first company in the world to change over its production to pure, crystallized insulin. One year later, in 1938, Hoechst developed NATIV-INSULIN, a suitable depot preparation.

In 1939, Hoechst brought out yet another outstanding preparation — Dolantin — which achieved great fame among the many analgesics that were then available. The drug had four times the efficacy of Pyramidon and at the same time exhibited spasmolytic properties. Dolantin, a purely synthetic substance, made the use of the alkaloid morphine and its not altogether harmless derivatives largely unnecessary, even in cases of grave colic.

PYRAMIDON, NOVOCAIN, SALVARSAN, INSULIN and now DOLANTIN — these, together with the important sera, were the products with which Hoechst secured for itself its place in the history of medicine. They were the jewels in the Hoechst pharmaceutical crown, creations that filled every employee with pride in the Hoechst sign which lit not only the streets of their own towns and villages but which shone brightly even in the darkest corners of the earth.

After Hoechst had been integrated in the I.G. complex, there came a day, however, when these products were no longer sold under the Hoechst emblem but bore the Bayer cross. At first, there was at least the by-line «manufactured in the Hoechst works of the I.G. Farbenindustrie AG»; but eventually even this modest acknowledgement was omitted in the larger interests of the company.

There were, no doubt, good reasons for this policy and perhaps it was not a very

serious matter in the context of the larger events. Hoechst had taken the big step and its independent history had to all intents and purposes come to its irrevocable end. Who in Germany at that time had even the slightest inkling of the transience of this alleged irrevocability.

The Hoechst AG is formed

For eight years, a period equal to the life of the former «little I.G.», the divided I.G. complex remained under allied control. But, during the course of the years, more and more functions had been transferred to German hands. There was FARDIP, the German assessors' committee, there were the German study groups formed as part of TRIFCO, there were the trustees of the various companies and the liquidators appointed by the allies. All of them had done their best to get the victorious nations to approve the establishment of at least three large successor companies that would be able to maintain themselves against the intense international competitive conditions. The changed political constellation and the growing authority of the Federal Government had a favourable effect on these efforts. Also, it became clearer every day that it was anachronistic to keep under quarantine, in the midst of a free and prosperous economy, a complex of a magnitude such as was represented by the major I.G. successor companies in spite of all the destruction and amputations that they had suffered.

It was, therefore, almost inevitable that at the end of 1951 the 100,000 DM Hoechst AG should be formed, to be followed shortly afterwards by the constitution of the new administrative apparatus which only then, after heartbreaking processes of stocktaking, was able to gain an adequate picture of the available manufacturing capacity. Until then, all decisions made at Hoechst had been subject to the uncertainty of the provisional. That it was possible, nevertheless, during these years of interregnum, to lay a great many of the foundations for the later reconstruction is part of the phenomenon that has been less than adequately interpreted by the concept of the economic miracle.

1952 had seen the final phase of the I.G. dismemberment and the first steps towards reconstitution. 1953 was dominated by renewed freedom of action. The newly-formed limited companies, Hoechst, Ludwigshafen and Leverkusen had been consolidated to such an extent that their economic development could proceed freely. On 27th March 1953, almost eight years after the end of the war, the first extraordinary general meeting took place at Hoechst. The most important decision was the increase in capital from 100,000 to 285.7 million DM and the formal incorporation of the Hoechst, Gries-heim, Offenbach and Gersthofen plants into the Farbwerke Hoechst AG. Knapsack, Kalle, Behringwerke and Bobingen became subsidiaries.

Following the annual general meeting, the founders, the Hoechst supervisory board and board of management, the boards of management of the subsidiaries and the works councils and delegations of the employees of the new companies met in the auditorium of the Hoechst administration building. The chairman of the board of management, *Karl Winnacker*, seized on this occasion to make a now famous speech. It was significant for two reasons. Firstly, it was a courageous and unqualified defence of the board of management and the supervisory board of the former I.G. Secondly, the speech laid down the boundaries within which the new company was to operate. Since this speech represents an important chapter in the history of the company, its full text is given below. Winnacker declared:

«As of today, allied control has ended. The company has regained its full rights and responsibilities in accordance with German law. When some eight years ago, on 23rd March 1945, we gave the order for the complete stoppage of all plants in view of the advancing battle front, all life ceased in our ninety-year old works. During those weeks, we saw in our country, as the fearful consequence of a war conducted with inhumanity to the point of disintegration, the collapse of all that had been created during centuries of tradition. Economy, state und law collapsed.

In mute resignation, we experienced the end of our statehood. If today, after the first years of reconstruction, we have regained full jurisdiction over our company, which is again in full operation, then this shows that we overestimated the power of destruction.

Under the shadow of impending disaster, we forgot that somehow life always continues. It has continued, in spite of death and destruction. If the fight for our existence and the efforts involved in our reconstruction have left us little time for reflection, then on this day of joy our first duty is to recall those friends and collaborators that have not survived this most fearful catastrophe in the history of our people.

In the companies and works now belonging to Hoechst, 1933 employees were killed in battle, or by bombs, or are missing. Our thoughts are with them and their kin. Let them remind us at all times that we must never again gamble with the precious gift of peace.

One of the most far-reaching steps that the Allies took in consequence of their victory, was the Control Commission Law No. 9 of 30th November 1945 which sanctioned the confiscation of the I.G. Farbenindustrie on 5th July 1945 and which formed the basis of the dismemberment of the I.G. in conformity with the later Law No. 35 of the Allied High Commission. Almost unnoticed by the majority of the people, who were preoccupied with the fight for their existence, this meant the destruction of the most important undertaking that German science and technology and German enterprise had ever developed.

In a trial fought with great bitterness, the responsible leaders of the I.G. Farbenindustrie AG, and thus our entire company, were able to rebut all the charges of war crimes, robbery and plunder levied against them. We feel closely linked with all the former leaders of the I.G. Farbenindustrie AG and with all the old friends of this company and we are happy that a number of them are able to be with us today.

Up to the present, reconstruction of the old works has been carried out under allied control. These works had been partly destroyed by bombs and their organisation had been completely upset by dismissals. Their links with subsidiaries, on whom they had come to rely for all stages of manufacture as a result of twenty years of collaboration, had been completely severed. The central selling organisation no longer existed and a provisional system had to be established in the individual works. With untiring effort, the employees of our factories, under their new management, have achieved an admirable feat of reconstruction.

We thank the staff and workers that helped us in this task and that stayed loyal to their former works. We also thank the managers and trustees who succeeded, within the limitations of narrow and stringent regulations imposed by the Allies, in bringing the works back to full production and making them competitive once more.

The work of reconstruction in the various plants was accompanied by a bitter fight concerning the future economic organisation of the I.G. successor companies. As both victor and vanquished slowly drew back from the atmosphere of hate and destruction, they became more reasonable and the plans for the reconstruction of what remained were put on an economically sounder footing.

We have succeeded in preventing complete disintegration of the I.G. and in confining the division of the I.G. Farbenindustrie to the minimum number of companies so as to maintain viable units. This has in no small measure been due to the control authorities who had been charged by their countries with the dismemberment of the I.G. Farbenindustrie AG und who could in many cases be persuaded to take another view and to accept our plans for the foundation of economically practicable units.

The German government intervened in these arguments at an early date and used its authority to help ensure that instead of an infinite number of uneconomic plants, three large successor companies were formed. In tough diplomatic negotiations the basis of the present arrangement was hammered out, the arguments in respect of each company frequently extending over many months.

We should like to seize on this occasion to thank the Federal government, led by Chancellor Dr. *Adenauer*, who at the decisive moment, intervened personally in the negotiations, and especially in matters concerning the Hoechst works. We also thank the Federal Minister of Economics, Prof. Dr. *Erhard* and Secretary of State, *Westrick* and his collaborators, particularly Dr. *Prentzel*, who have effectively supported us in the protacted negotiations. Hoechst also offers its thanks to the government of Hesse and in particular to Dr. *Zinn*, its president. He displayed at all times a considerable interest in our many special problems and he has often intervened personally, with great determination and considerable success, on behalf of Farbwerke Hoechst.

Our thanks are also due to the Bavarian government with whom we are closely linked through our plants and interests in Bavaria. The negotiations extended over many years and involved considerable differences of opinion. That they have nevertheless led to a reasonable and economically viable result, is due in no small measure to the valuable part played by press and radio.

We also thank the I.G. liquidators, Dr. *Brinkmann*, Dr. *Reuter* and Dr. *Schmidt* for their efficient support and their helpful mediation.

Finally, I feel I must thank all those members of our company, of whatever level, who have tried to find a practical solution to our problems. Above all, I must thank our founders who have given practical expression to the solution at which we arrived. At last constituted and freed from Allied control, Farbwerke Hoechst AG thus sets out on its future. Its companions are Leverkusen, Ludwigshafen, Cassella Farbwerke Main-

kur AG and Chemische Werke Hüls, who have now also been reconstituted. All these companies are linked by an association that has lasted over many years. Their dissection after the war has left many wounds. We are closely linked with regard to the supply of starting products and intermediates and we also supplement our respective selling ranges. We shall be able to face future economic competition and we shall be able to fulfil our economic obligations only if competition — which can have beneficial effects — is honest and reasonable. The close, and in many cases personal, friendship between management and employees, which has linked us over a long period of common history, will help us in this.

The company that we have christened today may be a complex not readily understood by the outsider. Those, however, who have followed our struggle for enlargement from a knowledge of the old Farbwerke Hoechst and the relationships of the old I.G. Farbenindustrie, will know that these efforts were not merely concerned with an increase in turnover or the acquisition of additional interests, but that they aimed at completing the intricate pattern of our activities.

One of the most important divisions of Hoechst continues to be the dyestuffs division which has now been supplemented by Naphtol-Chemie Offenbach. Hoechst dyestuffs manufacture is based on our intermediates production which has now been supplemented by Griesheim and Lech-Chemie.

The pharmaceuticals division has regained its traditional complement, namely Behringwerke. To be economic, our sulphuric acid production relies to a large extent on collaboration with the Duisburg Kupferhütte and for this reason, we warmly welcome the re-establishment of the former close relationship. An important contribution to the fertilizer and plant protection field are the calcium cyanamide production of Knapsack and the pesticides produced in Gersthofen.

The solvents and plastics divisions developed at Hoechst have long been based on Knapsack carbide and acetaldehyde. This field, too, has now been extended in important respects by the Perlon factory in Bobingen.

The Kalle plants, which are concerned with the processing of plastics, will closely collaborate with Hoechst's plastics division and we believe that this collaboration will provide a fresh and strong impetus for both. In this field, the old link with Wacker-Chemie GmbH is also of great value. Together, we have promoted the development of acetylene chemistry for more than thirty years. We have a large stake in the electrochemical field. There are the phosphorus and ferrous alloys from Knapsack, carbon from Griesheim, graphite from Sigri, common salt electrolysis at Hoechst, Gersthofen

Professor Winnacker addresses
the Annual General Meeting in March 1953

and Wacker, and sodium production in Gersthofen. There is finally the important field of welding techniques, with carbide production at Knapsack and the manufacture of oxygen and welding equipment in a number of widely scattered plants. It is not possible, on this occasion, to follow thes relationships more closely. Prerequisite for progressive development in all these extensive fields is adequate research. After great initial difficulties, some 992 chemists, engineers, doctors and pharmacists are now once more employed in our scientific laboratories and in our plants. We hope that we shall succeed in filling the gaps of the past and in helping German chemical industry to get back on its feet. We must, however, be clear that we shall find it difficult to realize the large vision that the former I.G. Farbenindustrie pursued.

One of our most rewarding tasks will be the promotion of a spirit of co-operation throughout our establishments. We believe that the form of organisation that we have chosen will, for historical and factual reasons, be particularly conducive to this end. While the basic production is concentrated in the Hoechst, Griesheim, Offenbach and Gersthofen complex, the structure of the subsidiaries is based on specific, self-contained fields that have a worthwhile sales potential.

The involuntary long separation faces us with tremendous organisational tasks that will require outstanding human qualities.

We shall, all of us, have to show a great deal of confidence and understanding so that a high degree of fusion is achieved.

At this moment of satisfaction over our regained freedom and over the chance of a new start, we should remain conscious of the responsibility that we assume. Our shareholders have had to bear heavy sacrifices as a result of the dissolution of the I.G. Not only the large shareholders but tens of thousands of small savers that supported the I.G. Farbenindustrie with confidence and loyalty for many years have been hard hit in these years. Worries about the future fate of their hard-earned assets were re-awakened during the discussions concerning the nominal capital of the new companies. The opening DM balance sheet of the I.G., published in spring 1952, created many misunderstandings concerning the actual capital situation among savers not familiar with all the details of these intricate financial questions.

If the current rate of exchange of 10 : 9 causes dissatisfaction amongst some, we beg them to realize the seriousness of our present circumstances. The successor companies and plants that are now going to look after the former I.G. capital together own no more than 36 pc of the assets of the I.G. Farbenindustrie. Fourteen per cent have been lost abroad and fifty per cent in the Eastern zone and beyond.

The loss of all our patents and trademarks abroad, the publication of all our trade secrets, the extensive damage suffered during dismantling and the curtailment of many important and profitable industrial activities have caused us serious harm. In contrast, the rest of the world has used the post-war era to build up its industries and to lay the foundations for a successful future.

We must therefore ask you to understand why we have evaluated so soberly the assets that have been made over to us. We were not guided by any desire to make life easy for ourselves. In fixing the nominal capital, we were conscious of our great responsibility towards our former I.G. shareholders. Once the transition period of the share exchange has passed, our shares will again become the classic, safe investment in the German stock market, an investment in which shareholders can have faith, even in times of crisis, because it is based on a long-term, balanced and sustained dividend policy.

Now that the shareholders' committee has signified its support of our decisions, we propose to remain faithful to our shareholders if they continue to be faithful to us. After the most careful examination of our business prospects, we are confident that we can accept this responsibility under present conditions. We hope, of course, that the government will facilitate our fulfilment of this obligation by a forward-looking financial and fiscal policy so that, apart from meeting our dividend obligations, the expansion of the company remains safeguarded.

We should like to assure our pensioners that we shall extend the same loyalty to them also. For some years after the end of the war, we were not allowed to resume pension payments and it was later still before we were permitted to make up the payment arrears that had accrued in the meantime. The pension regulations now decreed by the Allies have as their main purpose the distribution of the pension liabilities of the I.G. Farbenindustrie AG over the successor companies. They also safeguard the present pension of all I.G. pensioners, including those that did not work in any of the plants of the successor companies. But even more important than this regulation is the firm resolve of management and employees to continue the personnel policies initiated by the former I.G. Farbenindustrie.

We shall regard the fate of our pensioners as our own — as indeed it is — for a cardinal principle of any personnel policy is care for the aged and the infirm. It must, of course, be realized that this duty imposes great responsibilities on our plants.

Just how great a burden this represents is strikingly illustrated by the fact that for every two active employees in our company, there is one pensioner.

In this hour of the rebirth of Farbwerke Hoechst, I appeal on behalf of the management to all employees to extend to us their wholehearted co-operation. There has for many years been understanding and friendship between us and these have survived even the greatest calamities. We are accustomed to close collaboration with the works councils. If we wish to solve the tremendous personnel problems ahead of us, this collaboration will have to be even closer than before.»

The foundations of reconstruction

It was indeed a sober report that Winnacker presented to his audience. Everyone present realized the gravity of the tasks ahead. And everyone caught the spirit of determination to tackle and to master the many problems that the company had to face. In almost grim silence, the audience listened to the closing words of Professor Winnacker: «At this moment of our re-creation, we must realize that our work for the company imposes upon us great and serious duties. Unsparing devotion and a sense of responsibility at all levels — in the plants, the workshops, the offices, the management — a deep understanding of the human factor — whether in the boardroom or on the shop floor — these are the foundations of our new, and yet so old, company. If we accept these obligations, seriously and conscientiously, we shall be able to evolve that social pattern for which our people, chastened by catastrophe, so earnestly strive. Then our company will prosper; then we shall find security for our families both during active life and in retirement; then we shall find satisfaction and happiness in our work without which no life is worth living.»

The formation of the new company coincided with another event. The plants and interests from the I.G. heritage that had been promised to Hoechst were now officially made over. Farbwerke Hoechst thus comprised the plants of Hoechst, Chemische Fabrik Griesheim, Naphtol-Chemie Offenbach and Lech-Chemie Gersthofen. Some 15,000 people worked in this group.

In addition, Hoechst acquired the entire capital of Knapsack-Griesheim AG, Kalle & Co. AG, Bobingen AG and Behringwerke AG. This meant that some 27,000 people worked in the Hoechst complex.

Apart from some minor interests, Hoechst was given 49 pc of the shares of Wacker Chemie GmbH (share capital 40 million; employees 4,000) and some 30 pc of the Duisburg Kupferhütte. This latter company had been founded in 1867 by several sulphuric acid producers in order to process the residues obtained in the roasting of foreign pyrites. Its capital in 1953 was 24 million DM and it gave employment to some 3,300 people.

Hoechst had pursued the return of its former interests with great tenacity. In this, it was guided not only by historical considerations but even more by simple issues of self-interest whose significance could not be denied by anyone concerned with a factual approach to the problem. For almost forty years, Hoechst had operated entirely on its own. At the end of the century, it joined forces with Gersthofen so as to have access to the cheap power provided by the Lech, power that Hoechst badly needed for its indigo synthesis. When the future importance of acetylene chemistry came to be realized, Hoechst acquired the Knapsack carbide plant in the lignite fields of the Rhineland.

During the succeeding years, technical interdependence became so close that Hoechst lost its original autocratic character. The subsidiaries had become indispensable. Hoechst could no longer function without Knapsack's carbide which had become the foundation of the entire acetylene chemistry.

Knapsack was hit hard during the war. Almost 70 pc of the plants had been destroyed. «Knapsack should have ceased to exist after the bombing of 28th October 1944, for what remained was smoke, but not the smoke of production but only that of ruins and ashes», wrote the authors of a festival brochure on the occasion of the fiftieth anniversary of Knapsack.

But by 1948, the carbide furnaces were belching smoke again and in each succeeding year, the company presented new products: granulated calcium cyanamide, ferrosilicon, monochloracetic acid, and finally, acetone based on isopropylalcohol. To crown this development, Knapsack — by then already under the aegis of Hoechst — was able to start up the first phosphorus plant in the Federal Republic. Today, the products from this plant find wide application, especially for detergents, plasticizers for plastics, baking powder or agricultural fertilizers.

Phosphorus manufacture was based on the electrothermal process developed by *Gustav Pistor* in Griesheim and Bitterfeld. This had proved highly successful in the phosphorus plant at Piesteritz on the Elbe, part of the I.G. set-up, where in 1927 four phosphorus furnaces with a load of 10,000 kW each had gone on stream. The process was perfected at Knapsack. The first furnace had a load of 20,000 kW which was increased to 50,000 kW in the second and third furnaces.

Together with Knapsack, the wholly-owned subsidiary of Gebr. Wandesleben GmbH of Stromberg in the Hunsrück also came to Hoechst. This company produces the slaked lime so vital to carbide manufacture.

Knapsack could hardly have survived as an independent company. Its production range was too narrow and the basis for reconstruction too small. The fact that in 1951 the

Allies merged Knapsack with Griesheim-Autogen and the other oxygen plants of the former I.G. and that they gave it a 70 pc holding in Friedrich Uhde GmbH, made the company more attractive than ever.

Friedrich Uhde GmbH had been founded as a design office in 1921. Initially, it occupied itself with the design and construction of nitrogen plants but extended its activities to the mineral oil field when the Leunawerke of the I.G. acquired an interest in it. At the present time, Uhde is concerned with the design and construction of plant for the chemical industry. Its Hagen works supplies high-pressure fittings for ammonia syntheses, hydrogenation plants and other high-pressure processes. It operates processes developed or perfected in Farbwerke Hoechst or its associated companies. Nitrogen and fertilizer plants, refineries, ethylene and plastics plants, chlorine-alkali electrolyses, man-made fibre-plants — all these and many more have been erected by Uhde throughout the world. On the other hand, Kalle with its cellophane production, which the Allies proposed to sell to the highest bidder, could not do without Hoechst. At an early date, therefore, the Kalle management tried to re-establish contact with Hoechst. After tough negotiations, the American decartellization chief — *Newman* — was won over. But the economic committee of the Allied High Commission for a long time rejected the plan out of hand. A decision in favour of Hoechst could be secured only after an exhausting tug-of-war and after the Federal and Länder governments had intervened. Hoechst was, however, required to pass 18 pc of the share capital to a French industrial group. This was intended as compensation for old contractual obligations about which no agreement could be reached. Later on, these 18 pc were, by amicable agreement, returned to Hoechst so that Kalle once again became a wholly-owned subsidiary of Hoechst.

Adenauer intervenes on behalf of Hoechst

It proved just as difficult to re-establish the links between Wacker and Hoechst. At first, the Americans played with the idea of selling the Wacker shares to a banker's consortium. At this point, the then German Federal Chancellor, *Adenauer,* and his cabinet intervened on Hoechst's behalf. In March 1952, he wrote to the Allies: «For economic, legal and political reasons, the cabinet has come to the conclusion that it cannot agree to the Wacker arrangement proposed by the economic commission of the Allied High Commission. In view of this decision by the Federal Government, arrived at after a great deal of careful thought, I would ask you to request the economic committee of the Allied High Commission to re-examine its attitude in this matter and, if necessary, to enter into negotiations with the Federal Ministry of Economics.»

This démarche was not without success. At the end of 1952, the economic commission of the Allied High Commission revised its earlier decision. Hoechst was allowed to acquire the former I.G. holding in this company.

This had also been the wish of Wacker Chemie which had been closely associated with Hoechst since 1921. Hoechst was, however, required to sell 1 pc of its holding to the Wacker family so as to reduce it to 49 pc. In 1958, however, the former 50/50 partnership was re-established in agreement with the family.

Behring returns

It is surely superfluous to emphasise the traditional collaboration between Hoechst and the Behringwerke at Marburg. The latter's diphtheria and tetanus sera, as well as many vaccines, will forever occupy a proud place in the annals of medical history. During the dismemberment of the I.G., serious differences of opinion arose over the future fate of Behringwerke. The government of Hesse energetically supported the interests of Hoechst so that eventually, Behringwerke, too, returned to the fold.

Bobingen — courted by many

Bobingen was a newcomer to the Hoechst complex. This was not the fortuitous result of the dismemberment of the I.G., but the fruit of a hard-fought battle. In the past, there had been no points of contact between Hoechst and Bobingen. The company had been formed in the second half of the last century. For almost thirty years, Bobingen was a bleaching works. In 1899, it was converted into an artificial silk plant producing, from 1902 onwards, collodion silk and artificial horsehair. During the first world war, Bobingen nitrated cellulose to produce gun cotton and, in consequence — in conformity with the provisions of the treaty of Versailles — the factory was demolished in 1919. Later on, Bobingen came under the wing of the Köln-Rottweil AG, Berlin, which reformed the company as an artificial silk producer. When the Köln-Rottweil AG, together with its subsidiary, became a part of the I.G., a period of prosperity began for Bobingen. The number of spinning machines was trebled and production was increased during the second world war to approximately seven tons per day. At the end of the war, the company was away to an early start. As early as October 1945, part of the plant was producing again and in February 1946 the first viscose bristles were produced. Bobingen had also gained early experience in the manufacture of perlon fibre. The Allies had no intention whatever of joining Bobingen to Hoechst. Their plan was to merge Bobingen, Rottweil and Dormagen into one great artificial silk complex. At

the same time, Cassella — which was then greatly interested in man-made fibres — cast covetous eyes at Bobingen.

Hoechst had never produced man-made fibres and during the I.G. era it had not been concerned in the field of mouldable plastics and synthetic fibres. The re-formation of Hoechst, therefore, presented practically the last chance of staking out a claim in this new field. In this concept, a vital role was played by Knapsack as raw material producer and Kalle and Bobingen as plastics processors.

Hoechst had clearly recognised that its position in the dyestuffs and organic and inorganic field would not be sufficient in the long run to enable it to meet the competition from abroad. Du Pont with its nylon, or ICI with its Terylene, had long since established themselves in the man-made fibres field. The I.G., too, had occupied itself with man-made fibres before war broke out. In 1938, *Paul Schlack* had discovered Perlon in the I.G. works of Berlin-Lichtenberg but development of this fibre was greatly retarded by the outbreak of war.

Because of its involvement in acetylene chemistry, Hoechst had already become closely concerned with high polymers. Now it had to follow the leading companies in this field, both at home and abroad. This meant the rapid erection of a man-made fibre plant or the acquisition of an existing artificial silk works. The technical standard of Bobingen was not exactly outstanding. Nevertheless, Hoechst decided upon this alternative. For at Bobingen, there was not only a well-tried staff of experts but in this comparative haven, many former man-made fibre experts of the I.G. had sought refuge from the ravages of war. They had begun Perlon production on a modest scale.

When, therefore, «Bobingen AG für Textil-Faser» became a subsidiary of Hoechst in 1952, the company acquired a firm base from which to operate in this new field.

Pre-requisites

Although, with the exception of Cassella, reunion of the former Hoechst subsidiaries had been successfully accomplished, and although even new members had been added to the family, the management was by no means overcome by optimism. True, in spite of the ruthless dismemberment, the old bonds between Hoechst, Leverkusen and Ludwigshafen had not been entirely severed. On the other hand, the former partners in the I.G. had once more become competitors. And so far as Leverkusen and Ludwigshafen were concerned, competitors that had a good start on Hoechst as both their capital and assets showed.

The works in the Main area had suffered little from the war. But all of them suffered from shortcomings whose origins went back over many years. Immediately after the formation of the I.G. Farbenindustrie, a tough fight had started between the various groups concerning rationalization of the manufacture of coal tar dyes and their starting products. After all, the main purpose of the I.G. merger had been the elimination of duplicated production and the achievement of greater and more economic manufacturing units.

The problems of the Main works

In these conflicts, the works in the Main region found themselves at a considerable disadvantage. Many of the plants were in a bad state of repair. Earlier, false economies now claimed their price. The ruthless cost comparison carried out at the time showed that Hoechst was handicapped in many ways in relation to Leverkusen and Ludwigshafen. Thanks to *Duisberg,* Leverkusen had had available well-planned economic plants since the turn of the century. Ludwigshafen, too, disposed of an integrated plant system. Hoechst suddenly realized that it needed complete technical re-organization if it wanted to be competitive. The company had lost a large part of its dyestuffs and starting products manufacture to other large I.G. works.

By way of compensation, Hoechst was allowed to take over certain products from other works. For some of these, new plant had to be built. It was also planned that Hoechst should get the Offenbach production, since for the time being Offenbach was scheduled for shut-down.

The sword of Damocles also hovered over the organic plants of Griesheim. After the large electrochemical plants had moved to Bitterfeld where power was cheap, there was a trend to abandon manufacture in Griesheim altogether. There was a violent fight for the inheritance.

Looking back, therefore, it is not difficult to understand why the I.G. era was a mixed blessing for the Main works. The constant threat of shut-down was not calculated to improve morale.

Once the economic crisis receded, it was too late to realize all the grandiose plans. The movement of Offenbach and Griesheim plants to Hoechst proved suddenly no longer possible. It was found that human loyalties, even to antiquated plants, were stronger than sober calculations. The plants stayed where they were and when Hoechst was reconstituted, they rejoined it in their original form.

The Third Reich four-year-plan called for a flood of investments, but the flood by-passed Hoechst. It poured instead into the Central German plants. From 1935, the I.G. assets gravitated more and more to Central and Eastern Germany. The profits of the com-

Wiesbaden-Biebrich works,
Kalle AG

Production plant at Hoechst

Bobingen works

panies on the Rhine and the Main were used to expand the plants in the East. The result was doubly calamitous for the Maingau members of the I.G. giant: firstly, existing plant could not be renewed. And secondly, many a promising development to which Hoechst might justifiably have laid claim went East.

No wonder that the new board of management was faced by many grave worries as it analysed its inheritance in 1953 and measured it against domestic and foreign competition.

Out-of-date research laboratories

There was an even more serious aspect. For more than twenty years, German research had stood still, or to be more precise, had been deflected from its true tasks. Since the beginning of the war, research had been confined to a few special problems. Many laboratories had gradually come to look like museums.

Practically no new research buildings were constructed during this period. In Hoechst, nothing had been built since 1936. The standard of German research laboratories did not improve until 1951, when new buildings were constructed and new equipment installed. Thanks to the thrifty policies of trustee *Michael Erlenbach*, the funds needed for this were available.

But, in order to branch out into new fields of production, Hoechst had to borrow. At first, of course, the investment programme existed in outline only. 1952 was too uncertain a year for large-scale planning. In 1951, political factors had produced a tremendous boom in German industry to be followed, less than twelve months later, by a sudden depression. This was particularly serious for Hoechst because the organisation of the new company had not had time to become consolidated. Some works were operating as much as 50 pc below capacity and the spectre of unemployment hung heavy over Hoechst. Dismissals were avoided only by slashing profits.

Turnover almost 1,000 million

It was not until 1953 that the boom barometer began to steady on the fair weather mark. Hoechst's turnover started to approach 1,000 million DM and Hoechst's biggest problem was how to balance the company's long-term interests against the legitimate hopes of shareholders, disappointed for so long.

It was not an easy matter. Hoechst knew only too well the tremendous effort that would be needed to enable it to catch up with international chemical industry. The board of management did not seek to hide these matters from the supervisory board: «The fact that we regained our economic freedom in 1953 does not mean that we have overcome the consequences of the war or that we have reached the point where we can compete with the chemical industry of the world as equals . . . The investment of approximately 320 million DM since the currency reform and the expenditure of 420 million DM on repair work during the same period, do not alter this fact.» On the other hand, the management had no wish to ignore the legitimate hopes of shareholders.

The largest share transaction in Germany

These long-suffering shareholders had no voting rights at the annual general meeting of the reconstituted Farbwerke Hoechst in September 1953. The transfer of the I.G. assets to their actual owners was, of course, a highly complicated affair which has been described as one of the largest share transactions ever carried out in Germany.

Some two million shares had to be issued and distributed according to a specific key. Initially, only the share transfer to the three major successor companies — BASF, Hoechst, Bayer — and Cassella was settled. One former 1,000 DM share of the I.G. entitled the holder to 250 DM nominal of BASF shares, 285 DM nominal of Bayer shares, 210 DM nominal of Hoechst shares and 25 DM nominal of Cassella shares. Later on, 50 DM nominal of Rheinische Stahlwerke shares and 60 DM nominal of Chemie-Verwaltungs-AG were added, making a total of 880 DM, not an unfavourable conversion ratio if one takes into account the currency reform.

The former I.G. fusion was thus reversed by making each shareholder a participant in all the successor companies. Investigation had shown that the former I.G. shares were held by some 180,000 people. In October 1953, these shares were quoted for the first time on the German stock exchange. On 22nd December 1953, they were officially recognised. The official rates on that day were $122^1/_4$ for the Hoechst shares, $125^1/_2$ for the Bayer shares and $120^1/_4$ for the BASF shares, rates that seem rather unreal at the present time.

According to allied provisions, the owners of the new shares continued to be restricted in their rights until 60 pc of the I.G. shares had been exchanged. Until then, specially appointed trustees safeguarded shareholders' rights.

In October 1953, the Allies had given the green light for the share exchange. In March 1954, the operation was concluded. Apart from the liquidation law, the legal and economic structure of the new companies had been settled. The era of the I.G. Farbenindustrie had finally come to an end.

Hoechst looks to the future

Now the moment had come for Hoechst to look to the future. The tempo at which the company had to enter the world markets left little time for retrospection. The focal point of reference was the American chemical industry which had taken the international lead during the past twenty-five years. Between 1938 and 1953, turnover of the German chemical industry had risen from 6,600 million DM to 12,000 million DM. During the same period, turnover of the American chemical industry had catapulted from 9,000 million marks to 80,000 million marks. Germany's turnover had doubled. America's had gone up nearly ten times. Figures like these served to save companies like Hoechst from overestimating their own potential.

Although it was soon found that the old name had managed to retain much of its former lustre, tremendous efforts had to be made to justify the quite unexpected amount of goodwill that was accorded to the new «Tower and Bridge» symbol. At every meeting of the supervisory board, the board of management produced piles of data in justification of the vast investment programmes which had to be paid for from the company's coffers and by way of public loans.

Millions are needed

Investments were stepped up by vast sums year after year and there appeared no end to the process. When, in 1954, the chairman of the board of management submitted a new investment plan to the supervisory board, he said: «An investment plan of 417 million marks is no bagatelle. In addition, it is more than likely that we shall not come to a halt when this money has been invested. There are no breaks in the progress of chemistry. We are therefore forced to invest continuously. We believe, however, that our present measures do not pursue senseless expansion but are simply the consequences of an age in which chemistry is invading every aspect of daily life and steadily gaining an increasing share of industrial production.»

Only a small part of the investments went into plants for the production of the classic Hoechst products such as dyestuffs, pharmaceuticals and fertilizers. The bulk was applied to solvents and the new plastics and fibres fields for which market research predicted a considerable future. Hoechst simply could not stand aside from these developments. To do so would have reduced the company to the status of a medium-sized undertaking that, at the same time, would have had to withstand unabated pressure in respect of its conventional products. In any case, a broad manufac-

Gendorf works

turing programme provided the best protection against boom fluctuations and selling crises.

As a result of all this, Hoechst had to face up to the urgent raw material problem. The new production had to be based on a broad raw material basis. No matter how many barges brought coal from the Ruhr or carbide from Knapsack — additional supplies of carbide had to be bought at ever-increasing prices, in spite of new capacity at Knapsack — supplies were inadequate to meet the gigantic demands. There was only one solution, which the Americans had already adopted. Hoechst drew a deep breath and then also took the plunge. It turned to petroleum, an apparently inexhaustible raw material source. The hour of petrochemistry had struck.

Chemistry and Petroleum

The beginning of Hoechst's petrochemistry is marked by a tower. Black, awe-inspiring, it rises for almost 100 metres — a sharp contrast to the silvery-grey pipes of the distillation columns all around it. At the top of this tower, referred to as the «coker», a yellow flame dances in the sky, day after day, night after night. It can be seen from many miles away — the symbol of a large chemical works, of Hoechst. Previously, large plant buildings for pigments and pharmaceuticals, silos for fertilizers and massive nitric acid towers have always formed the silhouette of this town of chemistry by the banks of the Main.

A factory-owned, reinforced concrete bridge, harbour installations with the most modern loading facilities and wide roads filled with an incessant stream of traffic determine the rhythm of this metropolis of industry. But its external architecture is changing more quickly than elsewhere. The inexorable progress of plastics has produced new focal points in the Hoechst constellation.

How are olefins obtained?

The big tower, completed in January 1956, was the starting signal for a new chapter in the history of Hoechst. Inside it, reactions that until then had been fond dreams of Hoechst's chemists were realized for the first time. This «coker» at long last enabled Hoechst to undertake its own production of olefins from crude oil. Olefins are highly reactive gases such as PROPYLENE, BUTYLENE, and the universally useful ETHYLENE — raw materials that in modern chemistry have gained the same significance as coal and carbide. Although they had been known for a long time, their production used to be too expensive because they had to be obtained by complicated methods from coal or acetylene. The cost of these methods prevented the manufacture of olefins on a large scale.

There was another factor. The coal tar required by chemical industry, and the aromatics such as benzene, toluene, xylene, naphthalene and anthracene produced from it, are really no more than by-products of coke production. The amount in which they were obtained was determined not by the chemical industry but the steel industry. To this extent, therefore, the chemical industry was always dependent to a certain degree on the production plans of the steel works, a dependency that showed itself more and more clearly as plastics and man-made fibres came to be more and more widely used. The time was not far off when the amounts available from coal tar were no longer sufficient for the needs of the chemical industry.

Petrochemistry in America

In America, a country rich in raw materials, other avenues had been explored early in the twenties. Here oil derricks sprout out of the soil in immense profusion and the refineries were able to supply the chemical factories with any desired amount of raw material. The refineries were, however, not content simply with supplying the chemical industry. Since their technical facilities and know-how could also be used for the production of chemical starting products such as ethylene, they entered the traditional fields of the chemical industry. Today, for example, almost ten per cent of the total turnover of Shell is in chemical products.

To avoid being overtaken by the expansive designs of the refineries, many major chemical producers transferred to the Gulf coast of the United States where most of the oil was gushing. Many refineries erected pipelines that supplied the chemical factories, four or even five hundred kilometres away, with starting products pumped

through half a dozen branch lines. Even so, the requirements of the American chemical companies amount to no more than 5 pc of the total annual output of crude oil of 400 million tons so that the raw material basis of the American chemical industry is secured for a long time ahead.

The search for other ways

The German chemical companies were completely shut off from this development until the end of the war. They knew, of course, exactly what was happening in the States. Since it was impossible to start from petroleum in Germany, other routes to obtain hydrocarbons were tried. The need to produce motor fuel from domestic coal, a need dictated by the foreign exchange position at that time, provided the spur for all the work that was carried out as part of what was later to become known as petrochemistry. In this way, a close exchange of ideas took place, until the beginning of the war in 1939, between the former I.G. Farbenindustrie and the large American oil companies.

Motor fuels from coal

The self-sufficiency aspirations of the Third Reich caused German chemistry to produce the required amounts of fuel for cars, planes and other vehicles from coal, the inexhaustible raw material reservoir. Numerous hydrogenation plants were built which operated by the I.G.-developed coal liquefaction process. The raw material was lignite and later on coal. At the same time, plants using the Fischer-Tropsch syntheses were also set up. They were the result of a tremendous effort which could have served a better purpose in a free economy. There developed therefore a strong national fuel industry of a high technical standard and with a tremendous amount of valuable experience whose successes did not go unnoticed by the foreign petroleum companies. The production of synthetic fuels was bound to remain uneconomic in international competition.

Not enough coal and carbide

At the end of the war, however, things looked very different. The shackles of a nationalised, planned economy were removed in favour of a completely liberalised system. Particularly the large chemical companies faced an entirely new situation. Hoechst had never been blessed with a superabundance of raw materials but matters were even worse now. Prices of raw materials rose higher and higher and the costs for electric power looked like swallowing up entirely the already narrow profit margins. The calculations carried out at Hoechst showed with alarming clarity that coal and carbide were no longer sufficient in order to meet the raw material requirements. To be a successful competitor, Hoechst needed a broader raw material basis. If this was not provided, Hoechst would in but a few years entirely lose its position in the world market. Already, the Americans were making moves to flood Europe with cheap chemicals from the «oil can».

How could the situation be met? The coal hydrogenation plants in Leuna near Magdeburg, for example, were now in the eastern zone and the production of synthetic naphtha in West Germany had been prohibited by the Allies. The large crude oil refineries were all located on the North German coast and had no thoughts at that time of advancing by pipeline into the heart of Germany.

Hoechst had no choice. However unusual it might be for a chemical company to produce its raw materials, this was the road Hoechst had to travel.

Hoechst decides on crude oil

It did not take long to decide whether the indispensable olefins were to be produced from crude oil or light naphtha. The light naphtha, rich in hydrogen, would have been the more ideal starting material but it was too rare and too expensive. A ton of light naphtha at that time cost 250 marks while crude oil cost only 70—80 marks per ton. Even this price tended to fall and there was no longer any shortage of crude oil.

The petroleum companies at that time were particularly interested in crude oils with a high amount of naphtha and diesel oil. That the remaining lubricating and fuel oils might one day be in great demand nobody dreamt for a moment at that time.

These heavy fractions, ignored by most, had been thoroughly analysed by the chemists who had found that, in contrast to the low-molecular petrol, they consisted of large molecules that formed long chains and that provided the product with a high-boiling, viscous character. It was necessary to burst these chains, to disintegrate and crack them. For this sort of work, chemistry does not use hammers or knives — it falls back on its old ally—heat. The thermal cracking of heavy oil makes it possible to split large hydrocarbons into gaseous fragments.

It started in a metal tube

Until 1953, no more than theoretical investigations in this field had been carried out by Hoechst. But then came a clear directive to the chemists and engineers: realisation of a crude oil cracking plant.

The erection of such a cracker was preceeded by a great deal of work in the laboratory using small-scale models. The starting point was an externally heated metal tube. It was clear from the beginning that temperatures of at least 700 °C would be involved. This needed special metal alloys whose melting point was high enough to withstand 800 °C without difficulty.

Symbiosis of chemists and engineers

Twenty chemists and as many engineers worked on the project. A number of them were former I.G. experts who had been working in the mineral oil industry. This industry was perhaps the nearest example of what Hoechst was trying to achieve. During this phase of the work, chemists and engineers formed a kind of symbiosis. For where the problem is the development of suitable equipment for a new chemical process, the number of cooks, for once, cannot be large enough.

Indeed, it was because of such close associations that the chemical industry had progressed from one-man workshops to the modern large-scale plants. Without a good engineer even the best idea of a chemist is no more than an abstract formula. The realisation of such ideas, particularly where large-scale processes are involved, requires equipment, and the production of such equipment needs perfect collaboration between chemist and engineer, not forgetting the part played by physics.

Four thousand measuring instruments

At Hoechst the engineering deportment is responsible for the development of chemical equipment and for the erection, maintenance and supply of plants. The number of people working in this division is in inverse proportion to the number of people in the production plant. The Hoechst workshops alone employ some 5,000 people. This figure will be readily understood if one thinks not only of the hundreds of workshops but also of the many kilometres of pipelines through which the site is supplied with power, gas, steam and compressed air and the numerous base chemicals such as nitrogen, acetylene, chlorine or sulphuric acid.

More than 4,000 measuring instruments control production at Hoechst. It has been found that although the number of employees working directly on the plant can be reduced again and again, this is achieved at the expense of an increased number of people in the measuring and control sections. This is also the reason why in a modern chemical concern, the ratio of skilled to unskilled labour is tending to shift in favour of the former.

Experimental plants 30 metres high

Following the first laboratory experiments, an experimental plant for crude oil cracking was erected. It is, of course, clear that such a plant, intended for the development of a major chemical process, cannot be of miniature dimensions. Where mechanical phenomena are to be studied, where information is sought concerning the behaviour of material or equipment, where the performance of pumps, compressors, valves and control systems is to be evaluated, where the controls, the material flow and also the accumulation of contaminants has to be checked, the pilot plant is frequently as high as a ten-storey building. In a miniature piece of equipment, faults that can have catastrophic consequences in large-scale production frequently escape detection. The first pilot plant at Hoechst, therefore, was thirty metres high and this is hardly surprising inview of the fact that the final resul of these experiments, the actual coker, has a height of 100 metres. But in 1953, matters had not yet progressed thus far. In the pilot plant, the process that was to be used in the coker is tried out again and again. This pilot plant therefore has the same design characteristics as the later coker.

A Hoechst premiere

The things that were going on in this experimental plant were tantamount to a world premiere in chemistry. The heat cracking of crude oil by thermal treatment at temperatures of 800 °C to give olefins was carried out at Hoechst in an almost sensational manner. For it was realized that with this cracking process it would soon be possible to produce, in situ, both ETHYLENE and PROPYLENE, another raw material that was to become as interesting as ethylene.

Of course, molecular cracking had long been familiar in modern refinery technology. It was generally employed in naphtha production from heavy crude oil. But the purpose and the method were considerably different. At any rate so far as the refineries in Germany were concerned, their purpose then was not the production of gases but of low boiling liquids of the naphtha type.

Coke pebbles from the tablet press

Apart from crude oil, the coker is charged with coke pebbles with a diameter of between 5—12 mm, produced during electrode manufacture in Griesheim.

The method of making these pebbles was quite original. The pharmaceuticals division provived the means — an old tablet press which produced a veritable avalanche of pebbles.

Assembly of the coker tower

◀ *Plant for the separation of liquid components from the crude gas produced during high temperature pyrolysis*

Distribution system for the gaseous end products

A stream of gas transports the pebbles to the top of the tower. From there they travel downwards through a system of metal tubes which are heated externally to such a degree that the pebbles become red-hot. The pre-heated crude oil is then sprayed on to this incandescent mass. Almost instantly, it is cracked into solid, liquid and gaseous substances, the pebbles becoming cooled at the same time. After this «refreshment», the pebbles resume their travels inside the coker. The gas stream again transports them to the top. The solid matter that is formed — the coke — coats the pebbles with a thin layer, like a skin around a hazelnut. If the pebbles become too large, they are eliminated from the coke cycle by means of sieves. It is interesting to note that the amount of pebbles moved in an hourly cycle is far larger than the amount of crude oil used.

Indirect heat transfer was deliberately chosen for the coker. Originally, Hoechst intended to use heavy residue oils from the refineries instead of crude oil. With such oils, a great deal of coke would have been split off which Hoechst intended to pass on to the electrode production at Griesheim. This electrode coke, however, must be very pure. In the direct transfer of heat, the coke would have come into unavoidable contact with sulphur dioxide in the flue gases and would, therefore, have been contaminated. However, market analyses carried out meanwhile necessitated a change of plans. The analyses had shown that the prices for crude oil and residue oil were almost identical. In view of all this, a decision was taken to use crude oil.

With crude oil, the yield of gaseous hydrocarbons is greater. Approximately 60 pc of gaseous hydrocarbons are obtained and only half the amount of liquid products. On the other hand, crude oil does not yield a great deal of coke, no more than about 2–3 pc. But the decisive criterion was that the new Hoechst production programme relied entirely on olefins. The name «coker» is therefore somewhat of a misnomer and it was in fact valid only while residue oil was being considered.

The Hoechst experimental plant was ready to go on stream at the end of 1953. For more than a year, it was used to try out all possible grades of crude oil and their reaction conditions. At the same time, complicated material tests had to be carried out. In particular, it was necessary to establish the maximum temperatures that the metal alloys would tolerate, for the higwer the temperature, the greater the cracking intensity.

Difficult material tests

Whether the alloy withstood maximum temperatures for a few hours was unimportant. What mattered was the permanent stability, whether the equipment was able to withstand extreme stresses month after month, year after year. Again and again, therefore, the Hoechst material testing laboratories were called into action with their microscopes and X-ray equipment. During this work the experience gained in the high pressure techniques of the I.G. proved of great value to the Hoechst chemists and engineers. The analysts had to fulfil different tasks. They had to find new methods of gas analysis, for example with the aid of gas chromatography, in order to be able to observe the new reactions.

In 1954, the green light for the construction of the coker was given all along the line. By the end of 1955, the first cold and hot trial runs were carried out. Although the experimental plant was of considerable size, a number of questions arose. Will it be possible to equal the yield of the experimental plant, are the power calculations correct, will it really be possible to push up the coke pebbles for 76 metres? These were anxious questions. But when the chief of Hoechst's petrochemistry pushed the button on 1st February 1956, it was found that everything was according to plan. The first crude oil cracking plant for the production of olefinic gases had gone on stream.

After the long period of raw material scarcity, there was great satisfaction at Hoechst over this first success in petrochemistry. But the Hoechst chemists had no time to rest on their laurels. For in the progress of chemistry, time seems to pass even more quickly than elsewhere. Even before the first ton of crude oil had been fed to the coker, new problems had arisen.

Cracking furnaces for ethane and propane

The coker had originally been laid out for an output of approximately 10,000 tons of ethylene per annum. Although later it yielded almost twice this amount with a greater crude oil throughput, it was found after a fairly short period of time that even this amount would not be sufficient to meet future needs. Chemists, therefore, turned their attention to two valuable hydrocarbons that were also obtained during crude oil cracking—ethane and propane.

The conversion of these cracking gases into ethylene and propylene had already been tried at an earlier date. A different type of furnace had to be constructed. It was not a conventional type of furnace but rather a giant pipe system. The pipes were about 10 cm in diameter and they were heated from the outside. In such plant, ethane and propane were cracked into ethylene and propylene at a temperature of 820 °C. Stubborn gases that would not subject to this cracking during the first treatment were returned to the furnace until they were completely decomposed. In this way, the yield of ethylene and propylene was considerably increased. The ethylene is used by the Hoechst plastics plants and the propylene is converted into isopropyl alcohol and, at Knapsack, into acetone.

Methane — a gas with two faces

A third product from the Hoechst coker is METHANE, a gaseous hydrocarbon which has long been known. Mixed with oxygen, it is an extremely explosive substance which causes firedamp in mines. As a natural gas it is a valuable provider of energy. Its formula is CH_4. This formula is commonly used in chemical teaching to demonstrate the concept of valency — the four arms with which one carbon atom grabs four hydrogen atoms.

Before the coker had started to operate, Hoechst had been supplied with methane from the Ruhr. Of course, this Ruhr methane had to be processed in a Hoechst plant to give it that degree of purity necessary for chemical operations. From 1954 onwards — in other words, two years before the coker went on stream — the Ruhr methane was supplemented by pure natural gas from the drillings of the DEA at Pfungstadt. Later, only Pfungstadt gas was used. This was transported from Pfungstadt to Hoechst through a 40 kilometre long pipeline.

Methane chlorination is an old Hoechst activity. The foundations for this had been laid by *Paul Duden* at the end of the first world war. His object at the time was the synthetic preparation of the rather rare methyl alcohol which was obtained in only small amounts from the wood coking industry. Duden chlorinated the methane to obtain methyl chloride which, in turn, was saponified to give methyl alcohol.

The experimental work had been successfully concluded in 1922. However, shortly before the large plant was to start up, news was received that high pressure synthesis of methyl alcohol from carbon monoxide and hydrogen had been successfully accomplished in the Oppau works of BASF. Hoechst was not able to compete with this process. Duden therefore had the methyl alcohol plant dismantled again but continued to work intensively on methane chlorination.

New markets for chlorination products

During chlorination, mainly methyl chloride and methylene chloride are formed. Minor by-products are chloroform and carbon tetrachloride. Before production could be started, it was necessary to find adequate markets for the individual products. This meant, as usual, that the development department had to take a hand. Research and

147

development chemists succeeded in achieving this goal. Methyl chloride was found to be suitable as a methylating agent for which a tremendous market was opened up when Kalle began to manufacture methyl cellulose discovered at Hoechst.

This product, marketed under the trade name Tylose, was used as emulsifying agent for detergents. Methylene chloride conquered a great field as extractant and solvent. Large amounts of it are used for the production of acetate rayon and non-flammable film. The usage of carbon tetrachloride is also steadily increasing. This product is used either as a standard solvent or converted into Frigen. The Frigen grades are non-toxic and non-inflammable chlorinated and fluorinated methane compounds with whose help Hoechst has gained a firm place in the field of refrigeration techniques. Frigen is indispensable in refrigerators. It has also become highly successful as a propellent in pressure packaging.

The process employed in the manufacture of the various products from Hoechst's methane chlorination plant are rather original. In successive reactors, four chlorine atoms are gradually added on to the methane molecules. The heat is absorbed in the reactor itself by way of an internal circulation. Methyl chloride, methylene chloride, chloroform and carbon tetrachloride are formed. During this process, the methane is only partially reacted. The unreacted part can be returned to the reactors. At present, some 20 million cubic metres of pure methane per annum are processed in the methane chlorination plant. This methane is obtained partly from natural gas sources and partly from petro-chemical cracking plants.

Using up left-overs is not only a domestic problem but also a problem of the chemical industry. Such a left-over, for example, is a gas obtained during the processing of coker gas. It consists mainly of hydrogen and a small amount of methane. This gas is taken over by the ammonia factory which produces pure hydrogen from it. If this hydrogen is mixed with nitrogen, synthesis gas is formed, the starting product for ammonia. The ammonia plant, however, cannot manage with the residual gas from the petrochemical plants alone. For this reason, Hoechst takes supplies of crude gas for the production of synthesis gas from other sources as well.

Even the first petrochemical plants had provided a broad raw material base which was able to support quite a number of manufacturing divisions.

Fuel oil changes the market

While the Hoechst chemists and engineers were still congratulating themselves on the coker and the cracking furnaces, an upset in the market caused them to turn their thoughts to fresh exploits. New trends became discernible in the petroleum market. There was now little doubt that the price difference between crude oil and light naphtha would gradually disappear. This made the men at Hoechst sit up. There had been enough warning signs: vastly increasing crude oil output, new petroleum fields in the Middle East, higher yields in America, and especially a tremendous increase in the sale of heavy oils. Fuel oil began its triumphant march forward in industry, in trade and in the crafts and also in the home where coal had to give way to oil-fired heating. The oil was cheaper, easier to transport and less dirty.

With every additional ton of fuel oil, the amount of petrol obtained also increased. It was therefore not very difficult for Hoechst to calculate the day when petrol would not cost very much more than the same amount of crude oil.

Although, even at that time, every fourteenth citizen of the Federal Republic owned his own car, petrol consumption did not increase to the same extent as the requirements of fuel oil. Petrol was not going to be in short supply for much longer.

All these thoughts drove Hoechst to the conclusion that it would have to acquire its own plant for the processing of petrol, namely the medium temperature pyrolysis plant. This term embraces cracking furnaces for petrol equipped with a very similar pipe system and operating at approximately the same temperatures as the furnaces in which ethane and propane were decomposed. In 1957, the first petrol cracking furnace at Hoechst was started up. A year later, the second steam cracker went on stream. The coker, the ethane-propane cracking and the petrol furnaces together yielded more than 20,000 tons of ethylene. The method of separating the gases into pure products was the same for all cracking plants.

Acetylene, too, from petroleum

This meant that in the field of petrochemistry, only one big object remained. Ethylene had become one of the most important raw materials for the chemical operations at Hoechst. Nevertheless, it was unable to displace acetylene from the gas kettles.

In the twenties, the carbide gases had found manifold application in industry. The first solvents and plastics like polyvinyl acetate were acetylene derivatives. Indeed, this was the reason why the Knapsack works with their carbide furnaces had become so important to Hoechst. Many millions of marks had been spent on expanding the Knapsack site to a capacity of 400 thousand tons of carbide per annum, using the most modern plants. The production of carbide, however, requires so much current that power costs become an intolerable item in the budget even of large undertakings. Hoechst, therefore, attempted to relieve Knapsack, at least partially, of carbide production and to involve it in other types of manufacture.

Knapsack produces acetylene from carbide. Hoechst manufactures it from petroleum, or to be more precise, from petrol. Cracking experiments of this type had first been undertaken in 1954. Since petrol, unlike crude oil, is a comparatively clean substance, small quartz tubes were sufficient for the first experiments. Very soon, however, this modest experimental equipment was enlarged by a burner.

On one thing the Hoechst chemists and technicians were agreed from the very start: very high temperatures would be needed to permit the large-scale production of acetylene. 1600 °C were probably the lower limit. These temperatures were produced with the aid of a hydrogen-oxygen mixture, using ceramic burners.

The problem of burner cooling

It was soon found that ceramic burners were not suitable for these high temperatures. They were either unstable or they fused very quickly to form smoking, shapeless masses. Metal burners with a melting point of 1300 to 1400 degrees did not at first sight appear to be much more resistant. Unless, of course, thought the Hoechst design team which had also produced the coker, a perfect cooling system could be developed.

It took three years to realize such a perfect burner cooling system. This shows just how many difficulties in this field had to be overcome. The best solution was found to be a double-wall burner design in which the entire surface of the metal was uniformly surrounded by water. This water cooling had to satisfy one important condition. Literally every square millimetre of the burner wall had to be uniformly cooled. The slightest variation in water pressure, a minor variation in the flow, a small gas bubble — any of this would be sufficient to ruin the burner. Forthe metal wall then instantly assumes temperatures of 2000° or more, melts and is destroyed. Many fundamental physical studies were necessary in order to ensure that the burners would be protected against 'burning'. In 1957, the first experimental plant for this high temperature pyrolysis was erected. Its capacity was the same as that of the coker forerunner. It had been laid out for a throughput of 200 kilo petrol per hour. In this case, too, the governing principle was that even in an experimental plant a minimum volume is necessary in order to eliminate the great variety of causes of later failure in the full-scale plant.

The Hoechst HTP specialists concentrated mainly on those elements of the plant that represented new departures. These elements were the burner with its reactor, the cracking mechanism and the quenching of the reactor mixture.

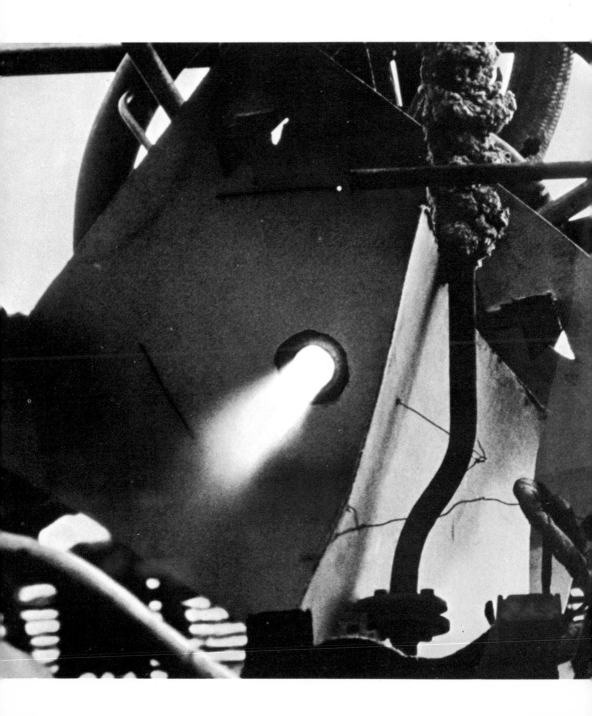

Testing the burner in the HTP experimental plant

How to separate, or in chemical terminology fractionate, the gases and vapours produced in the burner represented no problem for Hoechst. Special knowledge was however necessary for the separation of ethylene and acetylene. The mixture from the HTP plant consisted of 30 parts acetylene and approximately 70 parts ethylene.

Gases in the freezer

This separation had to take place in many phases. A temperature gradient from 2,500 degrees in the burner to −150 degrees in the low temperature separation of the residual gases had to be traversed. The major part of this fairly complicated procedure takes place in so-called separating columns. Many of these have up to sixty trays, each of which acts like a sieve. The acetylene or ethylene becomes purer from sieve to sieve. In Hoechst, a process and methods department had to be formed in order to calculate the exact characteristics of the separating columns. Distribution figures, the solvents, and the optimum conditions for pressure and temperature were established in special experimental departments at Hoechst. The low temperature separation was developed in collaboration with Linde AG. The main principle in this work was the modification of conventional plants so as to adapt them to the modern function of the separation of combustible gases.

The present-day high temperature pyrolysis was designed in the autumn of 1958. Precisely twelve months later, the burner experiments were carried out and in April 1960, the first tons of ethylene and acetylene with a purity of 99.9 per cent were produced.

In fractions of a second

Even in its purely external aspects, this Hoechst pyrolysis differs from the coker. The coker points, lonely almost, into the sky — a single, slightly clumsy tower. The high temperature pyrolysis, on the other hand, is a jungle of slim distillation towers and separating columns. The actual cracking centre accounts for only a small part of the entire plant.

It is located in an open building approximately twenty metres high which contains the four conical burners and their feed lines. The diameter of the burner is less than two metres. The actual cracking process is accomplished in fractions of a second. The dwelling time, that is the time spent by the naphtha mixture in the burner, is one hundredth of a second. The load of the burner is enormous, more than a thousand million kilocalories per cubic metre, per hour.

Remote-control production

Another characteristic of the high temperature cracking plant is that it requires only very few operators. One shift consists of no more than sixteen workers. The control station is of enormous size: Control lamps light up, automatic recorders plot mysterious graphs and every minute hundreds of figures are calculated to ensure careful control of the plant. In the control station, with its subdued light, there are only a few chemists, engineers and specialists. They do not spare a single glance for the distillation towers from which, every few minutes, white steam gushes forth. Their eyes are glued to the dials of the test equipment, a sophisticated control system that is a worthy complement to the technical wonder of petrochemistry.

But, of course, however seductive the creations of the chemists and engineers, in the end it is the calculating pencil of the economist that decides every issue. It is he who dictates whether a project is realized or whether an existing plant is still economical.

Naturally, there is frequent conflict of opinion between the sales people and the scientists until the board of management takes the final decision for which it has to account not only to the supervisory board but, in the last resort, also to its 250,000 shareholders.

New trends in petrochemistry

The past years have brought a surprising development in the mineral oil field. The fuel oil business has assumed astronomic proportions. Refineries have, therefore, been forced to change their processing techniques in order to meet this changing situation. As a result, petrol is being obtained in ever-increasing amounts and at continuously lower prices. This, in turn, has not been without consequence for Hoechst's petrochemistry. The alarming levelling-out of the prices of petrol and crude oil and the advantages of petrol as a basis for olefin production gave rise to a plan for changing over to petrol as raw material altogether. It was, however, not intended to produce this petrol any longer at Hoechst itself but to buy the surplus from the refineries. As a result, a final decision was taken at the end of 1960 to stop the production of olefins from crude oil and also to shut down the Hoechst distillation plant for crude oil from which part of Hoechst's petrol requirements were met. At this time, the HTP and the four cracking furnaces for petrol and ethane/propane were already in operation and provided a broad basis for Hoechst's petrochemistry.

The change-over from crude oil to petrol as raw material was smoothly carried out. The stream of ethylene, propylene, methane and synthesis gas continued to flow to the

processing plants. The coker and the Hoechst refinery now represent a kind of strategic reserve. For after all, nobody is able to predict with any degree of accuracy whether these plants may not one day have to be returned to active service once more, for the petroleum business, as Hoechst has had to learn, is full of surprises and rapid changes. The processing of crude oil and petrol was of great value to the company. When the time had come, and when the new olefin plastics had been sufficiently developed, Hoechst had available raw materials that could not be obtained elsewhere at that particular moment. But the most important point was that valuable experience had been gained by a large number of top experts which equipped them to deal with many other problems in this interesting field which is so important to Hoechst.

Hoechst's non-conformity in petrochemistry meant that the company was able to retain its freedom of action and that it was provided with a breathing space until the oil companies decided to extend their activities to the Frankfurt area which is becoming more and more important industrially. There never was any doubt that the day was near. It came, in fact, in 1961. The American petroleum company Caltex, which had already supplied Hoechst with crude oil, began to build a refinery near Hoechst. Under an agreement for a term of fifteen years, Caltex undertook to supply Hoechst with olefins. At the end of 1963, the first tons of ethylene were pumped through the pipelines from Kelsterbach to Hoechst. The first stage of the refinery has a throughput of two million tons of crude oil per year. It was due to the efforts of the government of Hesse and also of the civic authorities of Frankfurt that land was found for this important undertaking in spite of the over-population in the Frankfurt area. The Caltex refinery and new Hoechst plants will have room to expand at Kelsterbach for many years to come.

A similar development is taking place in the Cologne area. The Knapsack works, too, have had to change over to petrochemistry and electricity to reserve their supplies for special electrochemical purposes. As a result, close collaboration developed, especially during the post-war years, with the neighbouring Union Rheinische Braun-kohlen-Kraftstoff AG,Wesseling, which, as part of a long-term agreement, erected a special cracking plant for the production of olefins and thus became a potential supplier of raw material.

In this way, Farbwerke Hoechst has secured its petrochemical raw material basis at two of its most important production centres — in Frankfurt and in Knapsack near Cologne. In addition, of course, the Hoechst high and medium temperature pyrolysis will continue to supply ethylene and acetylene.

Hoechst acquires Gendorf

To this must be added the petrochemical products of one of the youngest Hoechst subsidiaries. This is the Gendorf works on the river Alz near Burghausen on the Bavarian/ Austrian frontier. Gendorf was built mainly with State funds and its output went almost entirely into the armament industry. For this reason, Gendorf was largely dismantled after 1945. All that remained was a skeleton: a small part of the power station, a part of the chlorine-alkali electrolysis and a plant for the production of ethylene oxide and glycol from carbide, purchased from the adjacent Süddeutsche Kalkstickstoff-Werke, via acetylene and ethylene. In this mutilated form, Gendorf was no longer viable. In order to provide its employees — mainly members of the old I.G. or refugees from the East — with a job, the State of Bavaria initially took over the plant but in 1955, it was acquired by Hoechst.

Gendorf presented Hoechst with a difficult problem. The labour force that it offered was, of course, more than welcome and the products manufactured at Gendorf fitted well as intermediates into the Hoechst range. But the Gendorf raw material basis and the route to the starting materials had to be fundamentally altered just as the whole works needed an entirely new concept.

Chemists have always had a fundamental objection to producing ethylene from acetylene. Acetylene has more energy and is, therefore, more valuable than ethylene. Nevertheless, Gendorf degraded acetylene into a lesser product, just as was done elsewhere in Germany, since ethylene was not available from petrochemical plants. At first, Hoechst was quite grateful for the ethylene that could be purchased in steel cylinders from Gendorf. For with its help the first polyethylene experiments were carried out in the Hoechst laboratories many months before the coker went into service. But later Gendorf attempted the development of an own more economical cracking process for ethylene and this was, in fact, adopted in 1958.

An ideal cracking process

The starting material was petrol which was then available in large amounts at reasonable prices. But there was another decisive factor. The unfavourable position of Gendorf with regard to communications made it necessary to derive the maximum amount of ethylene from every ton of petrol. For if the normal volume of by-products had been returned to the refinery, the transport costs would have become so high that Gendorf would have made hardly any profit at all. The need for Gendorf, therefore, was to produce the maximum yield of gas from the minimum of liquid raw material. In this way, a specific cracking process was developed in which hardly any liquid products at all were obtained. Things are different with the oil refineries. They do not require gas only for they can sell cracked petrol and fuel oil without difficulty.

The Gendorf process is similar to the high temperature pyrolysis at Hoechst. Cracking at Gendorf is also carried out at the very high temperatures at which the molecular chains are most easily and most extensively shattered. The more complete the cracking, the lower the molecular weights of the components that are obtained and thus, the greater the amount of ethylene. As a result of improvements over the next years, the Gendorf cracking specialists were able to increase the output of the plant by approximately 50 pc. Since the cracking plant in Gendorf produces practically only ethylene, the gas separation plant is simpler than that needed for the Hoechst HTP in which acetylene is also obtained as an important secondary product.

Half of the GLYCOL produced by Gendorf is used as an antifreeze under the trademark Genantin. It also forms one of the two raw materials for the production of the man-made polyester fibre TREVIRA. The starting product of glycol — ethylene oxide — is required in Gendorf and Hoechst for the manufacture of a variety of products such as textile and petroleum auxiliaries.

The age of plastics

Thus Farbwerke Hoechst's raw material basis has become broad and firm. Petrochemical production in Hoechst and Gendorf was supplemented at the end of 1963 by supplies from the Caltex refinery in Kelsterbach and from the UK Wesseling in Cologne. Indeed, if Hoechst had not developed its own petrochemical activities, the creation of new plastics would have been delayed until these further supplies became available. The great efforts and the great expense have been more than worthwhile.

What would have happened if Hoechst had patiently waited and had not followed the maxim — do it yourself? Even now, responsible people at Hoechst shudder at the thought. For there can be no doubt that if Hoechst had not taken the course it did, it would have missed the bus in a field of production whose future potentialities are even now immeasurable. Currently, some five million tons of plastics per annum are being produced throughout the world. During the next decades, this figure will multiply many times so that the term «the age of plastics» will be fully justified. That Hoechst did not become an «also-ran» in this field, and that it could secure for itself a proper share of the market, is due to its timely and courageous initiative which led to the construction of the coker, of the cracking furnaces and of the high temperature pyrolysis.

Plastics — wonders of chemistry

The production lines of one of the largest Hoechst plastics plants is behind a glass wall. Here ethylene from the pipelines of petrochemical plants is converted into polyethylene, a plastic. The most striking feature of this highly modern polymerisation plant is the absence of a single living soul. In the long building, there are kettle upon kettle and miles of pipes of every conceivable size but no workmen to operate them. The plant is supervised from huge control desks behind a glass wall and manned by a handful of trained operators. For all the world, it looks like the control room of a television studio.

The green light

Each piece of equipment and each one of its many feeder pipes behind the glass wall is monitored on the control desk. When the green lamps light up, the valves are opened and the process of polymerisation starts. Innumerable gas molecules join to form macromolecules. An infinite number of small building units — the monomers — form a large unit — the polymer.

Green light no. 1: The solving and dispersing agent flow into the polymerisation reactor. In this case, it is petrol which by itself will not polymerise. Its function is that of a reaction medium and it also serves to precipitate the polymer that is formed.

Green light no. 2: the catalysts are introduced. As almost always with these important accelerators of chemical reactions, only small quantities are needed. The amount of catalyst used in the production of polyethylene is less than a hundredth part of the amount of polyethylene.

Green light no. 3: ethylene flows into the kettle. The process of conversion — the polymerisation in which the small ethylene molecules are joined into giant molecules — takes place under comparatively gentle conditions. The polymer formed in the kettle floats on the petrol as a white powder. When a given amount of this powder has been produced, it is treated with a substance that poisons the catalyst. This terminates the polymerisation process.

Process control by television

The rest of the equipment serves the further processing of the primary product. First of all, the powder passes through filters which retain the dispersing agent. Processing is supervised by control installations fitted to the wall next to the control desks. A number of markers indicate the various stations. Two television screens show parts of the plant. The dispersing agent is regenerated and used again.

The powder then passes through driers and from there to a silo. This actually completes the process but some manufacturers prefer the material in the form of granulate. To produce this, part of the polyethylene — sold under the trade name Hostalen — is mixed with dyestuffs and stabilizers. The mixture then passes into a heated extruder, a machine like on oversized mincer, in which it is melted and pressed through a disc with hundreds of round or square holes. In front of the disc there are rotating knives which cut the continuous strand of polyethylene into uniform pieces. These then pass through a sieve after which they are weighed and packed.

The history of polyethylene

Hoechst's polyethylene is produced by the low-pressure process in contrast to the high pressure process developed in England in the thirties. ICI were the first to succeed in polymerising ethylene under very high pressure. Up to then, ethylene had always resised polymerisation — despite the fact that its molecules have an unsaturated chemical structure.

160

Hostalen granulate

Large plants using this process for the production of polyethylene were set up in Germany at BASF and one of its associates, Rheinische Olefin-Werke.

In Germany, Professor Karl Ziegler, director of the Max-Planck-Institute for carbon research in Mülheim on the Ruhr, had been engaged in an investigation of organic aluminium compounds ever since he became professor at the university of Heidelberg. At the end of the forties, in continuation of this work, he discovered an aluminium catalyst system to which ethylene added on. However, the growing chains that were formed as a result died prematurely—on average after approximately every hundred growth steps, as Ziegler once described them. The adding on of ethylene always petered out after a while and only low molecular compounds, but no true polyethylene, were obtained.

In an accidental discovery in Mülheim, which was duly recognised and scientifically exploited, it was found one day that the reaction was following a different course. In the apparatus used there were traces of a substance that acted as a cocatalyst. It was only after this undesirable trace catlyst had been eliminated, that the polymerisation process continued without difficulty. And when Ziegler finally found a suitable solvent — heavy naphtha — a new pressureless route for ethylene polymerisation had been found, a route whose basic principle was so simple that Prof. Ziegler was able to carry it in jam jars.

While it did not originally involve polyethylene Prof. Ziegler had a contractual relationship with Farbwerke Hoechst, and Hoechst chemists heard of this reaction. They immediately realized that the Ziegler reaction would make it possible for Hoechst to take up polyethylene production.

The classic plastics

Hoechst had been engaged in plastics even in the first world war. At that time, a shortage of raw materials helped a comparatively unimportant branch of industrial chemistry to assume tremendous significance. Prior to the war, nobody had even remotely guessed the amounts of raw materials that the present popularity of plastics would require. This was the reason why there was little jubilation when chemists promised the creation of a new plastic. Potential customers asked themselves what they were supposed to do with this material since there was already an abundance of natural products. And even the experts did not exactly rave over the chemists that had developed resinous structures from pungent smelling phenol and formaldehyde.

At that time, the orthodox school of chemistry was not interested in the indefinable

163

resins with which a large number of chemists was suddenly experimenting. Crystallisation was the vogue in organic chemistry at that time. Anything that could not be crystallised had a rather tarnished reputation in the laboratories. And even when the Belgian chemist Leo Hendrik Baekeland, the creator of bakelite, reported in the "Chemiker-Zeitung" in 1909 on his successful polycondensation experiments with phenol and formaldehyde, it did not cause any particular excitement. Many of his contemporaries did not have the necessary imagination, nor the scientific training, to grasp the revolutionary development that this was heralding. A lack of consumer interest in the new plastic initially prevented the industry from making large production plans.

But the first world war brought a decisive turn in events. Germany, poor in raw materials, was forced to close part of its import needs with plastics. The scarcity of certain materials aided the breakthrough of plastics. Farbwerke Hoechst specialised in a particular field, the processing of synthetic resins into Asplit cements based on phenol/formaldehyde. It was not until the end of the twenties that Hoechst took up the planned manufacture of plastics — polymerisation plastics.

Collaboration with Professor Staudinger

These polymer plastics were not of the phenolic resin type but vinyl compounds which have an unsaturated atom grouping similar to that of ethylene. If acetic acid or hydrochloric acid gas is added on to acetylene with the aid of catalysts, vinyl acetate or vinyl chloride is formed. Vinyl acetate polymerises very readily. Thanks to the early efforts of Professor Paul Duden concerning the development of acetylene chemistry at Hoechst, the chemists of the company came to be regarded as pioneers in this field.

In addition, there was a very happy collaboration with the Freiburg Professor Hermann Staudinger. Staudinger was the founder of macromolecular chemistry. And although this is today an expression used as a matter of course by the entire chemical industry, it should never be forgotten just what difficulties Staudinger had to face in introducing his ideas about macromolecules. He had recognised that strength, elasticity, film and filament formation of many natural materials, for example rubber, starch, silk or cellulose, were due to the agglomeration of simple unsaturated compounds to form giant molecules. When Staudinger once lectured about the high molecular character of rubber, the famous mineralogist Paul Niggli rose to declare laconically: "There is no such thing".

In his biography, Staudinger reminisces: 'Niggli started from the then conventional idea that a molecule could not be larger than the elementary cell of the product that could be recognised by X-ray methods. The results of X-ray investigation of crystallised poly-hydroxymethylene, which contradicted this view, were not published until 1927. Following this, Niggli soon changed his views and during later discussions he frequently recalled, with much amusement, his first rejection of macromolecules'.

Do macromolecules really exist?

As late as 1957, Professor Staudinger was confronted by the Japanese emperor, who was greatly interested in science, with the question "Professor, are macromolecules simply ideas that help you to explain many phenomena or is their existence scientifically proved. If so, by what methods?" Staudinger's reply was based on the finding that a macromolecular substance which is converted into derivatives does not change its degree of polymerisation.

Plastics in Hoechst

The man to whom Hoechst owes the development of its first plastic plants was Dr. Georg Kränzlein, the chief of the main Alizarin laboratory. It was he who had brought about the collaboration with Professor Staudinger. Under his management, the manufacture of polyvinyl acetate — sold under the trade name Mowilith — was taken up in a building of the Alizarin department. Kränzlein was also chairman of the plastics commission of the I.G. Farbenindustrie which controlled all the work in this field. It was thanks to his influence that the I.G., even under the great pressures resulting from the world economic crisis, did not stop development work in this field. It also was due to him that Hoechst was given a fair share of plastics production within the I.G.

Polyvinyl acetate, which heralded the plastics era at Hoechst, continues to occupy an important place in the manufacturing range of Hoechst. The starting product — vinyl acetate — is produced by the catalytic addition of acetic acid to acetylene. The vinyl acetate plant at Hoechst is one of the largest, if not the largest, in the world.

Apart from Hoechst, polyvinyl acetate is also produced by Wacker-Chemie GmbH, a firm in which Farbwerke Hoechst AG. has a 50 per cent share. Wacker-Chemie has played a key part in the development of this plastic.

Copolymerisation

If instead of the same molecule, two or three different types of molecules are polymerized together, the process is described as copolymerisation. Just as a painter by mixing two colours obtains a new third colour, so in copolymerisation a new plastic with new properties is produced from different starting materials. The best-known example of copolymerisation, which has gained tremendous economic significance, is SBR synthetic rubber. A copolymer in which brittle polystyrene is rendered elastic by the incorporation of butadiene.

The copolymerisation of vinyl compounds was investigated in the Hoechst laboratories as far back as the twenties. Among the copolymer plastics produced by Hoechst, the vinyl acetate copolymers have the greatest importance. Other copolymers in the Hoechst plastics range are based on vinyl chloride.

Mass polymerisation

Vinyl acetate molecules have a double bond — the characteristic vinyl group. This can be polymerised in a number of different ways. One of the simplest is mass polymerisation or block polymerisation. In this, vinyl acetate monomer is transformed into polyvinyl acetate through the action of catalysts but without the use of solvents or diluents. After a given time, vinyl acetate polymer issues from the large polymerisation kettles as a viscous colourless mass. It is allowed to cool and solidify and subsequently is broken up into small lumps. No further processing is needed.

Emulsion and suspension polymerisation

Other types of polymerisation, namely emulsion and suspension polymerisation, have however achieved greater importance for Hoechst plastics production. An emulsion is the fine distribution of a liquid in another liquid, for example oil in water. A suspension is the distribution of a solid substance in a liquid.

When vinyl acetate monomer is converted during emulsion or suspension polymerisation, water is first added to the polymerisation kettle. This is followed by emulsifiers and finally by the vinyl acetate. Emulsifiers have to be used since otherwise the vinyl acetate, which is practically insoluble in water, could not broken up into fine droplets. The water would remain at the bottom of the kettle and the lighter vinyl acetate would float on top. Even with rapid stirring, it would not be possible to produce a mixture, let alone an emulsion. The emulsifiers facilitate fine distribution of the vinyl acetate and small droplets of vinyl acetate in water are formed. If it were possible to look into the tightly-closed vessel, one would get the impression that it contained milk. Polymerisation is initiated with the aid of catalysts and heat. Each droplet begins to polymerise independently. The innumerable vinyl acetate molecules in the droplets do precisely what is expected of them. They join with one another to form macromolecules. At the beginning of polymerisation there are liquid droplets finely distributed in water. At the end, there are solid particles.

Polymerisation technology employs two processes which can be differentiated in practical respects although they do not differ in the strictly physical sense.

In suspension polymerisation, the initial vinyl acetate droplets are comparatively large and not emulsified to any particular degree. The polymerisation catalyst, however, becomes dissolved in these droplets and even the high-molecular product that is formed retains the approximate size of the original droplet. Once polymerisation is completed, polyvinyl acetate pellets of a mat white colour are formed. These pellets are filtered from the water.

In emulsion polymerisation, far finer vinyl acetate droplets are distributed in the water. In order to achieve this, protective colloids are added. On completion of polymerisation, they insure that solid polyvinyl acetate particles do not settle out. The emulsion — or, to be strictly accurate, the dispersion — remains homogenous. It is extraordinarily stable. Polyvinyl acetate dispersions can be shipped anywhere in the whole world and can be stored for comparatively long periods.

The more carefully emulsification is carried out, the more uniform is the final polymer — the plastic dispersion. When polyvinyl alcohol is used as an emulsifying agent, advantage can be taken of two of its important characteristics: it very readily emulsifies vinyl acetate in water and it acts as an outstanding colloid for the polyvinyl acetate particles.

Polyvinyl alcohol is produced from polyvinyl acetate by re-esterification. In this process, polyvinyl acetate is dissolved in methyl alcohol in the presence of an alkali or acid so that the acetic radical of the polyvinyl acetate combines with methyl alcohol to form methyl acetate and polyvinyl alcohol. A small part of polyvinyl acetate production is therefore continuously used up as emulsifying agent in the form of polyvinyl alcohol in order to produce polyvinyl acetate dispersion.

The various polyvinyl alcohol grades are marketed under the trade names Moviol and Vinarol. Both products are used in a wide variety of applications, for example as finishing and sizing agents in the textile industry.

Mowilith — the raw material with a thousand uses

With the development of the dispersion grades, the polyvinyl acetate business at Hoechst experienced a tremendous upsurge. The white milky dispersion is sent out to customers in green barrels. Every year, some 400,000 such barrels leave the factory.

In addition, the dispersions are also despatched in road and rail tankers. Hoechst and its foreign manufacturing facilities today supply more than 100,000 tons of Mowilith dispersion per year. This figure does not take into account Wacker's output.

A list of all the applications of polyvinyl acetate would fill a volume. Its most important uses are in paints for buildings and in the production of glues and adhesives. The applications for Mowilith are so numerous that the Hoechst advertising people have rightly dubbed it as the raw material with a thousand uses. Polyvinyl acetate accounts for the major share of Hoechst's plastics output. The needs of the building industry alone require continuous expansion in production capacity and provide fresh applications almost daily. Great importance has been attached at Hoechst to securing an adequate supply of vinyl acetate for a long time ahead.

New patents for Wacker and Hoechst

For many years, acetylene had been the starting product for vinyl acetate. It was, after all, the first rung in Duden's ladder. And although acetic acid was needed for vinyl acetate, this acid, too, was based — via acetaldehyde as intermediate — on acetylene, the progenitor of so many chemical products. A process discovered almost simultaneously by Wacker and Hoechst and developed by both companies appeared to be much more promising at first sight. In this process, acetaldehyde is obtained by direct oxidation of ethylene with air or oxygen. In 1958, more than 100 tons of acetaldehyde were prepared in this way. Once Hoechst's petrochemical plants were able to supply sufficient ethylene, acetaldehyde capacity was increased to several thousand tons per month. Today, the new acetaldehyde plant supplies a large part of Hoechst's requirements. In a few years time, acetaldehyde will be produced in Hoechst solely on the basis of ethylene. As a result of the rapid development of petroleum chemistry, the new process has gained great importance throughout the world and is already being used by many companies. In order to exploit the joint patents, Hoechst has founded the Aldehyd GmbH. in conjunction with Wacker.

Polyvinyl chloride

The polymerisation of vinyl chloride, although worked out in the scientific laboratories of Hoechst many years ago, was reserved during the I.G. period for the Ludwigshafen and Bitterfeld works and for Wacker-Chemie. Hoechst was able to take up the production of polyvinyl chloride only after the dismemberment of the I.G. Farbenindustrie. This was at a time when PVC had already gained a significant market for itself. Large companies both at home and abroad had built up massive capacities for this product. It will therefore be readily understood why Hoechst decided to concentrate its attention on various special grades of PVC. These are made available to the plastics processing industry under the trade name Hostalit and they are mainly polymers produced by either suspension or emulsion polymerisation.

Of particular interest is a novel polymer mixture in which a chlorination product of Hoechst low pressure polyethylene is added to PVC. These new special grades, which are marketed under the name Hostalit Z, are used particularly in the building industry. PVC is also produced in the Gendorf works where it is mostly converted into film. Wacker-Chemie, too, is an important PVC producer.

Fluorinated plastics

Hostaflon is the Hoechst trade name for fluorinated plastics. The largest part of these exclusive compounds consists of fluorine, an element closely related to chlorine. It belongs to the group of halogens and is found in nature as a calcium compound in fluorspar.

Work on fluorinated organic compounds was carried out at Hoechst as far back as the thirties. In 1934, Hoechst was able to consolidate its leading position by a sensational patent. This concerned the first method for the production of polymeric trifluorochloro-ethylene. The experience available at that time for the processing of plastics was however inadequate for the manufacture of useful products from fluoro-organic polymers.

At the end of the thirties, a young chemist at Du Pont had produced a similar fluorinated product — tetrafluoroethylene. His subsequent discovery was almost as accidental as Klatte's discovery of polyvinyl acetate several years before at Griesheim. The Du Pont chemist poured tetrafluoroethylene into a bottle. Then he turned to what he thought was more important work. It was not until some weeks later that he remembered the bottle. He opened it but found to his astonishment that the gas had disappeared. Instead, a waxy soft compound had formed at the bottom of the flask. Even the preliminary investigation of this accidental polymer — polytetrafluorethylene — caused a sensation in the laboratories of Du Pont. The new polymer resisted temperatures down to nearly absolute zero point and on the other end of the scale withstood heat that no ordinary plastic would tolerate. The strongest acids were unable to attack this super-plastic. Even aqua regia, a highly corrosive mixture of nitric acid and hydrochloric acid, was tamed by it. But even more impressive is the following fact: Various diaphragms, only 0.5 mm thick, have now been exposed for more than seven years to the attack of water vapour saturated chlorine gas at temperatures of around 70 °C without the slightest effect, even on the surface. Polymerisation work on fluorinated organic substances was taken up again at Hoechst both during and after the war. This work led to products that have been marketed under the trade name Hostaflon.

Hostaflon has found its main outlet in the chemical industry itself to protect its equipment against corrosive chemicals. In aviation, too, and in nuclear and reactor technology — in fact wherever the highest stresses are involved — this plastic is gaining ever-increasing importance. Its high price, however, is as yet preventing it from becoming a major product such as PVC or polyethylene.

From the test tube to large-scale production

Next to Mowilith, polyolefins are in the forefront of Hoechst's interest in terms of production tonnage. As always with new products, polyolefins posed the problem of how to translate a laboratory discovery into terms of large-scale production. Particularly in the chemical field, this is a far more difficult undertaking than the layman often imagines.

An invention, so the experts say, needs five to ten years in order to experience this translation from the successful test tube experiment to large-scale production. That Hoechst was able to abbreviate this interval to less than two years in the case of polyethylene was due entirely — as in petrochemistry — to the perfect harmony between chemists and technicians.

After short but intensive tests in the Hoechst laboratories where, as in Professor Ziegler's work in Mülheim, polyethylene was at first produced on a kilogram scale, the first pilot plant was erected. Its initial output was ten tons a month.

At this stage, of course, it could not be expected that every production detail had been fully mastered. Whether the desired degree of polymerisation could be obtained, whether undesirable by-products would be formed that were not encountered in the laboratory experiments, how the product would behave over long periods of time, whether the catalyst system could be varied — all these things had to be studied in great detail in order to make sure that the full scale plant would finally turn out a product of the desired quality.

The sum of all this experience is know-how. Know-how is a considerable asset to any company and comprises the manufacture and applications of the new products. It was therefore of considerable interest to Hoechst to enter into an exchange of know-how with the Hercules Powder Company which was also planning to become active in the field of thermoplastics. In this way, the Hoechst experts gained an early insight into the American plastics market.

Together with Hercules Powder Company, Hoechst has set up the Abieta Chemie GmbH, on the site of the Gersthofen works. This plant produces auxiliaries for modern Buna production at Hüls.

Farbwerke Hoechst AG also has a capital interest in Buna-Werke Hüls GmbH by way of the Synthesekautschuk-Beteiligungsgesellschaft. In this way, together with Bayer, BASF and Chemische Werke Hüls AG, it again has an interest in rubber synthesis, one of the first and most important plastics and a field full of tradition.

There was a special reason why Hoechst concentrated on plastics production from olefins. In spite of its great scientific pioneering work, Hoechst lagged far behind in this field after the second world war, especially so far as mouldable plastics were concerned.

This was not, of course, surprising in view of its restricted raw material basis at a time when plastics already accounted for 8.5 per cent of the total output of the chemical industry in the Federal Republic. In 1954, some 302,000 tons of plastics were produced in Germany. By 1961, plastics production had increased to 1.1 million tons. Half of this amount was accounted for by polymer plastics.

It was only after Hoechst had started to provide the essential raw materials from its own petrochemical plants that the picture changed. New developments took place at breathtaking speed. In August 1954, a lincence for the production of low-pressure polyethylene had been obtained from Professor Ziegler. One year later, at the end of 1955, the first large plant was in operation. It produced 250 tons a month. Today, this figure has risen to five thousand tons of polyolefins per month.

The role of the development chemist

At this time, the Hoechst development chemists, the link between production and customer, were fully engaged in putting across the new plastics. Their properties, their behaviour under all sorts of conditions and the most suitable method of application — all these aspects are of vital concern to the development chemists. Upon their answer depends whether a bridge can be built between a new product and its customers. This applies to newly-developed plastics as much as to a large number of other products which are marketed in continuously improved form. For this reason, the number of development chemists engaged at Hoechst is almost as large as the number of employees in a medium-sized factory — 2,000 including more than 200 scientists.

Hoechst's development chemists do not confine themselves to mere matters of theory. They have at their disposal a whole arsenal of complex production equipment, a factory on a miniature scale containing many plastics processing machines so that the introduction of the new products can be accelerated.

Equally important is control of production so as to ensure uniformly high quality. Other tasks for the Hoechst technical service men include the development of new processing techniques and of new applications for their products.

At the Brussels World Fair in 1958, Hoechst showed a polyethylene plant using the low-pressure process. Although this plant was on a miniature scale, it clearly showed the entire production process. Visitors saw the conversion of simple ethylene gas into a plastic from which a memorial plaque was moulded for each visitor. Brussels was, in fact, the debut of low-pressure polyethylene.

Pipes from polyethylene

This low pressure polyethylene proved an outstanding stable mate for high pressure polyethylene developed in England. The polyethylene produced by Hoechst — Hostalen G — consists of straight molecular chains. High pressure polyethylene on the other hand has far more widely branched chains. In contrast to high pressure polyethylene, low pressure polyethylene has a higher density and thus greater strength. Because of its molecular structure, it also has a very high melting point — around 130 °C. Hostalen is distinguished by its high resistance against chemicals and heat. In fact, it was a raw material that the pipe manufacturers could not afford to ignore.

The degree of polymerisation of polyethylene can be closely controlled. It is within the power of chemists to determine just how big the molecules will be. Hostalen can therefore be tailor-made and grades can be produced for almost every application and for a great variety of processing methods.

Polypropylene — Hostalen PP

Hostalen PP is another successful Hoechst plastic. Its starting product is propylene which, like ethylene to which it is chemically related, is a product of petrochemistry. Propylene is polymerised under conditions and with the aid of catalysts similar to those used in the polymerisation of ethylene.

Professor G. Natta applied the findings of Ziegler to propylene when the catalyst system developed by Ziegler became a major talking point among chemists throughout the world. Natta was able to show that the same metalorganic catalysts could also be used for propylene. But he also found that the same catalysts could yield different polymers: Propylene polymerisation can result in a soft amorphous mass or in crystalline plastics of such hardness and strength that they surpass even polyethylene. Natta found that this phenomenon was due to a different arrangement of the molecules in the chain. Of the three structural variations that occur, industrial chemistry prefers the isotactic structure because this alone imparts high strength to the products.

In the isotactic structure, the successive individual molecules in the polymer chain have the highest degree of symmetry. They are arranged like soldiers on parade. It is these uniform chains that yield the perfect polypropylene, a plastic of the lightest weight and yet able to tolerate the greatest stresses.

On the basis of Ziegler's and Natta's research work, and equipped with the scientific and technical experience gained with low pressure polyethylene, Hoechst began the large-scale manufacture of polypropylene at the end of 1958. The product is sold under the brand name HOSTALEN PP. Hoechst succeeded in so designing its process that practically only isotactic polypropylene was obtained. In comparison with polyethylene, Hostalen PP is distinguished by a higher melting point (160 °C) and greater rigidity and hardness. Hostalen PP is used for a variety of applications from vacuum cleaner casings to shoeheels, from articles for the electrical and precision engineering industries to vehicle and equipment construction.

Hostaform

A new and promising development in the field of macromolecular chemistry is the polymerisation of aldehydes. This field was investigated independently by Hoechst and the Celanese Corporation of America.

An exchange of know-how and the positive assessment of the products obtained by both sides led to the foundation of Ticona Polymerwerke GmbH in which Hoechst has a share of 59 pc and Celanese one of 41 pc. Production of polyformaldehyde started in Kelsterbach — 8 km away from Hoechst, and near the new Caltex refinery — at the end of 1963. The products will be used mainly in the technical sector, for example in automobile engineering, where they can frequently replace light metal components.

Since 1930, plastics have developed volume-wise far more strongly than metals, including aluminium. This comparison does not even take account of synthetic rubber or cellulose fibres. There is no reason to think that this development will abate in the near future. New products are being continuously developed and the price structure of plastics is subject to continuous change.

174

*Ethylene polymerization plant
at the Brussels World Fair*

Plastics everywhere

Plastics, like all other industrial products and especially chemical products, initially remain reserved for only a few applications because of their high price. As a result of intense development, and particularly as a result of technological progress, they even tually come within a price range where they are suitable for mass-production.

The reason that plastics are no longer regarded simply as an inferior substitute for a natural product is unlikely to be due to the fact that walls in atomic reactors, shells of rockets or the insulation in transatlantic underwater cables are made from synthetic high-molecular products. It is not their particular characteristics that have helped plastics to become working materials in the wider sense of the word. It is the thousands of items of every-day life, the gaily coloured toys and the virtually unbreakable plastic domestic equipment that have gained plastics the support of the man in the street. The ordinary man or woman hardly ever realises that nylon stockings, high-grade clothes or the film in which so many of our foods are now packed also belong to the family of plastics, the marvels of chemistry.

Films from cellulose and plastics

One of these marvels of chemistry is the plastic film. In taking a closer look at this group of plastic products, we have to move from Hoechst to Wiesbaden-Biebrich. One of the advertising slogans of Kalle AG, a wholly-owned subsidiary of Hoechst, is 'If it's films, ask Kalle'. This company, which celebrated its centenary in the summer of 1963, has had close links with Hoechst since 1907.

However, until 1925 the slogan should have read 'If it's dyes, ask Kalle'. For until that time, Kalle was a production centre for dyestuffs and pharmaceuticals. It was only following the reorganisation within the newly-founded I.G. Farbenindustrie that Kalle became 'unemployed' and had to look for new fields of activity.

One of these was CELLOPHAN. Kalle took up this field with such intensity, and with such success, that it has meanwhile become the largest European producer of this film. Today, Kalle employs some 7,000 people of which a part, however, is concerned with the manufacture of OZALID copying papers and reproductive equipment, the second largest field of Kalle.

The inventor of this process, which has long since replaced conventional blue-printing, was G. Kögel. Like one of the American pioneers in the field of synthetic rubber production, he wore the garment of a Catholic monk. Kögel, experimenting in Beuron

monastery with diazonium compounds, recognised their outstanding light sensitivity. It is not entirely without satisfaction that Kalle points out today that Kögel first offered his new photocopying paper, which can be developed dry, to the large constituent companies of the I.G. But these companies did not show any interest because sales did not seem likely to achieve the figures that they were used to. Kalle therefore took up the invention and began the production of Ozalid papers, at the same time producing the necessary equipment which was hired out to customers. In this way, availability of the important technical service was ensured. Although Ozalid at that time cost five times as much as ordinary blue-print paper — progress always costs money — it achieved success in a surprisingly short period of time. Kalle is currently engaged in developing new reproduction materials for special fields of application.

But back to Cellophan. The main achievement of Kalle was not so much the change-over in production from dyestuffs to the new cellulose product but the opening-up of applications for the new product. Almost every day, the development chemists of Kalle opened up new possibilities for the use of cellophane. In order to popularise these applications, Kalle sent battalions of representatives up and down the country, even to the smallest village grocer, to propagate the advantages of the new material. It was therefore not long before conventional, unattractive packaging materials were replaced by glass-clear cellophane.

Cellophane still tops

Thirty years later, in the age of plastic films, cellophane remains on top. It still accounts for almost half of film production at Kalle. The reason for the continuous success of cellophane is its unsurpassed transparency and brilliancy and also its outstanding machine properties when applied in automatic packaging plant. Cellophane is particularly valuable as a packaging material in the cigarette industry.

In the course of time, the manufacturing methods for cellophane have been widely rationalized. The current method is a follows: Cellulose is dissolved in caustic soda solution and carbon disulphide. Viscose is then formed, the same viscose as is used in viscose acetate production. In film manufacture, the viscose is pressed through a narrow slit, approximately 2 m long, into a precipitating bath. In this bath, cellulose is regenerated and converted into a band of film. This band of film passes over a system of rollers which are immersed in baths in which the band is subjected to a variety of treatments. Subsequently, it is dried down to a certain minimum moisture content. This is necessary because a completely dry band would be brittle and tear.

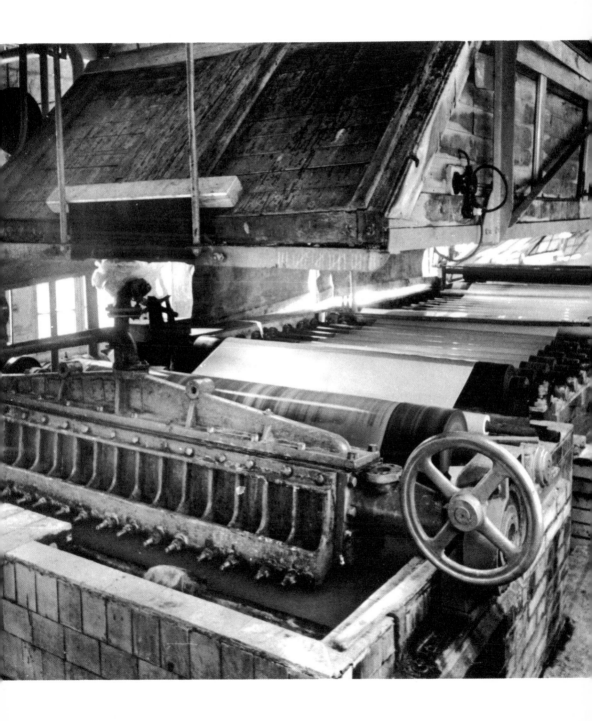

Highly complicated measuring and control instruments insure that during its 100 m long journey from roller to roller the band remains smooth and retains its standard width. From the last roller the band runs on to an automatically controlled winder to form large rolls which are then stacked in warehouses. Sales of cellophane were greatly enhanced by the development of the cellophane weatherproof grades. These grades are lacquered either on one or both sides so that the goods packed in them are largely protected against drying-out and moisture.

The rise of plastic films

Cellulose and cellophane are obtained from wood. They are therefore still natural products in the wider sense. In 1939, however, plastic films were born at Kalle. They owe their existence solely to chemical reactions. The starting point were the polyamides used in 1939 by Paul Schlack in the I.G.-Werk Berlin-Lichtenberg for Perlon manufacture. When this work on the first Perlon filaments and fibres was being carried out, Kalle was asked by the I.G. to develop films from polyamide.

Although Kalle was able to get the necessary raw material from BASF in Ludwigshafen, and although a usable production method could be developed fairly quickly, the enterprise remained stillborn because of the outbreak of war. The polyamide films show great versatility but they do not occupy an important place in the manufacturing programme of Kalle because other plastics have meanwhile gained greater importance in film production. Kalle resumed its operations in 1945 with 400 employees and, shortly afterwards, new developments were set in train, especially after Kalle had rejoined the Hoechst group.

SUPRATHEN, the first plastic film to gain any significance, is based largely on high pressure polyethylene. Even the layman not versed in chemical terminology will usually be right if he thinks of the plastic bags used for food in terms of polyethylene. Many of the transparent films that are used by the building trade during the winter or that find application in horticulture and agriculture are also made from this synthetic material.

Polyethylene film is extruded and extruders dominate the scene in many Kalle production plants. The machines are very long. At one end the colourless polyethylene granules are fed via a screw into a heated chamber where they are fused into a plastic mass which is then pressed through a die. Sometimes a broad slit die is used. With the aid of this die, wide film webs are produced. For the production of tubular films and bags, an annular die is used.

Two-way stretch

Some plastic films, particularly those produced from Hostalen G and PP, are stretched after extrusion to several times their length. This increases the tensile strength significantly.

In contrast to fibres, plastics films are usually stretched — or oriented — biaxially, i. e. both in length and width. For example, a film leaving the extruder in a width of 50 cm, is given a width of up to 2 m by this process in addition to the longitudinal extension. In this way, the film acquires not only far better physical properties but also a greater degree of brightness. Orientation therefore governs quality and appearance of a plastic film. Together with Hoechst, Kalle has acquired a great deal of know-how in this field and has been able to develop a large number of new techniques.

Orientation is particularly important in the case of HOSTAPHAN which is produced from polyterephthalic ester. This is the same material as that used in the production of Trevira, Hoechst's polyester fibre. The tensile strength of Hostaphan film is almost equal to that of steel. In addition, the film has a very high temperature resistance and an extraordinarily high electrical insulation value. For this reason, Hostaphan plays a large part in the electric industry, which is in any case partial to plastics, as insulating material for condensers and electric motors. Hostaphan film can also be coated with polyethylene to produce a composite film. The gas impermeability of Hostaphan is combined in this way with the considerable protective action of polyethylene against water vapour.

A film with a future

A film that Kalle believes to have a very great future is produced from Hoechst's polypropylene, HOSTALEN PP. Because of its outstanding clarity and high lustre, it meets the highest demands. This film can be converted into packs for foodstuffs resistant to boiling and suitable for sterilization and also into packs for hot-filled materials. It would therefore be an ideal packaging film for the steadily growing pre-cooked food industry. Like other plastic films, polypropylene can be welded. In the production shops of Kalle this is carried out with electrodes that do the job in a fraction of a second. In cooling, the welded points solidify and then have the same strength as the unwelded material. Cellophane, which is not a thermoplastic, cannot be welded. After lacquering, collophane is therefore simply heat-sealed.

Genotherm from Gendorf

Films from polyamide, acetyl cellulose and polyolefines, cellophane and Hostaphan are the most important products of the extensive Kalle range. PVC is the only major film not produced by the machines in Biebrich. From the beginning, this has been the particular baby of Gendorf.

Although pvc films have in the meantime gained a considerable share of the market, the beginnings in Gendorf were modest indeed. The Gendorf works were particularly badly hit during the war and when film production was again taken up, the only assets were a range of calenders, machines with large heated rollers that render the pvc plastic and roll it into very thin films. Gendorf today has available the most modern machinery and also rules over its own raw material supplies. The major item of production is Genotherm, rigid pvc film, of which many hundred tons are produced per month, in fact more than half of the entire output of rigid pvc film in Germany.

The many applications for pvc films include office equipment and carrier film for adhesive strips. Recently, two particularly interesting applications have been developed. Genotherm is used as a carrier material for records and recorder tapes as well as a material for food containers, for example for delicatessen, fats, and especially margarine. The former papier mâché has today been largely replaced by the more suitable rigid pvc. The film is also used for the packaging of pharmaceutical and cosmetic products. The containers are deep drawn on special forming machines. The output of one of these machines is more than 5,000 units per hour. A plastic sheet, heated to a very high temperature, is drawn over a form against which it fits very closely. In fractions of a second, the plastic formed in this way solidifies and thus retains the contour imparted to it by the form. There are of course machines that are provided with exchangeable forms so that boxes, cans and dishes can be produced on a large scale.

If during film manufacture, pvc is mixed with a suitable plasticizer, soft films can be produced which are especially suitable for use in the open. This soft film has proved highly successful in horticulture for cold frames and portable greenhouses. Tubular film extruded from soft pvc serves for the production of sachets used with great success especially in the cosmetic industry. The list of these interesting and often new film applications is endless. Kalle films for example are suitable for glossy laminations for printed magazines and for the protection of valuable documents.

Hoechst takes up man-made fibres

In 1954, France's convention-happy metropolis bore witness to a unique occasion. The man-made fibre producers of the world gathered to hold their first international conference, a week of resplendent receptions, lectures and exhibitions. Farbwerke Hoechst AG was very much an onlooker at these events. While the company was once more vigorously engaged in its traditional fields, the manufacture of man-made fibres was, at that date, still a closed book.

But eight years later, at the London rendezvous of the man-made fibre producers in 1962, the Hoechst delegates no longer needed to look upon themselves as outsiders. In this short period Hoechst had caught up with the man-made fibre giants.

Although the product range of Hoechst had become tremendously complex since its foundation the company's debut in the field of synthetic fibres did not take place for 90 years. Today Hoechst makes more than 20,000 products.

As soon as the company was reformed in 1952, fibres figured on the agenda of the meetings of the board. At that time, Hoechst was engaged in a search for new fields of production that would comprise the entire spectrum from the raw material to the chemical end-product. The intention was not only to produce chemical starting products for the new man-made fibres but also to engage in other manufacturing phases so as to get closer to the textile industry as such. Hoechst's emergence among the man-made fibre producers was preceded by extensive debates by management. There were many suggestions about new fields of production other than fibres. When, finally, the decision went in favour of fibres, there was no doubt at Hoechst that this step presented both tempting opportunities and serious risks.

Acquisition of Bobingen

In order not to lose any further time, Hoechst acquired the artificial silk factory of Bobingen near Augsburg which was one of the residues of the former I.G. complex. In 1952, Bobingen had celebrated its fiftieth anniversary as a producer of artificial silk. During those fifty years, Bobingen had experienced many ups and downs, a fate not uncommon to the companies that had engaged in the manufacture of artificial silk. Nevertheless, shortly after the turn of the century, Bobingen was able to spin some 400 kg of artificial silk per day from cotton waste. At that time, of course, artificial silk was by no means the equal of the natural product. Nevertheless, it found a ready market because it was possible to achieve with it a large number of fashionable effects. During the first ten years of the twentieth century, seven artificial silk factories had opened up in Germany. In 1913, the number had increased to twenty-two. Together, they represented a capital of over 27 million marks and produced some 1,200 tons of artificial silk. The larger of these companies soon experienced a considerable business upswing, particularly after artificial silk began to be generally accepted for underwear, dress satins and finally even for ladies' stockings. During the first years, it had been used only for fashion accessories such as braid, cord or similar items distinguished by a particularly high gloss.

For the smaller undertakings, however, the situation was by no means so promising. The rapid change in production methods and the high costs of development work to improve quality rendered the existence of these companies rather precarious. As a result, Bobingen, too, was forced to work out a new manufacturing process just when the last machines for the nitrate method had been installed. The actual inventors of the new method were three Englishmen who treated cellulose with caustic soda solution, obtained from electrolysis, and with carbon disulphide. In this way, a cellulose solution was formed which, because of its high consistency, was termed 'viscose'.

This viscose process offered two advantages. The solvent and the pine tree cellulose which it employed were far cheaper than the cotton linters and ether and alcohol of

which large amounts were required in the other processes. For example, 1 kg nitrate silk required approximately 13 litres of these solvents. As a consequence of all this, Bobingen stopped the nitrate silk plant in 1911 and took up the viscose process. The viscose was spun into fine filaments in an acid bath where they solidified.

Gun cotton

At the beginning of the First World War, the Bobingen viscose plants had stopped. But soon the military remembered that it was possible to produce gun cotton by the nitration of cellulose, that is by its treatment with concentrated nitric and sulphuric acid. In the course of this development, Bobingen became the gun cotton factory of the Vereinigte Köln-Rottweiler Pulverfabriken AG in Berlin. As part of this complex, it also shared its post-war fate. The plants that had served for war purposes were dismantled or destroyed.

Two years later, Bobingen was able to resume artificial silk production after the Köln-Rottweil AG — its less belligerent post-war name — had turned from explosives to more peaceful pursuits. In the main works at Premnitz on the Havel, which had been turned into a gunpowder factory during the war, momentous things were taking place. Although the work of the chemists continued to centre around cellulose, they were no longer concerned with nitration. Instead, attempts were made at Premnitz to develop from cellulose the first artificial staple fibre to compete with natural wool. Staple fibre is something different from the endless filaments of silk or artificial silk. Staple fibre has to be spun, either on its own or blended with natural fibres such as cotton or wool, to give the final yarn.

Vistra — the new rayon staple

The Köln-Rottweil AG christened its rayon staple Vistra and presented it to the public for the first time in 1922 at an exhibition in Munich. Although Vistra production in 1925 amounted to more than half a million kg., rayon staple did not at first prove a commercial success. The substitute materials of the war had not been forgotten by the German public. No matter how impressive the proof of quality, neither spinners nor public could be won over to the artificial rayon staple. The stores of the Köln-Rottweil AG were soon proving too small for housing all the unsold material that was accumulating.

And when, eventually, the originally promising export business also receded because of the high tariff walls erected by most countries, the Köln-Rottweil AG had to slam on the brakes. Together with its works at Premnitz, Rottweil and Bobingen, which had been closed for several months in 1926 because of the serious order position, the Köln-Rottweil AG took steps to join the I.G. Farbenindustrie AG which had been formed during that year. The artificial silk companies thought they would be able to sit out the storm of the approaching world economic crisis under the I.G. umbrella.

The I.G. had erected an artificial silk factory operating the viscose process as early as 1921 in connection with the Film-Fabrik Wolfen of Agfa. In 1926, it had started up a further factory in Dormagen which employed the cuprammonium process. By taking over the Köln-Rottweil AG, it was able to enlarge this field of production to which, in the past, the large chemical companies had not paid the degree of attention that might have been expected. The first step towards expansion of this field was to increase Vistra production in Premnitz to 100 tons of rayon staple per day. Moreover, Bobingen's artificial silk production was greatly enlarged and modernized. Bobingen was provided with 36 new spinning machines, with modern plants for the filtration of spinning acid and with new washing machines. In 1928, Bobingen was able to announce an annual production of 700,000 kg viscose. In the following years, these figures were increased threefold. Furthermore, in 1926 the I.G., together with Vereinigte Glanzstoff-Fabriken AG who withdrew from the arrangement some years later, erected an acetate silk factory in Berlin-Lichtenberg, the 'Aceta.'

The whirlpool of the world slump

But things were to take an entirely different turn for a time. The whirlpool of the world slump which set in during 1929 depressed prices on the textile raw material market to their lowest levels. For a time, wool became cheaper than rayon staple. The world cotton price dropped from something like 22 cents in the 1928/29 season to approximately 4 cents. The I.G. had no choice. Together with a number of spinners it formed the Vistra association. Its aim was not to increase prices unnecessarily but to stabilize them at a sensible level. This the association achieved long before the self-sufficiency ambitions of the Third Reich unbalanced the interplay of forces of a normal market economy. During the years following, the rise of rayon staple output continued irresistibly. Soon Vistra was outselling artificial silk, and eventually there came the day when more rayon staple than natural wool was produced in the world. But there also came a day when the reaction vessels of the chemical industry produced a new competitor to rayon staple and artificial silk. Both these products were the off-spring of a mixed marriage between the plant raw material cellulose and the science of chemistry and this earned them the description semi-synthetics. But the new fibres that were now announced to the world were 100 pc man-made.

The birth of the man-made fibres

A famous name in the history of man-made fibres was *Dr. Fritz Klatte* who first developed a commercial synthesis for POLYVINYL CHLORIDE and POLYVINYL ACETATE in the present Griesheim works of the Hoechst AG. Klatte succeeded in producing vinyl chloride, until then known only as a laboratory preparation, on an industrial scale, as early as 1913. Klatte, with his fine nose for the future potential of a product, regarded vinyl chloride as an excellent raw material for man-made fibres. But as yet, chemists did not know how to render the gaseous vinyl chloride into the solid state or how to polymerise it in an economic manner. This was simply because science at that time did not know enough about high polymers. The breeding of macromolecules from simple small molecules was only in its infancy. In particular, there was as yet no *Hermann Staudinger,* the later Nobel prize winner, who provided chemistry with its first ordinance maps, and who charted the wonderland of the macromolecules of which a single one is often made up of millions of atoms. Staudinger was also the first person to develop a reliable method for measuring the degree of polymerisation of chemical substances.

It was not until the early 1930's that chemists really mastered industrial polymerisation. But once this had been achieved, the Wolfen Works of the I.G. did not waste any more time and turned to the classic vinyl chloride. This substance, which can be produced quite cheaply from acetylene and hydrochloric acid gas, was to yield the first man-made textile fibres in the world. The most difficult problem was in dissolving the polyvinyl chloride in a cheap solvent. This was solved by aftertreating the polyvinyl chloride with chlorine. Acetone could now be used as a cheap solvent. When this spinning solution was passed through a nozzle and the acetone removed, the PVC solidified to form fibres.

This so-called Pe-Ce-fibre offered many advantages. It was unaffected by acids, water or putrefactive media. It was distinguished by high tensile strength and non-inflammability, characteristics of tremendous importance to the textile producer. The only real danger to Pe-Ce fibre was hot washing and ironing because, unfortunately, the fibre softened at 70 °C. Pe-Ce fibre was, therefore, not suitable for ordinary suits and dresses, but because of its high chemical resistance, it gained considerable importance in the technical sector.

The German chemists then turned to a new fibre made from polyacrylonitrile but meanwhile the lead in the field of man-made fibres was taken over by their American colleagues. In the laboratories of the Du Pont group work had been going on for a long time on man-made fibres. Like Germany the United States realized that the answer was to be found in suitable polymerisation methods. In charge of this work was the young chemist *Wallace Hume Carothers* who carried out a large number of experiments in this field. Eventually, Carothers and his co-workers obtained substances that could be rendered into filaments in their molten state and that showed the phenomenon of cold stretch, hitherto unknown with synthetic materials. The filaments could be extended without difficulty to three or four times their original length.

Du Pont markets nylon

It took another five years from the date of this discovery in 1934 before Du Pont was able to market nylon, just before the war. The great advantage of nylon was that it did not consist of uninterrupted carbon chains like Pe-Ce fibre. Like wool and natural silk, nylon, apart from the regular carbon formations, also contained carbonamide groups which made it stable even in tropical heat. Its other properties, too, stamped it as the queen of the man-made fibres.

The I.G. follows with Perlon

The next move was with the I.G. Before Du Pont actually marketed its nylon, *Paul Schlack* had read several articles concerning Carothers' work. Schlack was scientific director of the I.G. works at Berlin-Lichtenberg — the Aceta works — and had been engaged for many years in a study of the polyamides which include nylon. During an outing to the Tegel Lake in Berlin in the summer of 1937, Schlack studied the first patents of Carothers and decided to pursue his own work as intensely as possible. Schlack, who later became director of a scientific department in Hoechst, was at that time engaged in so many other things that he was able to devote only a fraction of his time to polyamide research. Since laboratory chiefs do not normally work on the bench themselves, Schlack did not in fact have any laboratory facilities of his own. Almost all the experiments had to be carried out by his assistants in accordance with his directions. Schlack and laboratory assistant Ahrens initially concentrated on ammonium caproic acid and then on caprolactam which has a cyclic structure. Carothers had also investigated this caprolactam but had declared it expressly as unsuitable for polyamide synthesis.

Less than three months after he had taken up the experiments, Schlack obtained his first caprolactam polymer, a tough, horn-like compound, from whose melt endless

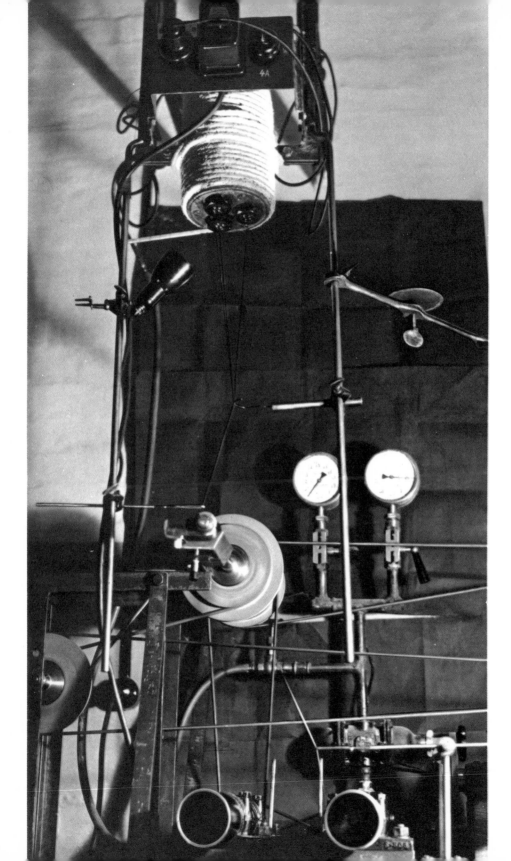

filaments could be drawn with a glass rod. The threads could be streched in the cold without difficulty, exhibiting extraordinarily high tensile strength.

The polymerisation of this substance — the birth of PERLON — took place during the night from the 28th to the 29th January 1938. The caprolactam, in a thick-walled glass tube, was heated in a furnace at approximately 240 °C for the whole night, in the presence of a catalyst.

The next step was obvious — to develop a technically useful process for caprolactam, for its polymerisation and its spinning. Since at that time equipment from high-grade alloyed steels required a special permit which was granted only in exceptional cases, Schlack had to content himself with a stainless steel kettle, such as is used in large catering establishments, which he obtained by devious routes. In this kettle, small amounts of cyclohexanonoxime were produced. In a second room, a solution of the oxime in 90 p. c. sulphuric acid was passed through a tubular furnace where, accompanied by violent hissing, the oxime was converted into caprolactam. This was then processed and vacuum-distilled. In this way, it was possible to produce one to two kg of caprolactam daily. In an adjoining room there was a spinning unit that had in the meantime been constructed. The caprolactam was polymerised with heat using a catalyst and the melt pressed through a nozzle with the aid of a stream of nitrogen. The Perlon filaments were extruded through the fine capillary openings of this nozzle.

The 'chemical spider'

Shortly afterwards, several leading men of the I.G. inspected this primitive 'chemical spider' and the endless filament that it produced. 'Don't these filaments break?' was their astonished question. To which the Perlon pioneers proudly answered: 'The machine has been running for five hours. The filament will break only when our stock of spinning compound is exhausted.' This comparative unbreakability of the Perlon thread was one of the most important conditions for its production on a large scale.

Code names for raw materials

During the first period, the Perlon discovery was kept strictly secret. All the raw materials were given code names — the term Perlon is made up of some of these codes — and even the patent was filed only months after polycaprolactam had been developed. This was really a risky course to take. After all, many countries were experimenting with polyamides so that there was a great danger that other companies might anticipate the patent applications of the I.G. On the other hand, the I.G. was able in this way to secure comparatively comprehensive patent protection without laying its cards on the table prematurely. The effort at secrecy proved entirely successful. When in the summer of 1938, a number of Du Pont directors came to Berlin to carry out licence discussions on the strength of their nylon success, they were somewhat surprised when they were shown high-grade Perlon filaments and Perlon knits together with pattern cards and fastness evaluations. The first neutral evaluation of Perlon was carried out by the coloristic department of Hoechst. This was not under the control of the photo and artificial silk division of the I.G.

Although the I.G. Farbenindustrie, following its agreements and its intensive exchange of know-how with Du Pont, would have been in a position to produce nylon instead of Perlon, the company stuck to Perlon. The main reason for this was that the starting material, caprolactam polymer, could be produced more easily and in a continuous process.

Six months after Schlack's discovery, the first few pairs of ladies' stockings from Perlon were produced. By 1939, there was an experimental Perlon factory in Berlin-Lichtenberg which produced Perlon bristles. At the same time, Du Pont was erecting its first nylon works in Seaford.

During the war years that followed, new Perlon factories were constructed in Berlin, Premnitz and particularly in Landsberg on the Warthe. Every ton of Perlon produced, however, went into the armaments industry. The air force in particular, required great amounts of Perlon for parachutes and for the reinforcement of aeroplane tyres.

A minimum of expenditure

Perlon is one of those rare discoveries in which a minimum of financial expenditure has resulted in a maximum of economic success. Even the most generous calculation shows that the entire Perlon development work did not use up more than five million marks. This is really very modest compared with the 40 million marks which had been spent several years before on indigo synthesis by Hoechst and BASF. A modest amount also if it is considered that for many years the I.G. invested no less than 5 pc of its thousand million marks turnover on pure research.

Bobingen: meeting point for the I.G. fibre experts

Shortly before the Russian troops hoisted their flag on the I.G. works of Landsberg on the Warthe and Premnitz in Brandenburg, a complete experimental polymerisation plant and spinning unit were transferred to Bobingen. When Paul Schlack and a

Countless Trevira filaments passing to the warp beams

The Offenbach plant for the production of Trevira raw material

number of other fibre experts of the I.G. were reunited in the Bobingen works after the end of the war, they were more than happy to find this equipment there.

Until then, Bobingen had produced artificial silk and from 1944 onwards reinforced artificial silk for tyre cord. Shortly before the war started, new centrifuge plants had been installed for this purpose. But apart from this the I.G. had no other plans for Bobingen. For the large-scale production of man-made fibres, central Germany and Rottweil had been selected.

With the discoverer of Perlon in its own midst, however, and equipped with a plant, however modest, Bobingen's ambitions grew. In 1946, a decision was taken to manufacture PERLON bristles and in 1950 to manufacture PERLON fibres. This required courage, not only because of the inadequate technical equipment of the plant but also because American occupation forces were unwilling for a long time to give permission to produce. When they did so, the French made difficulties. They permitted the export of only small amounts of caprolactam — produced in Ludwigshafen — from their zone of occupation.

Compared with today, Perlon production was not very important when Bobingen joined Hoechst in 1952. Nevertheless, Bobingen had managed to secure in good time a certain share of the Perlon market. It required, however, a system of continuous improvisation and makeshift solutions. There were insufficient means for modern plants and for the development of a comprehensive sales organisation. The manufacture of Perlon filament in particular, far exceeded the capital resources of Bobingen. The Bobingen chemists and physicists were also lacking in money and other facilities for the execution of a proper research and development program.

Hoechst and Perlon

As in 1926, when Bobingen, together with the Köln-Rottweil AG., first jointed the I.G. complex, so in 1953 modernization of the Bobingen works was again begun under the patronage of Hoechst. First of all, manufacturing facilities for Perlon filament were set up with the aid of an investment programme involving millions of marks.

Although Hoechst was extremely generous in its treatment of Bobingen, the board of management realized that it was too late for the company to gain a dominant market position with Perlon. Before anyone in Germany or Europe had even heard the name of Perlon, Du Pont had already sold vast quantities of nylon for millions of stockings. Even in Germany itself, powerful competitors had become active while the former I.G. companies were still smarting from the agonies of dismemberment.

New man-made fibres

Hoechst had no illusions concerning this situation. And it was precisely for this reason that the company decided to base the future of man-made fibres not on Perlon filament alone. Attempts were therefore made to develop another fibre which was to be a one hundred per cent Hoechst product from beginning to end. 'We were looking for a fibre', remarked one of the present leaders of Hoechst 'that would have the highest possible state of refinement. This of course had to be another fully-synthetic product'. There were even thoughts in Hoechst of developing an entirely new chemical fibre. But there were numerous economic doubts about this. All the calculations showed that the development of a new fibre from the first experiments in the laboratory to the point of selling, required a period of 8–10 years. No matter how perfect the product, by that time it would be faced by a market that had no longer any room at all for new man-made fibres. It was, therefore, necessary to adopt a fibre that had already been developed. The choice was between polyacrylonitrile and polyester. Both fibres had been fully developed at the beginning of the 1950's. The only thing in doubt was which one of the two gave the better technical and textile properties. It was equally open to question which one of the two would eventually prove to be the public favourite. Even the most intensive market research in the United States was not able to provide the answer to this problem.

Orlon and Dralon

Work on polyacrylonitrile fibres had been carried out simultaneously in Germany and America. In terms of time, the I.G. probably had a slight lead. The birthplace of this fully-synthetic fibre was the I.G. works at Wolfen and its creator was the chemist Dr. *Herbert Rein.*

After the war, the Du Pont group in America pursued the production of polyacrylonitrile fibres with great intensity. It was called Orlon in America and Du Pont aimed at nothing less than the conquest of the world textile market with this product that was so much like wool. The first experimental plant in Wilmington, Delaware went on stream in 1946. Three years later, the first 100,000 men's suits and costumes from Orlon fibre decorated the shop windows of the American textile stores.

In Germany work on the manufacture of polyacrylonitrile fibres had been resumed after the war by Farbenfabriken Bayer and Cassella Farbwerke Mainkur. Bayer, whose Dormagen works was already producing man-made fibres, marketed Dralon at the beginning of the fifties. Cassella began the development of a continuous filament that was to be marketed under the name Pan. In 1954, however, Cassella left the large-scale technical development of this product to Farbenfabriken Bayer where both Dralon fibres and filaments are now being produced.

The history of polyester fibres

Since the polyacrylonitrile fibres were part of the heritage of the I.G., Hoechst could also have taken up the production of this fibre, particularly since there were facilities at Knapsack for producing the raw material. That the decision was in favour of polyester fibre, which required a licence from ICI in England, was due to various reasons. The polyester compounds were not entirely new to the chemical companies outside the British Isles. Even nylon discoverer Carothers had experimented with polyesters before he turned to polyamides. Indeed, the importance of polyester was realized by the I.G. fibre works as early as the 1930's. But one thing was not known in Germany, namely that at almost the same time, work was proceeding in England on high melting point polyester fibres.

These fibres are linear, long-stretched filamentous molecules which are obtained industrially from a simple ester. Esters are reaction products between alcohol and acids and they occur widely. For example, the fats taken up by the human body are esters, namely those of glycerine.

Carothers had formed his polyester compounds from straight-chain carbons, so-called aliphatics but two chemists in England provided these chains with special benzene rings. Their idea was the same as those of their colleagues at the I.G.: to increase, in some way or other, the resistance of the filaments and to render them resistant to high temperatures.

The aromatic acid used was terephthalic acid and the alcohol employed was ethylene glycol which is very similar to glycerine. Terephthalic acid has two acid groups on its benzene ring, i.e. two hooks that enter into a firm bond with the eyes of the bivalent glycol during ester formation. The addition of these ester molecules to form macromolecules is rather different from normal polymerisation processes and is described as polycondensation. The two English chemists that had spun this aromatic filament were *John R. Whinfield* and *James T. Dickson* who were both working for the Calico Printers Association. Their discovery was taken over by ICI and soon after the end of the war this company presented its Terylene fibre to the world. It became England's favourite in the international fibre Derby.

In 1953, Hoechst negotiated a Terylene licence with ICI. This was, however, not done until intensive investigation had been carried out as to whether the conditions for an adequate and undisturbed raw material supply existed. For on this depended whether the fibre could be produced economically and whether it could be sold at a price that would permit mass-production. The supply of the necessary glycol did not present any problem. It was provided by Gendorf which had been engaged for a long time in its production, first on the basis of acetylene and later on the basis of ethylene obtained from Gendorf's own petrochemical plant. One difficulty appeared to be the supply of paraxylene, the starting product for terephthalic acid. Although it is possible to distil paraxylene from coal tar, where it occurs together with ortho- and metaxylene, it does not provide those vast quantities that are necessary for large-scale fibre production.

Paraxylol from petroleum refineries

The rapid development of the petroleum refineries, however, provided a supply source that is not likely to dry up in the foreseeable future. It was found that the large American refineries were in a position to supply paraxylene in ever-increasing quantities and at constantly lower prices. For this reason, Hoechst did not pursue a method developed in its own laboratories. Instead, long-term delivery contracts were concluded with American petroleum companies who sent the product to Germany in tankers. Recently, paraxylol can also be obtained from European refineries.

The conversion of paraxylene into TEREPHTHALIC ACID is effected at Offenbach and Hoechst. Offenbach was entrusted with the preliminary stages of polyester production in order to secure for this site a wider manufacturing basis. Offenbach and Hoechst use different methods for the production of terephthalic acid. Hoechst adopted the ICI process in which paraxylene is oxidised with nitric acid to form terephthalic acid. In Offenbach air is used as oxidant.

Unfortunately, therephthalic acid is a rather difficult substance. It does not dissolve in conventional solvents and it cannot be melted. For this reason, it is first converted into a compound that is more amenable to reactions. The route is via the dimethyl ester which, when re-esterified with glycol, yields the terephthalic bis–glycol ester.

The next step is the condensation of this glycol ester. During this process, it is of extreme importance that the temperature is kept constant. Heating up, too, must take place with a very high degree of uniformity. All these processes take place in kettles several metres high — the standard polymerisation and polycondensation equipment. From these melt kettles, the polycondensate issues as a wide band. After a short period in a water bath, huge 'meat mincers' set about chopping up this band, producing every minute tens of thousands of polyester chips.

Polyester becomes Trevira

These chips, whether from Hoechst or from Offenbach, are placed in special railway wagons and transported to Bobingen. Here they pass through huge driers before entering the spinning machines. Since they are already polycondensed, the most important production phase in Bobingen is the actual spinning. In the case of polyester, the melt spinning process is employed. The melted polyester filaments are spun from nozzles with 250 or more apertures, looking something like oversized showers. In the spinning shaft, the Trevira material does not, at first sight, look like filaments at all but rather like infinitely thin jets that solidify during cooling. It is only when several of these jets have been joined that they give the white filaments which, following their final finishing, are sold by Hoechst under the trade name TREVIRA.

The rack for filaments

In the interior of these filaments, which solidify during cooling, there is a veritable molecular anarchy. The filaments are therefore pulled apart and stretched to approximately four times their original length. Although the filaments become thinner in the heated 'rack' used for this purpose, they acquire extreme tensile strength and can be pulled apart only by a major effort. This tensile strength is caused by the fact that during orienting of the filaments, the previously disorderly molecular chains become rearranged in the order desired by their chemical creators.

Following this straightening-up of the molecules, the filaments are subjected to a complex series of special treatments. Unfortunately, at this stage of a works tour the otherwise quite forthcoming fibre chemists suddenly seem to run out of details and precise numerical data. Whatever type of fibre manufactuae is involved, the production of man-made fibres requires special know-how which each company has had to acquire for itself. There is, therefore, an understandable reluctance to allow outsiders to look into one's cards. Just as wine connoisseurs are able to state the location of a vineyard, even for the same type of wine, so real fibre experts can name the manufacturers of dozens of different polyester samples. This shows how widely production methods vary. Common characteristics of all polyester plastics are, however, their dimensional stability and water repellency. The suit kept by ICI in water for many months without losing its creases has become legendary. In the wide field of technical uses for polyester and

the Hoechst Trevira grades there is no better demonstration of the outstanding tensile strenght of these materials than car safety belts from TREVIRA HIGH TENACITY.

Close quality control

Continuous quality control marks every phase of polyester manufacture, whether in Hoechst, Offenbach or Bobingen. As with pharmaceuticals, very high degrees of purity are specified in fibre production. This, of course, makes enormous demands on the homogeneity of the raw material. At Bobingen there is an apparently endless arsenal of test instruments. There are electronic uniformity testers in which the strength of the filaments, their tensile characteristics and their extensibility are tested. On the other benches, fabric samples are investigated to see whether they are water resistant, air-permeable and abrasion resistant. There is a hot bench on which fabrics are heated up to their melting point, their behaviour under the microscope then being studied. Another machine does nothing else but bend a polyester filament several times per second. This is continued for many days so as to be able to determine whether the flexural strength meets the strict specification. The specified length of the fibres is measured with the aid of special combs. Complicated machines determine the maximum load that a fabric will withstand.

The Bobingen experts stress that all these experiments are designed to determine the consequence that may flow from factors that can well occur under practical conditions. As in all other Hoechst fields of production, such as dyestuffs and plastics, random sampling is continuously carried out in order to check that the batch involved is true to type.

Technical service brings new impulses

The technical service department for fibres at both Hoechst and Bobingen maintains its own spinning shops, and knitting and weaving plants. Although this involves a great deal of expenditure, there can be no doubt that the final assessment of the quality and characteristics of a material can be made only if the material is processed under practical conditions. The experience gained in these experimental plants is passed on by the technical service people to textile manufacturers who are thus kept abreast of modern processing methods and the latest special fibre blends. Thus numerous valuable impulses emanate from technical service that lead eventually to new scientific, manufacturing and commercial experience.

In Hoechst every attempt is made to avoid even the most insignificant quality variations in Trevira. For this reason, every user of Trevira is invited to enter into a contract under the terms of which he undertakes to send samples of his finished products to Hoechst. So far, more than 8000 customers have signed such contracts. The samples are investigated to see whether, for example, in a given length of suiting the specified ratio between synthetic and natural fibres has been maintained, whether the cloth is sufficiently colour-fast, whether crease recovery is satisfactory and whether the cloth pills. Pilling is an undesirable characteristic of woven and knitted materials from spun yarns. It manifests itself in nodules formed by long projecting fibres at abrasion points. If the investigation is not entirely satisfactory the processor undertakes to improve the quality of his products. Only when the renewed investigation at Hoechst is entirely satisfactory, can the Trevira label be used.

Man-made fibres from Hoechst

Although a tremendous amount of money and effort has been invested in this customer service, it has been decisive for the fame of Hoechst's man-made fibres. Nothing proves this better than the continuous capacity extensions upon which the company has had to embark ever since the first experimental Trevira plant went on stream in 1955 with an output of 50 tons a year.

When TREVIRA appeared officially on the market in 1957, total capacity was some 5,000 tons per annum. By 1960, this figure had been increased to three times the amount. This upward trend has continued unchecked since then and today, Bobingen produces 2,000 tons of Trevira per month.

The market share of PERLON, which was temporarily neglected in favour of Trevira, has also been enlarged in recent years. So as to increase its Perlon filament capacity, Hoechst acquired in 1960 a majority share in the Spinnstofffabrik Zehlendorf in Berlin. This factory, which employs some 1500 people, produces Perlon as well as rayon staple.

The success that Hoechst has gained, especially with Trevira, was not achieved without a great deal of effort. The progress of man-made fibres was slow but today they occupy an important place in the production programme of Hoechst. Recognition for the breakthrough of these products is due not only to chemists and technical service men. A significant contribution has also been made by the engineering, selling and advertising departments. Planned team work has once again borne rich fruit.

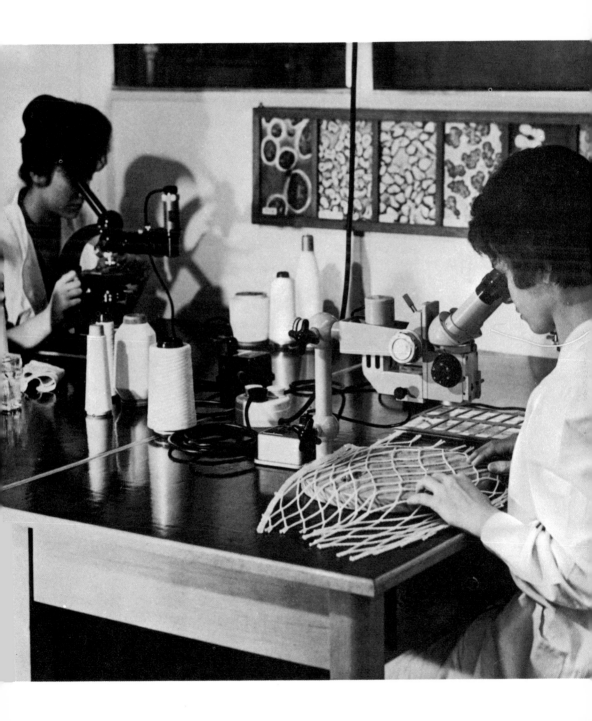

Dyestuffs for man-made fibres

However jubilant the fibres experts might have been when Hoechst joined the polyester fibre producers, their colleagues in the dyestuffs division by no means shared their enthusiasm since there were as yet no suitable dyestuffs for the new fibres in the Hoechst range. The development of man-made fibres had been fairly problematical and the difficulties encountered in the development of suitable dyestuffs were no less formidable. A new textile fibre, however outstanding its properties in textile respects, is not likely to achieve public acclaim if it cannot be dyed and printed in the shades demanded by fashion. Moreover, the fastness properties of such dyeings and prints must withstand the conditions to which the material is subjected during use.

Right from the beginning, these considerations played a big part in Hoechst's decision to take up the manufacture of Trevira. Although Hoechst had available numerous dyestuffs ranges for a variety of applications, the traditional products in this field were not suitable, or hardly suitable, for Trevira. This was, basically, the twenties' all over again. At that time, acetate rayon, a chemically modified cellulose, had just been marketed but none of the available dyestuffs proved successful with this fibre. Entirely new products had to be synthesised and entirely new ranges of dyestuffs had to be developed. A complete dyestuffs range must provide for the production of every shade from yellow to red and from blue to black. Not a single one of these colours can be omitted from the palette if it is desired to keep in step with fashion requirements. The creation from dispersion dyestuffs of such a range suitable for acetate fibres was achieved only after sustained efforts and with considerable help from the Hoechst dyestuffs laboratories. Because of the manufacturing programme laid down by the I.G., the production of this range had been given to the works at Ludwigshafen.

It was natural that Hoechst should try to utilize the experience gained with dispersion dyestuffs when the age of polyester fibres arrived. It was found that for this fibre, too, the coloristic principle employed for the acetate fibres could be applied. The laboratories and dyestuffs development department created a range of products suitable for polyester fibres in a comparatively short time and by utilizing the most readily accessible dispersion dyestuffs. The new range was given the trade name SAMARON. In contrast to acetate fibres, temperatures of more than 100 degrees Celsius must be employed for polyester fibres since they will not absorb such dyestuffs at lower temperatures. Dyeing therefore requires the use of closed dyeing apparatus and high pressures. For this reason, dyeing methods were developed that allowed dyeing of the polyester fibre at temperatures of about 100° C, using conventional dyeing equipment and dyeing accelerators, so-called carriers. For black dyeings, Hoechst invented an extraordinarily fast dyestuff, AZANIL BLACK. Continuing the famous developments by Offenbach in the field of Naphthol AS products, a valuable group of such dyestuffs was also developed for Trevira — the INTRAMIN dyestuffs.

The birth of a dyestuff

The development of a new dyestuff takes an extraordinarily long time, on average about two years. Out of the many individual dyestuffs prepared in the laboratory in the course of the year — there may be more than one thousand — the technical service department selects those that have better properties than the products already available on the market. New dyestuffs are tested especially for their affinity and fastness properties: Are the dyeings light fast and fast to washing? How do they behave in dry cleaning or during pressing? Light fastness is determined in accelerated exposure instruments, especially during the autumn and winter months when there is little sun. In these fastness testers, the dyeings are exposed to intensive radiation. The result is checked by an exposure to natural sunlight which may extend for six months or even more.

During this period, the behaviour of the dyestuff is observed almost with suspicion. A dossier is prepared in which all the characteristics of the new potential dyestuff are meticulously registered. If its brilliance does not withstand exposure or if the dyed or printed material shows signs of staining during washing or pressing, its fate is sealed. If, however, favourable results are obtained, the laboratories will prepare a few kg of the dyestuff. A series of further stringent tests follows. At the same time, other important questions are investigated: What are the chances of large-scale production, what are the economics of the dyestuffs, what are its selling chances, what is the patent position?

The final choice is made by the coloristic commission of the company which is made up of representatives from research, technical service and sales. This commission not only decides what new dyestuffs are to be marketed but also which older types should be withdrawn.

On average, Hoechst markets some fifty new dyestuffs each year and, in return, some products that no longer sell well are withdrawn. Today, Hoechst has available a range of some 1100 different dyestuffs. Approximately 800 of these are produced in Hoechst and the remaining 300 in Offenbach.

Novel dyestuffs

Before Hoechst introduced the Samaron dyestuffs range, which is based largely on existing products, research had followed a new direction and was soon able to score a notable success.

This success was the fulfilment of a pipe dream pursued by chemists throughout the world from times immemorial, namely the creation of a dyestuff that becomes firmly combined with the fibre as a result of chemical reaction. For in this way, the frequently brilliant dyestuffs can also satisfy the high requirements made on their fastness properties. It had long been known that wool, silk and polyamide fibres contained reactive amino groups. It should therefore be possible to produce true chemical combinations in the dyestuffs molecules by reacting these amino groups with suitable partners. Experiments in Hoechst confirmed this theory not only with regard to these fibres. It was found that the hydroxyl groups present in cotton could also react with suitable dyestuffs. This meant that reactive dyestuffs were also suitable for cellulose fibres.

As early as 1949, Hoechst was able to submit a basic patent concerning reactive dyestuffs. Three years later, the company marketed REMALAN BRILLIANT BLUE B, the first reactive dyestuff in the world, which combines chemically with wool.

Further development which had become necessary when the textile industry found it necessary to dye and print cellulose fibres led to the creation of an entire range of reactive dyestuffs for cellulose fibres.

The further extension of the reactive dyestuffs range was made possible only by creating sufficient capacity for the intermediate products required for the preliminary stages. In many cases, starting from simple aromatic compounds such as benzene, toluene, naphthalene and others, more than ten different chemical reactions such as nitration, reduction, oxidation, sulphonation, chlorination or methylation must be carried out in order to develop the desired dyestuff.

The first six representatives of this reactive range for cotton were marketed in 1957 under the trade name REMAZOL. In the meantime, the range has grown to over twenty types to which new shades are added each year.

The INTHION dyestuffs also broke new ground. In the presence of sulphur-containing compounds, these initially water-soluble polycondensation dyestuffs lose their solubility, the molecule becoming enlarged at the same time. Excellent fastness properties on cellulose fibres are obtained in this way. This class of dyestuffs opened up considerable possibilities for economic, high-speed dyeing processes.

Impulses for dyestuff research

Prior to the war, dyestuffs chemistry — measured against the development rate of modern chemistry — was occasionally dismissed as an antiquated and out-of-date field. It was regarded as part of classical chemistry, a thoroughly exploited field from which revolutionary new developments were hardly to be expected. The post-war period has, however, shown that fashion and technical progress as well as the advent of novel fibres will always provide new impulses and problems. In addition, soon after the end of the war, each of the former I.G. works had to try and build up a complete dyestuffs range of its own. During the I.G. era, each one of these individual works had limited itself to certain dyestuffs types. Now, the truncated ranges over which the former I.G. works disposed had to be supplemented as quickly as possible and some entirely new dyestuffs had to be included in the production program. In the meantime, new requirements had arisen: the users of dyestuffs had largely rationalised their methods.

This applied, of course, primarily to the textile industry but also to the printing industry, the paint industry, plastics, wallpapers and other paper groups. In contrast to conventional methods, modern dyeing processes had become largely continuous. For such continuous processes, however, many of the conventional dyestuffs were no longer suitable, whatever their advantages with regard to range of shades or fastness properties might be. Particular difficulties were encountered with the dyestuffs of the Indanthren series, the elite of all the dyestuffs, including in its ranks only the coloristically most valuable products. These Indanthren dyestuffs could be converted into a water-soluble form only by an expensive process but for dyeing they were required in this water-soluble form. The aqueous solutions — the vats — are very sensitive. In particular, they readily react with atmospheric oxygen. Continuous dyeing with such unstable compounds was therefore out of the question.

Modern techniques

This state of affairs persisted until a fundamentally new technique had been found. In this, the insoluble dyestuff is so finely distributed as a result of special preparation and grinding that it can be easily rendered into a dispersion in water, very similar to a dyestuff solution. The dyestuff particles distributed in water are hardly a thousandth of a millimetre in size. If a cotton fabric is impregnated with such a dispersion and dried, the tiny dyestuff particles are uniformly distributed over the fabric. Once this had been achieved, the next step was to find methods by which the dyestuff could be finally and firmly fixed on the fibre. This is now accomplished in a few seconds by converting the dyestuff on the fibre from its dispersion form into the vat where is then absorbed to give a fast dyeing. Through this technique, it has become possible to dye more than sixty metres of cotton fabric per minute with vat dyestuffs. Previously, it took twenty times as long. Moreover, with batch dyeing, certain variations in shade were unavoidable. Hoechst met this development by the marketing of its Colloisol paste and powder grades.

Apart from the new dyestuffs, other important dyestuffs groups, which have long formed the backbone of Hoechst's traditional field, have continued to develop. Foremost among these are the Naphtol AS dyestuffs produced in Offenbach.

Through continuous improvement and extension of this range — the most recent new-comers are the Variogen bases which give very fast dyeings — the Naphtol AS products have retained their great popularity. The damage done to the Naphtol AS field by the Second World War and the subsequent period has been repaired and the former fame throughout the world has been regained. The turnover figures show this very strikingly.

New pigments

The field of organic pigments, which Hoechst first entered triumphantly in 1909 with Hansa Yellow, has also been steadily enlarged. The Hansa Yellow dyestuffs, which are distinguished by very clear, strong and lightfast shades still form the core of the Hoechst organic pigment range together with the Hansa Red and Scarlet grades.

Requests by dyestuffs users for improved properties, for example higher brilliance, have been met by a number of new developments in the famous Permanent range of dyestuffs so that today a full range of Hoechst-produced red, yellow and violet shades is available.

More than 100 different grades of organic pigments are produced in a single Hoechst dyestuff plant. The most important production equipment is the large stirring vats which are arranged in rows and some of which have a capacity of up to 50 cubic metres. The reaction of the diazonium solution with the coupling components is carried out in these large vessels. Brilliant dyestuffs are formed in these vessels from colourless solutions in almost magical fashion. These dyestuffs are subsequently separated, dried and ground. In order to facilitate the work of the users of organic pigments, many of these products are marketed by Hoechst as non-dusting powders or as granulates.

Organic pigments have even penetrated the field of textile dyestuffs. The pigments are printed on the textiles with various binders and by a variety of methods, for example the Hoechst IMPERON method. Then they are fixed. Naturally, in these developments, the most recent progress of Hoechst's plastics research has been widely utilized. Whether it is the paintwork on a car, the cover page of an illustrated journal, the paint on houses and on walls, or the gay pattern of floor coverings — Hoechst organic pigments are probably involved.

Coal tar as raw material

After a hundred years, organic pigments—the first activity of Hoechst—still represent an important cornerstone of the company in spite of the world-wide competition that has since arisen.

However complex the world of dyestuffs has become today, and however much it reflects the ups and downs of modern fashion, one point has remained relatively unchanged. Coal tar is still one of the most important starting materials. But as petrochemistry is developing, coal tar is at last encountering a real competitor, at any rate in Europe. The final outcome of this contest can by no means be foreseen. While in the days of Runge or Hofmann or of the founders of Farbwerke Hoechst, coal tar was an indispensable raw material source, increasing amounts of aromatics are today being obtained from petroleum.

These aromatics also play an important part in many of Hoechst's classic medicaments, among them Antipyrin, Pyramidon and Novocain. These have meanwhile been joined by new pharmaceuticals such as sera, vaccines and insulin which are based on other starting products. But whether we are talking about antibiotics such as penicillin, streptomycin or Reverin, or about antidiabetics like Rastinon, or about the cardiac specific Segontin, they all continue the great Hoechst pharmaceutical tradition whose origin is so closely linked to dyestuffs.

Pharmaceuticals under the sign of tower and bridge

The glass tube in the cupboard of the Hoechst penicillin laboratory looks like thousands of others. It appears to contain nothing but a few grams of yellow-brown earth. Inside this earth, invisible to the human eye, there is, however, a precious organism, a culture of moulds. It differs from the numerous other known moulds by one outstanding characteristic: from the metabolic products of this mould, one of the most effective drugs ever known to mankind is derived. If, during the last war, at least some German pharmaceutical companies had possessed this tube with its contents thousands of soldiers in field grey would not have died from wound infections.

But the test tube with its invaluable contents came to Germany only in 1950, per airmail. It had been sent by Merck, the American pharmaceutical company in Rahway. The recipients were Farbwerke Hoechst. The Americans were at that time supporting, as part of the ERP aid, the development of German penicillin production. They made available their know-how in large-scale fermentation and they also provided an especially active mould strain — Penicillium notatum, Westling strain. This had enabled the Allies during the war to produce antibiotics by the ton. The fame of this PENICILLIN became legendary in the field hospitals of the fronts in North Africa, in Italy, in Normandy and above all in the Pacific. It was truly marvellous and with it even those cases could be saved that would previously have been abandoned as utterly hopeless.

A spoiled bacterial culture and its consequences

The Allies, too, had required many years before their doctors were able to use this wonder preparation in their syringes. As far back as 1928, *Alexander Fleming* had made a discovery that is now popularly described as sensational. Unfortunately, at that time, it caused anything but a sensation. The history of penicillin began quietly and without any drama. Nothing was further from Fleming's mind than to present a new drug to mankind. He was concerned in his laboratory in London University with the testing of a bacterial culture. In the course of his work, he made a surprising observation: on the nutrient medium of the staphylococci culture, a greenish mould had formed. This mould had probably penetrated through an open window in the laboratory and had settled, in spite of the glass cover, in the vessel containing the bacterial culture. This, of course, spoilt the culture. An irritating but by no means uncommon occurrence. The end of such episodes was usually that the spoilt culture was unceremoniously poured down the drain.

Death zone for microbes

But this time, events followed another course. Dr. Fleming subjected the plate with the staphylococci germs to a thorough inspection. And he noticed something quite unusual: in the area of the greenish mould there was a clear zone in which no staphylococci had grown. This appeared sufficiently remarkable to the bacteriologist Fleming to induce him to prepare more of these mould cultures. When Fleming took this decision, he had, in his own words, no idea that he was holding in his hand the key to the most important therapeutic substance that had ever been discovered for the treatment of bacterial infection in the human body.

The first task was to identify beyond doubt the mould that had caused this havoc among the staphylococci. This was difficult enough. There are thousands of moulds, on the crust of stale bread, on rotten fruit, Roquefort cheese and above all in the earth. Until then, science had not been greatly interested in them. There were in the whole world only a few dozen scientists that occupied themselves with these moulds. A great deal of time, therefore, passed until Fleming learned that the mould he had discovered belonged to a very definite strain which, because of its brush form, is termed penicillin.

Moulds against suppurant pathogens

Fleming bred a number of cultures from this mould and with it inoculated nutrient plates containing various pathogenic germs. To his great surprise, the reaction was the same in many cases. The bacteria were exterminated by the mould in a very short time. But not all of them. Although the staphylococci and streptococci, like most pathogens, were radically destroyed by the moulds, there were other germs that were unaffected

by Fleming's merciless microbe killers. The most prominent among them were the typhus and influenza bacilli. (At that time, the influenza pathogens were not yet classified as viruses.)

In general, however, Fleming was able to confirm that penicillin had an absolutely devastating effect on all so-called gram-positive bacteria. This bacteriological classification was proposed by the Danish scientist *Hans Christian Gram*. Depending on how certain bacteria responded to a staining method developed by him, he distinguished between gram-positive and gram-negative bacteria. Gram-positive bacteria, according to the Danish scientist, are staphylococci, streptococci, anthrax bacilli, pneumococci, tetanus bacilli, lactic acid bacteria and diphtheria bacteria. Gram-negative are the pathogens of gonorrhea, typhus, dysentery and the plague. It was, however, later found that penicillin was also able to deal with the aggressive gonococci and, in high doses, with spirochaetae.

Sulphonamides as antivitamins

Fleming's discovery was made in September 1928. In the same month, the British bacteriologist published his findings in the Lancet. The article was written with all the caution of a scientist who carefully rewords and rephrases a sentence many times before letting it see the light of day.

Perhaps this was the reason why Fleming's paper found only little interest in the scientific world. There was, of course, also the fact that many of his contemporaries did not have enough imagination and far-sightedness to recognize the revolutionary aspects of Fleming's research results or their potentialities. A few years later, *Gerhard Domagk* succeeded in the Elberfeld laboratory of the I.G. Farbenindustrie AG in the discovery of the sulphonamides. They were in the best tradition of the chemotherapy founded by *Paul Ehrlich* together with Farbwerke Hoechst. Investigation showed that it was possible to synthesise a long series of sulphur compounds which were tried out, with a great deal of success, in chemical laboratories throughout the world. Their power to deal effectively with what were until then usually fatal infectious diseases was greatly superior to Fleming's largely untried Penicillin.

The Oxford circle

But then the history of penicillin took a decisive turn. A group of Oxford scientists under the direction of the pathologist Professor *Walther Florey* and acting on the instructions of the British government, took a closer look at the neglected preparation. The realisation that Europe was faced by the imminence of another war accelerated the work of the Florey research group. The spread of infections had to be expected, coupled with the cessation of further supplies of German sulphonamides. At first, the Oxford circle had to face a great problem. Methods had to be developed for the derivation of significant quantities of pure penicillin from Fleming's mould. At the same time, it was necessary to eliminate from this preparation, by a complicated process, all those substances that did not act on the bacteria or that might be harmful to humans. After this had been finally achieved, a new problem arose, a problem full of drama and tension that faces the birth of every new drug: would the preparation confine its action to the pathogen only or would it also attack healthy cells?

As in the days of Paul Ehrlich, the first answer was provided by mice. Fifty of these faithful standard patients of the pharmacologists were inoculated with suppurant streptococci. Half of them were then treated with penicillin. The other twenty-five were left to their fate. The result was greatly encouraging for the Oxford scientists: Of the mice treated with penicillin, all survived. All those untreated died.

Tribute to progress

The experiments on mice or rats are usually followed by experiments on larger animals such as dogs or monkeys who pay their dues to human progress. Only then can the first clinical tests on humans be carried out. The important criterion is not only the action of the drug on the pathogen but also its side-effects, its possible action on the liver, the kidneys or other organs. Past experience had shown an almost tragic pattern. The more powerful the antibacterial substances developed by the chemists, the greater the undesirable side-effects. Almost always they made the application of the new drug impossible.

But penicilin was different. It was soon realised that this preparation came close to the ideal chased by pharmacologists. It was highly efficient against pathogens and it had very few side-effects. The liver in particular, which usually reacts with almost seismographic sensivity to chemotherapeuticals, was entirely unaffected by penicillin. The white blood corpuscles also suffered no damage as a result of the action of penicillin. Once this fact had been established beyond all doubt in numerous investigations conducted by the Oxford circle, the way to large-scale production was open. But at that time England was already in the first, and for England the most dangerous, phase of the war. Since a German invasion was an imminent danger, the large-scale production of penicillin was transferred to America.

Intense search for moulds

As it turned out, this was a fortunate decision. In the USA, development work on penicillin had been carried on with a great deal of energy. The day when this material would be available not in grams but in dozens of tons did not seem very far off. A prerequisite was, however, the discovery of new penicillin strains that would have a greater yield than Fleming's culture solution of the original strain which, until 1942, was the sole supplier of penicillin.

A large-scale hunt for possible mould-bearing soils was organised. Both in America and throughout the world an intense search was carried on. The American air force played its part in this and had strict orders to bring back soil samples from all the airports of the world open to it. And although some of the moulds obtained from these soils were able to produce penicillin, by far the most promising find was made on the doorstep of one the most important penicillin research institutes in America.

The scene was Peoria near Chicago and the leading actress in the drama was a young girl who sold her services to the institute as a searcher of moulds. This girl selected as her main area streets and markets. In the course of her search she found one day a melon which was covered all over by green mould. In the laboratory this mould was found to be the busiest penicillin producer that the microbiologists had ever had in their Petri dishes. But penicillin history was to be influenced by yet another fortunate discovery. Ordinary corn steep liquor was found to be an ideal nutrient for breeding penicillin in the culture medium. And when finally several mutations of the melon mould were successfully accomplished with the aid of ultra-violet light and X-rays, the American scientists were able to achieve penicillin yields of a thousand Oxford units per cubic centimetre.

These units had been laid down as an indispensable dosage standard by Professor Florey and his collaborators. The Oxford unit is that amount of penicillin which, dissolved in 50 grams bouillon, develops an action that is just sufficient to suppress the growth of a special staphylococci culture. In the early chapters of the penicillin saga, only the most meagre results could be expected. One cubic centimetre of the nutrient fluid generally produced barely more than 1—2 Oxford units.

This was very little indeed. In order to successfully treat most infections, tens of thousands of Oxford units were usually required. If, for some reason, penicillin production was interrupted, the results came near to catastrophe. Several of the patients that had already been successfully treated with penicillin died because the supplies of penicillin dried up during the first clinical tests.

When, however, the yield had finally been increased a thousand times and after a dozen of the large American pharmaceutical manufacturers had taken up penicillin production, the worst shortage of this precious preparation could be overcome. The largest amount of penicillin produced was flown to the field hospitals on the war fronts in the Pacific and in Europe where the new preparation successfully conquered many fatal diseases.

Penicillin from Hoechst

Penicillin was known in Germany from the first papers published by Fleming in the Lancet and also from an important paper published by the Oxford circle in the same journal. This latter edition of the Lancet had found its way in August 1941 via Sweden to the desk of the chief of the Hoechst pharmaceutical division. But thereafter, a curtain of secrecy had descended over any further news concerning work on penicillin in England and the United States. Penicillin had become a top secret among the Allies. Nothing was allowed to be published about the newly-bred, high-yield mould strains. The Hoechst management immediately recognized the importance of the discovery even from the sparse material available to it. In 1942 it decided to engage in penicillin research. The audacity of this project soon became clear to everybody although the experience of the company in the pharmaceutical field was considerable enough to justify the start of such pioneering work. Hoechst had after all produced many preparations that had become famous throughout the world—Antipyrin, Pyramidon, Novocain, Salvarsan, Dolantin.

In the case of penicillin, however, the Hoechst pharmaceutical chemists, pharmacologists and biologists were faced by completely new tasks. There were in Germany no suitable mould strains. No one knew what were the right nutrient solutions or fermentation methods. But above all, there was in Germany at that time no trained personnel, no raw material, no apparatus, not even people who might go and search for moulds. For in Germany, as previously in America, the initial task was the finding of suitable samples for the laboratory from mouldy food such as old cheese, or from earth or from refuse heaps. But in the laboratory the chemist could not just look at a mould sample and decide which one was useful and which one had to be rejected. Each mould that belonged to the group of penicillium notatum had to be specially bred. Only then was it possible to test the metabolic products for their antibiotic efficacy.

There weren't many people at Hoechst engaged in this task. Indeed, the actual research team consisted of only two. One of these worked in the pharmaceutical laboratory on the preparation of the cultures and the other was engaged on testing. They were supported by half a dozen laboratory assistants and other helpers. Later on, after a protracted tug-of-war with several authorities, it was possible to enlist the help of several chemists and biologists. But even so, it took less than two years before, out of thousands of cultures, several mould strains were obtained that provided a basis for an adequate penicillin production.

A considerable contribution to this work was made by Professor *Hans Schmidt*, who was then working at Behringwerke in Marburg, and also by the Dutch archive for mould cultures in The Hague. The yield of these strains was small enough, particularly if they were compared with those of Peoria. It may well be that the Hoechst biochemists would have regarded the situation as hopeless if they had known the figures from the United States. But the findings of the chemotherapeutical laboratory were beyond all doubt. It really was penicillin that was being produced from the metabolic products of the mould strains found in Hoechst.

Like the first American preparation, the Hoechst penicillin, too, was not white but yellow. This was due to the fact that the moulds also produced a dyestuff which fortunately, however, was not harmful. The complicated investigations and the animal experiments took up a great deal of precious time. But then regard for human life dictated that the new substance should be subjected to the maximum number of tests. It was Paul Ehrlich, the creator of Salvarsan, who had indoctrinated the Hoechst chemists with this principle so thoroughly that it was passed on from one generation of scientists to the next.

Staphylococci from the Hoechst sick-bay

Special methods had to be developed in order to determine the action of the individual penicillin solutions precisely. Like the Oxford circle, Hoechst used a carefully selected laboratory strain of staphylococci that could be bred over many years with a constant penicillin sensitivity. Incidentally, Hoechst was able to meet its own needs also in this case. The first germs of this staphylococci strain originated in the company's sick-bay at Hoechst. A worker from the factory had been sent there with such an infection. Even today, the derivatives of this now famous strain — SG 511 — are used in all German laboratories to standardise penicillin. Naturally, at that time nothing was known at Hoechst about Oxford units. For this reason, Hoechst set up the Hoechst bacteriostatic unit. But even before the war finished, Hoechst chemists were able to enjoy a particular piece of good luck. Among American prisoners-of-war, penicillin tablets of 2000 units each were found. These tablets were immediately dissolved and analysed in Hoechst and the unit established was found to be completely identical with that of the Oxford scientists.

Penicillin production in Hoechst began in 1943. The surface method was employed. In this method, penicillin manufacture does not take place in huge fermenters as in the United States and England but in shallow bottles. Hundreds of them are daily inoculated with new germs or "harvested". Soon afterwards, the first experiments were conducted at Hoechst using the submersion process. In this, penicillin is obtained in high kettles that are supplied with air not only from the surface, as in the case of the bottle cultures, but also from below through the liquid. In the last few months of 1943, the amount of penicillin produced was a few hundred thousand units. At the beginning of 1945, it had been increased to around ten million. This was still only a tiny amount, just sufficient to treat serious infections in a few patients. On the other hand, however, it showed the inexorable progress that was being made. It confirmed that Hoechst had taken the right road in spite of its complete exclusion from the scientific progress of the world. On the other hand, the men at Hoechst did not know at this point whether the rest of the world had succeeded in establishing the constitutional formula and whether the chemical synthesis of the drug was being realised. It was not until the end of the war that they knew that even America was nowhere near synthesis. This goal was reached only in 1960. Until then, production had to be continued in fermenters, for the moulds produced penicillin more cheaply than the chemists.

The first penicillin ampoules in Hoechst

In the last years of the war, Hoechst chemists were more than happy to derive at least 50 units per cubic centimetre from their mould strain. In October 1944, an injection preparation in ampoules with 20,000 units could for the first time be submitted for clinical testing. A typewritten label served as provisional instruction sheet. But there was little hope at that time of getting any clinical tests done in Germany.

One of the Hoechst chemists, therefore, simply placed a few penicillin ampoules in his pocket. His wife was working as a doctor in Edenkoben hospital. She had told him of a patient who was suffering from apparently incurable mastitis. The doctors had abandoned all hope. This patient was the first one to be injected with penicillin from Hoechst. Three ampoules over a period of three days. The success was sensational: the patient was saved.

The main amount of the penicillin produced in Hoechst was, however, not used for injection preparations but for antiseptic powder. This powder was provided free of charge to field hospitals and clinics. Although it required comparatively few units, its production was interrupted as soon as the mould yield in the Hoechst laboratory went down. This happened whenever bacteria entered the cultures and destroyed the penicillin and was, of course, achieved only by bacteria not sensitive to penicillin. They can degrade penicillin and render it ineffective. That, in fact, is the reason for their insensitivity.

Reports about the experience with this antiseptic powder were only sparse because there were already large gaps in the German communications system. Nevertheless, the Hoechst penicillin specialists drew up a plan on 15th January 1945 for the vigorous expansion of penicillin production.

Fundamentally, this was really no more than the construction of a larger experimental plant. But this plant, so the chemists thought, would allow them to get away at long last from the laboratory production scale. Alas, it was already too late. The collapse of Hitler's Germany was at hand. Indeed, a few weeks later, on 29th March, the first American tanks thundered through Hoechst. Just prior to this, one of the State agencies that still functioned had optimistically enquired of Hoechst how many tons of penicillin per day were already being produced.

Under American supervision

It wasn't long before the American occupation forces permitted further work on penicillin. Soon afterwards, the first reports concerning penicillin production in the United States arrived. The Hoechst people were at last able to compare their own efforts with those in the United States — carried out on a gigantic scale.

There was no hope of a practical evaluation of the American experience. Not enough was known at Hoechst about the technology of large-scale fermentation of these antibiotics. There were insufficient raw materials, not enough equipment, and even the most primitive laboratory material was lacking. To get the few thousand glass bottles that were required continuously for the cultures and filtrates caused an immense amount of difficulty. Improvisation was the order of the day.

The penicillin produced under these adverse circumstances was extremely precious. It was stored, like precious jewels, behind a tight net of security precautions before being sent out to the clinics.

Hoechst veterans recalled the early days of Salvarsan. Soon after Ehrlich's and Hata's successes with this preparation had become known and Hoechst had taken up the production of the new preparation, wealthy patients came to Hoechst from all over the world. Their aim was to get some of this magic Salvarsan at any cost. To achieve this end, any means seemed justified. Eventually, Hoechst was forced to construct a brick wall with a barbed wire top around the manufacturing plant and to engage an especially reliable doorkeeper. No one was allowed in without a special permit.

Salvarsan in the safe

Alfred Ammelburg, a member of the board of the company and then chief of the pharmaceuticals division, appeared every evening in the Salvarsan factory and placed the daily output of approximately 200 bottles in a briefcase which he then locked up in a safe in his office. Of course, these conditions lasted for only a few months until Salvarsan production was running at full speed and Hoechst was able to produce enough of this therapeutic to meet the most urgent requirements. For almost forty years Salvarsan remained the leading standard preparation against spirochaetae.

Today the visitor to Hoechst will look in vain for this historic plant. In 1962, it was pulled down to make room for a new building. The reason for this was that penicillin was found to be even more powerful against spirochaetae than Salvarsan. Ehrlich's preparation is now produced on only a very modest scale in very small kettles by a sub-division of other pharmaceutical plants.

In 1946 Hoechst was able to offer penicillin to the German medical world only in the form of an antiseptic powder. At that time penicillin was discussed at Hoechst in grams and kilograms while in America the antibiotic was being produced by the ton and discussed in terms of mega units. Moreover, the USA was already engaged in introducing other types of mould into antibiotic therapy.

American aid for Hoechst

The tough fight that was fought at Hoechst for a German penicillin impressed the American officers. They sent a few samples to a laboratory in Washington. Following this, an American general visited Farbwerke Hoechst. The result was the beginning of collaboration between Farbwerke Hoechst and American pharmaceutical companies. One of the largest of these American companies was Merck in Rahway who had become one of the biggest American producers of penicillin during the war. The first negotiations were concluded successfully. Merck provided Hoechst with a particularly efficient mould strain and with indispensable know-how for the development of a large-scale production plant of penicillin.

This was the great hour for the Hoechst process engineers and microbiologists. A half-finished building was available for the large-scale production of penicillin. This had originally been intended for an expansion of Dolantin production. Dolantin, an analgesic, is one of the most successful preparations in the glittering array of spasmolytics and analgesics that Hoechst had developed when it first took up pharmaceuticals production. Dolantin synthesis had been successfully accomplished in 1939.

The fight against pain

The analgesic action of Dolantin is four times that of Pyramidon. Moreover, it has a spasmolytic action that manifests itself even in cases of very acute colic. A quite novel characteristic of Dolantin is that it has a central analgesic action, i.e. one that emanates from the brain. Such action had previously been exhibited only by morphine and its derivatives. Hoechst was, however, not satisfied with Dolantin alone. During the war, a whole number of similar substances were developed which also had a central analgesic action. The most important among them was POLAMIDON which is one of the most powerful analgesics known. Its potency is twenty times that of Dolantin.

As the war went on, and as more and more blood flowed, so the demand for analgesics grew greatly in Germany. In 1944, when the chemists of Hoechst were still experimenting with modest grams of penicillin, more than 650 tons of Antipyrin and Pyramidon were produced. The production of Dolantin in 1944 was 1,600 kilograms. But after the end of the war in 1945, production of Dolantin came to a sudden stop. The patents had been requisitioned and exploited by foreign competitors. It was for these reasons that Hoechst came to the decision to dedicate the half-finished Dolantin building to penicillin production.

A special laboratory in which the mould cultures were stored and new ones were bred was also erected. In these rooms, which are inaccessible to the outsider, the first stage of penicillin production takes place in a tiny glass dish. This dish contains a nutrient medium from spice and agar-agar. This latter substance, a delicacy to the moulds, is an extract from certain seaweeds. It is frequently used by bacteriologists in place of gelatine. The nutrient medium is then inoculated with mould spores and the mould growth thus produced bred on other nutrient media. Once a sufficient amount of mould has formed, large shaking flasks are inoculated. Subsequently, the solution is introduced into a 400 litre fermenter. From this first fermenter it passes into a further kettle containing ten times the amount of nutrient medium and so on until finally, in a fermenter containing some ten thousand litres, the bulk of the penicillium grows and gives off penicillin to the solution.

From ten grams to five tons

Normally it takes eight days before the large-scale fermenter can be "harvested". During this brief interval of time, the moulds exhibit almost biblical fertility. Approximately ten grams of mould multiply into about five tons. The nutrient medium is separated from the mould pulp by means of large filters. Since penicillin is a metabolic product of the moulds it is not so much this pulp that is of interest to the chemists but the nutrient solution with the secretions of the moulds. Usually, the nutrient medium contains the penicillin in very dilute form. Some 40 tons have to be processed in order to obtain a few kilograms of the antibiotic.

The fermentation process is dominated by an inviolable requirement. All the substances and implements must be absolutely sterile. The extraction of the penicillin from the aqueous filtrate by means of organic solvents is subject to a succession of precautionary measures. The preparation of penicillin is not a chemical process, comparable, say, to dyestuffs production but a sensitive biological growth process which can be readily upset by minute germ traces.

The extraction of penicillin involves numerous phases until the actual substance is precipitated. The final and most important stage is sterile metathesis in which the various penicillin salts are prepared. From the moment when the first nutrient medium is inoculated to the despatch of the penicillin to the filling plants, no less than twenty sterility tests have to be passed.

In May 1950, the Hoechst penicillin factory went on stream as the most modern and largest in continental Europe. In the fifteen years that have followed this happy event, the Hoechst chemists have not remained idle. They have perfected manufacturing techniques in many respects so that new yield records were achieved again and again. Furthermore, with the aid of continuous mutations and selections, the mould strains were trained to almost olympic performance. Because of these improvements in the breeding of the cultures and also in the methods, something like ten thousand units per cubic centimetre of nutrient medium have been achieved. This is an extraordinary increase if it is remembered that in 1944 the Hoechst chemists thought themselves fortunate with yields of around 50 units.

Pharmaceutical packaging — a house without windows

Parallel with this steep increase in production went the increase in sales. At Hoechst, next to the main gateway into the factory, there is the impressive pharmaceutical packaging building. It is a structure without windows and no daylight gets into it. All the doors to the antibiotic filling department are tightly closed, because conditions here must be just as sterile as in the production plant. The girls operating the highly modern packaging machines are dressed entirely in white. Blue light from the ultra-violet lamps floods the white-tiled room. An air-conditioning plant ensures continuous filtration of the air. In one corner of the long room with its conveyor belts and automatic filling machines there is a small modest implement underneath a glass hood. In the midst of the shiny chromium-plated equipment, it looks like a museum piece — which indeed it is. A little notice on it says "With this machine, penicillin filling was started in 1950. Daily output 2000 bottles". Today, 200,000 or more ampoules per day are filled in Hoechst.

New penicillin preparations and new penicillins

The Hoechst pharmaceutical chemists were not content with these achievements. Other developments that had been taking place in the last fifteen years in penicillin manufacture were just as important to them. For example, a number of years ago, the USA succeeded in combining penicillin with novocain. The salt of novocain with penicillin only gradually dissolves in the body and thus has a long-term action.

Novocain is an anesthetic that was introduced by Hoechst in 1905 as part of its pharmaceutical range. Although since then, thousands of similar substances have been synthesised, Novocain has remained a pharmaceutical evergreen. Under the name Procain, it is widely used throughout the world as the local anesthetic par excellence. In recent years, it has been used not only for anesthetic purposes but also in the therapy of certain diseases.

Hoechst's chemists were also looking for other penicillin combinations. During this search they came across a mixture of novocain/penicillin with omnadin. The main action of omnadin is that it mobilises the defensive mechanism of the body in a very short period of time.

Meanwhile the time had come for at any rate partial synthesis of penicillin. This only became possible when in 1945 its chemical structure was finally clarified. With the aid of modified penicillins it was now possible to fight bacterial strains that had meanwhile become resistant to the standard preparation. By far the greatest credit for these semi-synthetic penicillins must go to the Beecham Laboratories in Great Britain. The new products were found to be largely resistant to penicillinase whose action had originally dampened the great and enthusiastic hopes that had been placed in penicillin. Penicillinase is an enzyme produced by many bacteria and this protective substance used by many microbes destroys penicillin or at any rate reduces its potency.

John J. McCloy,
former U.S. High Commissioner for Germany,
at the opening of the penicillin factory

Hoechst marketed partially synthetic penicillin under the trade names CINOPENIL and CRYPTOCILLIN. These were effective particularly against resistant staphylococci.

No magic formulae for chemists

Scientists are by and large sober and down-to-earth people. They shy away from the exaggerations with which a part of the press and some popular science writers describe chemical or biological processes. Chemists do not like to be identified with magic formulae, magic drugs or the witches' cauldron of modern chemistry. And although the pharmaceutical chemist, like any other, doubtlessly requires a little bit of intuition in order to be successful in his work, his main task is the painstaking execution of series of experiments, the confirmation of individual data, indeed a circumspect, gradual feeling-forward along a dark road that may, more often than not, turn out to be a dead end. And even if he is successful, it is more than likely that his success will only prove that Ehrlich's magic bullet to combat all diseases will for ever remain an unattainable dream. And yet, perhaps there is after all something magic about the fact that penicillin is able to destroy no less than 89 different types of pathogenic bacteria and that it fights to a considerable degree 16 further such bacteria. Or that many of the most dangerous bacteria that defy penicillin are dealt with by STREPTOMYCIN.

A new weapon in the fight against microbes

Only a few years after penicillin had become a world topic and millions of sick had been healed with its aid, the arsenal of the antibiotics was enriched by a further most valuable weapon. The main credit for this achievement is due to an American doctor, Dr. *Selman Waksman*. He had been engaged since 1915 with certain actinomyces which botanists classify between bacteria and mould. Both the atmosphere and the earth are full of these minute organisms whose most important species for medicine is streptomyces griseus. Waksman had discovered this species during the first world war. But nearly thirty years went by before he found a strain among them from which he could derive a useful antibiotic. This time it did not take as long as in the case of penicillin before the world recognised the importance of this new weapon in the fight against microbes. Only a few years later, the American pharmaceutical companies decided to take up large-scale manufacture of streptomycin which is extremely effective against both gram-positive and gram-negative bacteria. The first patient to be treated with the new pharmaceutical was a young girl. She was suffering from tubercular meningitis and doctors held out no hope for her survival.

224

*100 000 pharmaceutical dragees per batch
are produced in these drums*

But after only a few streptomycin injections her condition improved extraordinarily. After a few weeks, there was no longer any doubt: the girl was cured. In the ensuing period, streptomycin proved equally powerful against the dreaded tuberculosis. Today, some 70 pc of all the streptomycin produced is used in the treatment of tuberculosis. It has also found successful application in influenza, the plague, dysentery, typhus and whooping cough. Streptomycin is typical of numerous medicaments which, in contrast to the remarkably non-toxic penicillin, show side-effects that it has not been possible so far to eliminate entirely. This poses for the doctor the question that is as old as the history of medicine itself: is the disease serious enough that it outweighs any side-effects produced by the medication employed to combat it? However carefully this question is weighed, it will not be possible in many cases to come to a decision that is entirely free of all risks.

Ten years streptomycin Hoechst

Farbwerke Hoechst engaged in the production of streptomycin at an early date. In 1952, STREPTOMYCIN SULFATE HOECHST and DIHYDROSTREPTOMYCIN SULFATE HOECHST were despatched for the first time. Streptomycin is produced in the same fermenters as those employed for the production of penicillin. As in the case of penicillin, highly active strain cultures have meanwhile been prepared and the original process has been considerably improved. In this way it has become possible to derive far higher yields of active ingredient. Nevertheless, it is still necessary for Hoechst to process some 350,000 to 500,000 litres of cultural medium, plus approximately 300,000 litres of methanol as solvent, in order to obtain two or three tons of streptomycin.

In 1952, Hoechst conducted its first experiments in the combination of streptomycin and penicillin. A year later, in 1953, Hoechst was also able to submit to doctors the new product STELLAMYCIN, a mixture of streptomycin and dihydrostreptomycin. The particular advantage of this preparation is that although it has the same antibiotic strength, it is less toxic than other streptomycin preparations.

Modern prospectors

The mould investigators were by no means satisfied with penicillin and streptomycin. The successes that modern medicine was able to achieve with the aid of these products spurred them on to further searches. Is it not possible, they asked themselves, that among the innumerable microorganisms there are some whose metabolic products have an even wider spectrum of action than those of the various Penicillium notatum strains and of Streptomyces griseus? Antibiotics, in other words, that would be effective against practically all gram-positive and gram-negative pathogens. And so, once again, thousands of modern prospectors searched the earth, not to find gold, but something infinitely more valuable.

The golden actinomyces

Once again it was an American scientist who was able to score the first successes in the field of the broad-spectrum antibiotics: *Benjamin Minge Duggar*, formerly professor for plant physiology at the University of Wisconsin and, after his retirement, consultant to the famous American Lederle pharmaceutical laboratories. Since 1944, he had examined some 2,000 earth samples from many parts of America and Europe. From these samples, he had obtained 6,000 different types of microbes. Finally, Duggar isolated an until then unknown mould from a specimen of slimy garden soil. Because of its golden colour, he named it Streptomyces aureofaciens.

The antibiotic obtained from the metabolism of these moulds, marketed under the name of 'Aureomycin', soon achieved considerable fame. Shortly afterwards, two further preparations were marketed: Terramycin and Tetracyclin. With regard to their chemical structure and their action, they can be regarded as closely related to aureomycin. The structural formula of all these broad-spectrum antibiotics contains a four-ring system of the same configuration. In the case of aureomycin, the first ring carries a chlorine atom while terramycin contains a hydroxyl group on its third ring. Tetracyclin has neither.

Tetracyclin caused considerable excitement among chemists and pharmacologists. It is readily compatible and forms high antibiotic levels in the blood.

Thereupon, Hoechst collaborated with the American company Bristol Laboratories, New York, in the manufacture of this highly efficient broad-spectrum antibiotic. Once again, as in the case of penicillin and streptomycin, this is carried out in large fermenters and under the same absolutely sterile conditions.

Tetracyclin in capsules

HOSTACYCLIN, the name given to Hoechst's tetracyclin, proved outstandingly successful in the fight against some of the most merciless bacterial enemies of humanity. But even so, the pharmaceutical chemists at Hoechst harboured one other big wish. Tetracyclin has one considerable disadvantage. It is not easily dissolved in water and must therefore be administered in the form of capsules or dragees.

This question of solubility may appear to the layman as an insignificant detail, particularly since in recent years antibiotics have been perfected more and more. But so far as the doctor is concerned, there are many cases in which intravenous or intramuscular application would appear much more promising. Where there is acute danger to life, it is of tremendous importance to get the antibiotic as quickly as possible and in the maximum concentration into the blood. The oral preparation, however, has first to pass through the gastro-intestinal canal before it can enter the blood. Where very high doses are used, this may well affect the intestinal flora. Unfortunately, the aggressive antibiotics are not always able to distinguish between harmful and useful bacteria.

A new problem for the Hoechst chemists

The medical people, therefore, clamoured for a tetracyclin that could be injected directly into the bloodstream and that would dissolve so quickly that help was possible even in the case of the most serious and the most acute infections. A group of three chemists, therefore, tackled this task at Hoechst. For their answer they went back to Pyramidon, one of the classic products of the Hoechst pharmaceutical division. Pyramidon, too, cannot be readily dissolved in water. For this reason, many attempts were made in Hoechst before the first world war to develop a preparation that would effectively treat inflammation but that, at the same time, was readily soluble so that it could be easily injected without causing irritation. These protracted efforts to modify the molecule of Antipyrin and Pyramidon were eventually crowned in 1921 by the development of NOVALGIN. This analgesic has three distinct characteristics: it can be dissolved without difficulty in water, it has outstanding compatibility and its toxicity is so low that it can be injected in a 50 pc solution. Its action is so clear and so reliable that it has been used to replace morphine in attacks of renal and gall-bladder colic.

In the case of tetracyclin, the well-tried method of molecular substitution proved, however, to be far more difficult. The structure of tetracyclin could be modified easily enough and, indeed, solubility was increased. At the same time, however, the antibiotic properties of the preparation were lost. All the numerous attempts made in this direction in the end led to nothing.

But the Hoechst workers were not discouraged. Having been thwarted in their attempts at molecular substitution, they attempted to incorporate an additional side-chain in the tetracyclin structure which consists of four hexagonal nuclei. This provided them with an infinite number of possibilities and it took in fact a year before the Hoechst research workers made their decisive discovery. If a pyrrolidinomethyl group is introduced into

227

the molecule, tetracyclin is instantly rendered soluble. In precise figures, the solubility increases by 2,000 times. In this way, it had at long last become possible to inject this partially synthetic and modified tetracyclin intravenously.

Reverin — the universal broad-spectrum antibiotic

When, following complicated and careful tests carried out in several university clinics, Reverin was made available to chemists and doctors, Hoechst had the satisfaction of knowing that in the first year it was injected in more than a million cases.

Practical experience fully confirmed the clinical investigations. Almost always, REVERIN was found to be a truly universal broad-spectrum antibiotic that was able to give help even in cases that had been given up as hopeless. The achievements are truly impressive. The success rate obtained in the clinical use of Reverin for gynaecological infections was 98 per cent, for urological infections 83.5 per cent, for gall-bladder infections 92.3 per cent, for surgical infections 96 per cent, for skin infections 95.9 per cent and for respiratory infections 90.4 per cent. It was also found that Reverin was not only more effective but also more compatible than any of the other tetracyclin derivatives.

In view of this tremendous success, Reverin manufacture in Hoechst has been continuously expanded since 1958. Reverin is a pharmaceutical that for the time being is considerably more expensive than the first antibiotic penicillin. The comparatively high price of Reverin is due in no small measure to the indispensable and complicated chemical conversion. This is necessary in order to produce Reverin from the micro-biologically produced tetracyclin powder.

As sterile as an operating theatre

Each one of these conversion phases takes place in manufacturing spaces that fully match the sterile conditions of an operating theatre. There is sterile air, radiation from bactericidal ultra-violet light, ceramic filters with pores so tiny that they trap any type of microbe, floors prepared with special disinfectants and many other precautions, all of them designed to ensure that absolutely germ-free production is possible. Each one of the comparatively few workers in this largely automated plant wears white sterilised clothes, mask, goggles and rubber gloves.

Antidiabetics

The Hoechst achievement in the field of antibiotics has been matched in recent years by no less glittering successes in the field of metabolic diseases. The most outstanding

development was, of course, RASTINON, the antidiabetic with whose aid the German pharmaceutical industry was able to re-establish international acclaim after the second world war.

With Rastinon, Hoechst was able to continue its famous INSULIN tradition. This preparation, obtained from the pancreas, had been developed in 1923. During the succeeding period it had been greatly improved. The insulin solution of the twenties contained foreign protein, but in 1937, Hoechst became the first insulin manufacturer in the world to base its entire production on pure crystallised hormone. The insulin solutions prepared in this way were free of foreign protein and were therefore well tolerated by the patient. But there was another big hurdle to be overcome. Injections with the original insulin maintained a normal blood sugar level for only a few hours. This meant that many diabetics were forced to inject themselves with insulin several times a day. Until the beginning of the second world war, therefore, all research work in Hoechst on the diabetes sector was directed towards finding insulin preparations that ensured a more sustained effect. This problem was eventually solved by DEPOT INSULIN, a delayed-action preparation made available in a number of forms.

With its insulin for the therapy of diabetes Hoechst had gained international renown. But its research in this field did not stand still. Scientists everywhere were engaged in the development of an antidiabetic that could be administered orally. At any rate some of the diabetic sufferers were to be relieved of the necessity of injections. The prerequisite for the realisation of this aim was however to find a preparation that, unlike insulin, was not resorbed in the gastro-intestinal tract.

An important discovery was made in 1955 by the clinical workers *Hans Franke* and *K. J. Fuchs* in Berlin while testing a chemotherapeutical of Messrs. Boehringer and Sons in Mannheim. This preparation resulted in a surprising lowering of the blood sugar level. Originally, it was intended to use this preparation, one of the groups of sulphonyl ureas, purely for the treatment of infectious diseases. The research work of the Berlin clinicians, which after the death of Franke was carried on initially by Professor *Ferdinand Bertram* in Hamburg, showed that the substance could be used for the therapy of diabetes.

At the same time, Farbwerke Hoechst had found a chemically related substance which was not a sulphonamide and did not, therefore, have an antibacterial action. This preparation, too, was able to reduce the blood sugar level. This development work resulted in a close association between Hoechst and Boehringer.

The Hoechst preparation gained its place in diabetes therapy under the name RASTINON.

This first oral antidiabetic marketed by Hoechst has not been surpassed to this day although in the meantime more than 1500 related substances have been tested by Hoechst alone. The announcement in September 1955 of the discovery of effective oral antidiabetics was a true sensation throughout the world. It also served as a tremendous impetus for further fundamental research into diabetes. As a result the laboratories of Farbwerke Hoechst were able to make valuable contributions concerning the mode of action of oral antidiabetics.

Rastinon is a pharmaceutical that has to be taken by the patient every day right to the end of his life. For this reason, it was obviously necessary to first carry out animal experiments on a very wide scale.

The sustained and consistently uniform reduction of the blood sugar level was accurately confirmed through experiments on dogs. An administration of only 10 milligram Rastinon per kilogram body weight to dogs resulted in a reduction of the blood sugar level of 30 per cent of the initial value within one hour.

The problem was, however, not simply to eliminate every possible side effect. Any possible hereditary damage had also to be established. This could only be done by generation experiments, that is to say by treating several animal generations with the preparation. Extensive tests and detailed macroscopic and histological examinations of the organs of the animals invariably showed that the preparation was harmless. As a result Hoechst decided in August 1955 to attempt clinical evalution.

The clinical trials were carried out by new methods. Simultaneous investigations went on in six of the most important German clinics. This ensured that a complete picture of the action of Rastinon would be gained in a comparatively short time. The clinical experience gained was made available to the public. This, too, was a novelty in the medical field.

How does Rastinon act?

Since then, more than two thousand articles have been written about Rastinon which has since become one of the outstanding products of Hoechst. Scientific congresses have made the preparation the centrepoint of their discussions. And although the mode of action of Rastinon has not yet been fully elucidated, a great deal of knowledge about the dreaded diabetes mellitus has been gained. It is, for example, now known that senile diabetes is in many cases not due to absolute failure of the pancreas. In fact, the pancreas is still able to produce varying amounts of the hormone but it is unable to transmit it to the blood. The vital insulin supply is blocked.

231

The sulphonyl ureas induce discharge of the hormone from the cells of the pancreas and thus provide an incentive for renewed synthesis. This novel effect of Rastinon means that insulin has lost nothing of its importance to the diabetic. In conventional insulin therapy, a hormone is supplied to the body which it can produce in only insufficient amounts. Doctors call this substitution treatment.

With certain patients, however, a combination of insulin and Rastinon may be appropriate. It must be realised, however, that insulin and Rastinon are two entirely different preparations. While Rastinon is taken orally and owes its existence entirely to chemical synthesis — its starting material is toluene — insulin is a hormone that is obtained from animal pancreas glands. It can be effective only if it gets into the body directly without passing through the digestive tract since it is rapidly destroyed in the stomach. There is no such thing as an insulin that can be taken orally. At any rate, all experiments in this field have been without success so far. In order to ensure the amount of insulin continuously required by the large number of diabetes patients is always available, a large organisation has to be maintained. Lorries equipped with their own refrigeration plant bring fresh animal pancreas glands to Hoechst day after day, week after week, not only from German slaughterhouses but also from those of many neighbouring countries. Each one of these glands weighs an average of about 250 gram. In order to produce 100 kilograms of insulin, the glands of some seven and a half million animals are needed.

Micro-organisms as steroid architects

Although these amounts seem enormous, it must be realised that hormones are effective in minimum doses. This also applies to steroids whose research and manufacture is another field of Hoechst. The important groups of steroids include, for example, sterine, bile acids, cardiac toxins, sexual hormones and above all the hormones of the suprarenal gland, the corticosteroids. The main supplier of the starting product, preformed by nature, are plants native to Latin America. These have recently been grown in special plantations.

Hoechst obtains such a chemically modified starting product from overseas in the form of a white powder. At Hoechst, this powder is further processed in alternate biochemical and purely chemical processes. The vital criterion in these reactions is the planned exchange and variation of the side groups on the seventeen carbon atoms that constitute the tetracyclic skeleton of the corticosteroids.

The substituents of the carbon atoms and their chemical modification are in the first instance matters for the chemist. If purely chemical means are no longer sufficient, micro-organisms such as moulds or bacteria are used. This interchange between chemical methods and the use of micro-organisms during the regrouping of the substituents of the carbon atom may be repeated several times. The final purpose is to increase the therapeutic potency of these preparations. In view of the complicated molecular structure of the steroids this is fairly difficult. On the other hand, steroids exhibit extraordinary efficacy even if applied in amounts of no more than fractions of a milligram. Corticosteroid tablets, for example, contain an amount of active ingredient that is no larger than the size of half a pinhead.

The therapeutic significance of the corticosteroids lies mainly in the treatment of inflammations. The preparations are, however, also highly effective in the treatment of rheumatism, the universal disease that used to confine millions of people to their beds. In order to increase the effectiveness of corticosteroids and their synthetic derivatives against inflammations, special forms of application have been developed.

These forms are decided upon by chemists specialising in this subject, who are therefore very important people in modern medicine. They decide the best form in which a pharmaceutical should be administered, whether as a tablet, dragee, emulsion, suppository or some other form. A particularly happy solution has been found in the case of DELMESON, a Hoechst corticosteroid preparation. Delmeson is available as an ointment or as a foam in pressure packs. For the latter, Frigen, the Hoechst safety propellant, is used in many cases.

In order to combine the effect of this preparation, which can be used only for local inflammations, with an antibacterial action, the steroid is combined with the antibiotic neomycin. In this way, both the syndrome and the cause of various skin diseases can be treated. The classic CORTISON, a suprarenal gland hormone marketed by Hoechst in 1953, has in the meantime had many important successors and additions. HOSTACORTIN, for example, in combination with the famous Pyramidon, serves as a specific therapeutic for the maintenance treatment of rheumatic complaints.

The number of steroids known today has grown to 15,000. Of these, however, only about 2 per cent are of interest to medicine. They include the yellow body hormones — female hormones that safeguard the normal course of a pregnancy. Although the special attention of chemists and doctors has for many years been directed to the hormones of the suprarenal gland, the hormones from the suprarenal medulla have not been forgotten. SUPRARENIN, a Hoechst creation and the first synthetic hormone in the world, is still widely in use as a circulatory hormone.

Closely related to Suprarenin is ARTERENOL. Although this was first marketed by Hoechst shortly after the turn of the century, it has come fully into its own only in recent years. It is one of the most important drugs available today to stabilise the circulation following cardiac infarction.

Hormones — still a large field for research

The entire human hormone system still needs a great deal of thorough scientific investigation. However important the functions of these vital substances may be for the human body, there is still a great deal we need to know about their mode of action. Hormone research workers of international repute do not hesitate to admit that they have to be content with interpretations that the years to come may show to have been wrong. The answers that may be provided one day might well have unforeseen consequences.

Radiochemists — important aids to research

Among the modern research aids that the pharmaceutical industry employs, radio-chemical methods are gaining ever-increasing importance. The main advantage of these radiochemical methods is that with their aid it is possible to identify even minimal concentrations. The radiation of the active atoms of such substances can be determined with an astonishing degree of accuracy by modern counters. A whole range of such counters are available to radiochemists. The best known, though by no means the most sensitive, is the Geiger counter.

The assistance that the radiochemist can render to the pharmacologist and doctor is particularly important if it is desired to study the behaviour of a new preparation in the organism or in the metabolism, its accumulation in the organs and many other such factors. Frequently, it is only possible to supply the organism with very small amounts. This is because every form of excess dosage — in relation to the later therapeutical use — would give false results.

The first problem in such investigations is the radioactive labelling of the chemical compound concerned. This means that radioactive atoms have to be built into the molecule without changing its chemical characteristics. Such radioactive atoms may be radioactive carbon, radioactive hydrogen or radioactive sulphur. If such a radioactively-labelled substance is then used in the animal experiment, it is possible to determine with a high degree of accuracy for how long and in what parts of the organism it remains. There is no other analytical method that provides such a sensitive test.

A laboratory with special protective devices

Radioactively-labelled preparations are also becoming more and more important for human diagnostics. For example, radioactive iodine is used in order to test the function of the pituitary gland. Other radioactive preparations serve to investigate the kidneys, intestinal function or blood volume. Impressive successes with radioactive preparations have also been achieved in therapy. An outstanding example is the treatment of cancer with gamma or electron radiation.

In view of the significance of radiochemistry, Farbwerke Hoechst constructed its own radiochemical laboratory in 1957. Such a laboratory requires special protective installations. These serve not only to screen the radiation or to store the preparations safely. They are also intended to avoid their dissemination throughout the neighbourhood. This means lead and concrete walls and windows from heavy gauge lead glass. Also, the radiochemical laboratory is throughout equipped with remote control handling devices which avoid direct contact between the operators and the harmful radiation. The inner and outer safety of the laboratory is further augmented by special ventilation methods. These methods ensure that there is always a slight vacuum throughout the entire radiochemical laboratory. The admission of air from the building to the neighbourhood is prevented in the same manner. Before the air is discharged, it is freed by means of special methods from any possible radioactive contamination. Effluents are purified in several stages by a special process.

The laboratory carries out metabolic investigations using the new pharmaceutical preparations developed by Hoechst. It also produces various radiodiagnostics and radiotherapeutics for both doctors and clinics.

Radiochemicals are also produced by this laboratory. They are used in chemical research and process engineering, provided to scientific institutes or sold to other companies that have a use for them. Radioactive substances have already been successfully introduced into industry, science and agriculture. They are employed in a variety of industries. They are frequently encountered in measuring and control techniques, for example in the continuous measuring of layer thicknesses as in the production of paper, tinplate or plastic films.

The range produced by the radioactive laboratory includes some 100 radioactive preparations to date. The reason why research, development and production are joined in one and the same building, and a laboratory at that, is quite simple. The amounts produced exceed the laboratory scale in only the rarest cases. Such an exception is for example radioactively-labelled sea sand. This is used on the North Sea and the Baltic Sea coasts in order to trace the movements of the sand at the bottom of the ocean. In this case, individual batches may attain the order of 100 kilograms. In most other cases, however, the substance involved amounts to no more than milligrams or micrograms.

In the Hoechst radiochemical laboratory, radioactive isotopes are used but not produced. These isotopes originate from nuclear reactors or from particle accelerators.

In Germany, there are at present no nuclear reactors or large radiation installations that would be suitable for the production of radioactive isotopes. The raw material for the chemical work of the laboratory, i. e. the radioactive isotopes themselves, are therefore obtained from France, England or the USA. It is anticipated, however, that isotope production will shortly be realised in the nuclear research centres in Karlsruhe and Jülich.

Life: thousands of years

The life of radioactive isotopes varies a great deal. The life of radioactive carbon, for example, is thousands of years. Radioactive iodine 131, on the other hand, loses half its activity within eight days. This is, of course, a significant aspect in the application or selling of these products. For example, very short-lived isotopes are frequently used for special investigations in technical equipment. This is done because the radioactivity will have disappeared from the equipment within a relatively short period of time. On the other hand, there is the disadvantage that such substances cannot be stocked. The production of the preparation, its supply to the customer and its application must be planned according to a close timetable. The more compact this timetable, the better for the preparation. This is one of the reasons why short-lived isotopes are usually transported by air.

The mysterious realm of the viruses

Research into and fighting of viruses is a field that is continuously engaging the attention of scientists throughout the world. As these pathogens of smallpox, poliomyelitis, yellow fever and possibly also certain types of cancer are masters of camouflage, research workers did not know for a very long time whether live or dead organisms were involved. It was only with the advent of the electronmicroscope that the mysterious realm of the numerous viruses was penetrated for the first time. Even the largest among these are so tiny that bacteria look like giants. Bacteria are usually measured in microns — a thousandth of a millimetre. Viruses on the other hand can be measured only in millimicrons or a millionth of a millimetre. The virus of polio-myelitis, for example, has a diameter of approximately 25 millimicrons.

Although it has been possible to get some idea of the size of most viruses — about 150 virus diseases are known to date — many questions remain unanswered. We know, for example, nothing about the method by which viruses multiply, about their locali-sation within the metabolic processes in the cells or about the precise routes by which a virus gets into the central nervous system. Scientists still have to travel a long way in the development of a chemotherapy for virus diseases.

This means that vaccines for the prophylaxis and sera for the therapeutic treatment of virus infections continue to have considerable significance. Both active and passive immunisation form part of the research and production domain of Behringwerke in Marburg, a wholly-owned subsidiary of Farbwerke Hoechst since 1952.

The classic vaccines developed by Behringwerke against diphtheria and tetanus have been joined recently by those against poliomyelitis. This vaccine was developed in America by *Jonas Salk*. In contrast to bacteria, viruses do not thrive on nutrient media but only on living tissue. This meant that the Marburg animal reserves — they comprise approximately 500 horses and several hundred sheep and cattle — had to be reinforced by a great many monkeys. Poliomyelitis viruses were used, in the inactivated form, as virus suspension or attenuated for oral vaccination. The anti-poliomyelitis vaccine VIRELON was joined in 1959 by TRI-VIRELON a combined vaccine against diphtheria, tetanus and polio.

Testing of vaccines, both of the finished product and during every phase of its manu-facture right up to the sealing of the ampoules, is subject to close official control. A delegate of the Paul Ehrlich Institute in Frankfurt is exercising continuous supervision in Marburg. But the Behringwerke have to observe not only the German regulations but also the foreign test regulations. Unfortunately, the development in the sera and vaccine field has led to widely differing specifications in almost every country. The short period during which many of these products can be used is also presenting considerable problems to the biologists and chemists in Marburg. Of almost 400 pre-parations produced in Marburg, more than 50 per cent are effective only for a period of no more than twelve months. 180 preparations must be stored in a refrigerator in a narrow low temperature range of from 4—6° C.

The breeding of dangerous viruses requires a large number of technical facilities and safety precautions. Every building of the Behringwerke in which vaccines are produced is completely isolated from the neighbourhood. Remote control air conditioning plants and a tremendous amount of control equipment are employed in order to prevent the penetration of germs. To guard against contamination of the canals, the effluents from these buildings are specially treated. Stringent precautions are also in force in the department producing vaccines against foot-and-mouth disease. This department, too, is strictly isolated and persons can enter or leave it only after they have effected a complete change of clothing and have passed through a sterile barrier. The sera contain extraneous proteins against which the human body frequently reacts negatively. By the fermentative degradation of protein, salt precipitation and certain physical methods, it has been possible to cumulate the antitoxins, the defensive substances, in the sera and to intensify their action. In this way it has also been possible to increase the compatibility of the sera and to reduce the injection volume. The present-day FERMO sera, for example, contain only a fraction of the protein amount of a native serum.

Blood diagnostics and substitutes

Animal and human blood is of interest to the Marburg chemists, doctors and biologists not only because of the sera content. Today, the Behringwerke in Marburg are large-scale producers of blood diagnostics. These are the reagents for example for the Wasser-mann test or for the determination of blood groups. For the blood group test sera, the rarest blood sub-groups are required. Since frequently only a few people throughout the Federal Republic have these rare blood groups, it is sometimes necessary to spend considerable sums of money. The discovery of a large number of blood sub-groups has rendered paternity determination highly accurate.

For the last sixteen years, Behringwerke have also been engaged in the preparation of drugs from human blood. The medical world knows today that it is by no means necessary in every case to carry out complete blood transfusions. In many cases, it is sufficient to supply the patient with certain components of the blood. A haemophiliac, for example, does not need a complete blood transfusion but only that part of the blood that will cause coagulation. As a result of this work, Behringwerke have been able to make available to doctors a number of special preparations obtained from human blood, for example, sera, albumen, gamma globulin and fibrinogen.

Gamma-Globulin, unfortunately not exactly a cheap preparation, is a concentrated solution of antigens from the human blood against infection. It can be used both for prophylaxis and therapy of infectious diseases. It is of particular importance in virus diseases against which no other drug is as yet available. Recently, a group of research workers in Behringwerke succeeded, for the first time, in producing a gamma-globulin preparation — GAMMA-VENIN — that can be injected into veins. This means that very quick help can be given to a patient whose life is in danger.

The research work of Behringwerke which led to the development of STREPTASE has also been an outstanding pioneering effort. Streptase is a preparation that initiates the dissolution of coagulated blood in the circulation of the human being.

An agent against thrombosis

In 1933, the American biologist *William S. Tillet* during his work on bacteria discovered a substance formed by streptococci which was able to dissolve human blood clots. In 1945, the Danish doctor *G. Royal Christensen* isolated this substance and named it Streptokinase. Following this discovery, it needed a considerable effort by biochemists, extending over a number of years, before a germ was found that could produce this valuable substance in large amounts and that yet was harmless to humans. The effective ingredient had to be purified before it could be used in human medicine. More than five years of clinical testing were necessary in order to specify the applications and the dosages of Streptokinase. With this substance industrial research has provided doctors with the most effective preparation yet produced against the dreaded thrombosis.

Blood substitute from Marburg

The blood substitute HAEMACCEL which can keep a patient alive immediately after serious accidents is another Marburg speciality. This plasma expander was developed in Hoechst and is produced in Marburg.

The genesis of a new medicament

The number of scientists engaged in the research laboratories and production plants of the chemical industry in the search for still more effective medicaments for man and animal is continuously increasing. These scientists belong to a large number of disciplines: chemists, biochemists, biologists, doctors, veterinarians, pharmacologists, virologists and chemists. Once production is being considered, process engineers, engineers and sales specialists are also involved.

The birth of a new pharmaceutical mostly takes place in the chemical laboratory. It is

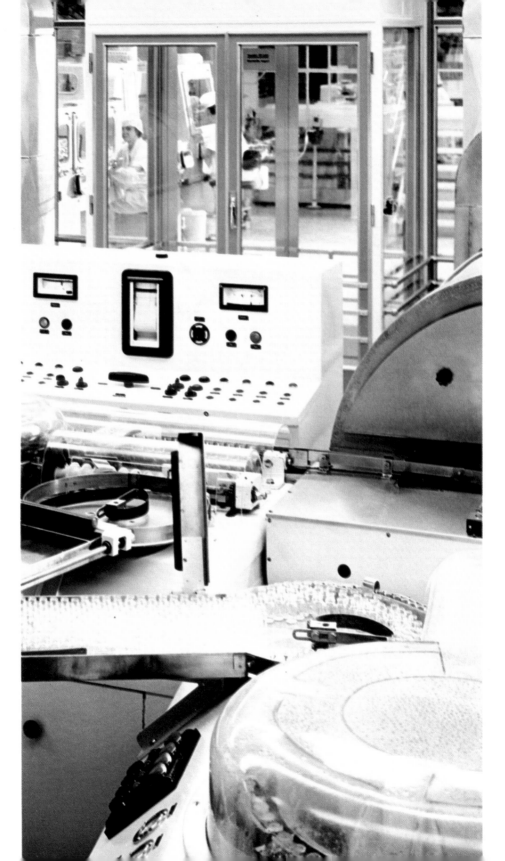

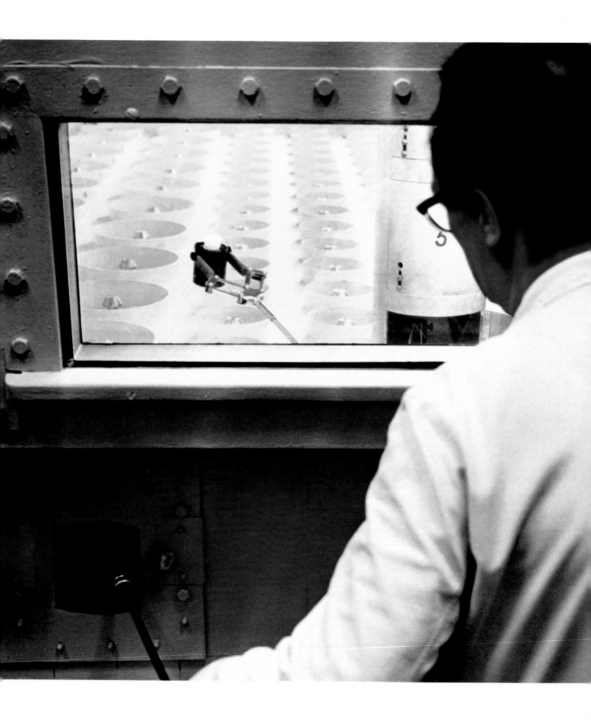

usually teamwork that produces the first substances of therapeutical interest. In Hoechst's experience, it requires something like 2,000 compounds before one promising one emerges.

The chemist is followed by the pharmacologist. It is his job to investigate the preparation for its therapeutic effect and above all its possible toxicity. Even the most effective medicament would be completely useless if, at the same time, it exhibited a degree of toxicity that would cause damage to the human organism.

The initial tests continue to be carried out on mice and rats. Their behaviour makes it possible to get some idea of the efficacy of a new preparation. Naturally, the data obtained from these animals are no more than general indications. This is because animals frequently react to pharmaceuticals in a different way from human beings. And in some cases, animal experiments are entirely useless. This applies particularly to the psychopharmaceuticals, preparations that act on the human psyche and that have assumed considerable significance in recent years.

A new range of test preparations

If the pharmacological investigations of mice and rats give a clear and generally satisfactory picture, then other animals such as guinea pigs, cats, chickens and monkeys are included in the tests. The preparations are given in higher doses and adjusted precisely to the body weight of the animals. Apart from the mode of action and the toxicity of the preparation, side effects are now also investigated. Such experiments sometimes last twelve months or longer. If the results obtained during this work are still encouraging, then the department for clinical testing at Hoechst comes into the picture. This department includes doctors who specialise in a number of fields. The final decision now rests with the clinicians who sit in judgement over the therapeutical value of a substance. Frequently there are considerable surprises. It is for example by no means rare that these clinicians will find that the preparation is suitable for an entirely different range of patients than was originally assumed by the chemists. In any case, only a small part of the screened preparations passes clinical tests. For many others, their career comes to a premature end at this stage. As a general rule, only one out of every two thousand new preparations eventually passes muster.

Before a preparation is generally released, it is dealt with by the galenic department. This is because initially the preparation was tested in its original state, just like chemists had synthesised it in a flask. The preparation of tablets, dragees, extracts or injection solutions is the problem of the galenic department. It

Testing a new cardiac preparation

have many factors to take into account. The commercial form must ensure maximum efficacy and must, at the same time, be suitable to the patient. The stability of the preparation under various conditions is also of decisive significance. Since Hoechst preparations are used throughout the entire world, they must be capable of tolerating climatic extremes and the most difficult storage conditions. Boxes containing Hoechst pharmaceuticals are continuously travelling throughout the world, by air and by sea, just for stability tests.

Experiments in Hoechst

The real test of a new preparation started, as explained, with the clinical examination. The medicament was tried out in one or two hospitals on several patients who had volunteered. But before these clinical tests were carried out, chemists and doctors who worked on the preparation in Hoechst used it on themselves. This was done primarily to determine the compatibility of the new drug.

No. 12512 — ten years of research

SEGONTIN is a good example of this prolonged and thorough testing. Segontin is a new type of preparation for the treatment of disturbances in the cardiac circulation. Angina pectoris and cardiac infarction are frequently results of an excessive reaction of the heart to internal and external stresses. Segontin protects both heart and circulation against such stresses. In addition, it promotes blood flow in the heart musculature.

The preparation had been made available to pharmacologists as early as 1950. It was produced by the pharmaceutical synthetic laboratory at Hoechst. The chemists had synthesised it as a possible circulatory specific under the number 12512. By the autumn of 1951, it had become clear that this substance was the most promising out of hundreds of compounds investigated by pharmacologists. On the desk of the research director there was a report which summarised the extensive tests: no. 12512 has a pronounced dilatory effect on the isolated heart and on the coronary vessels in the living animal. Since in therapeutic dosages the substance did not show any undesirable side effects it held out great hope for the future.

Newly-developed methods make it possible to record the favourable therapeutic action on the cardiac blood flow. In these methods, the blood flow in a coronary artery is determined directly. To do this, an air bubble has to be injected into the bloodstream and the travelling time of this air bubble is measured over a given distance. Subsequently, the air bubble is again removed from the blood stream. In this way, experimental animals did not suffer any damage. The greater the blood flow, the more quickly the air bubble travels.

At the end of 1953, there was no longer any doubt that preparation no. 12512 greatly increased the blood flow of the coronary vessels. The oxygen consumption of the heart was not increased and the heart frequency was reduced.

It was expected that clinical testing would show that no. 12512 had a favourable effect on angina pectoris and similar diseases of the heart. The preliminary clinical test confirmed these expectations fully.

And yet, the preparation had to be returned to the pharmacologists once more. The first orientating experiments had shown that Segontin was not a conventional preparation with vaso-dilatory properties but in fact a novel substance with a highly interesting mode of action. The compound appeared so valuable to Hoechst that it was investigated for a further four years as part of the research programme. By 1958, matters had progressed to the stage where clinical testing could be resumed on a large scale.

In these investigations, the preparation was administered in numerous clinics and sanatoria and also by doctors. In more than 70 per cent of all cases of angina pectoris, a reliable prophylactic action could be confirmed. Of particular importance was the observation made by all the testers that the best results were obtained in cases of arterio-sclerotic blood flow disturbances which hitherto had not been exactly amenable to treatment. These results were verified under the most stringent test conditions — in the double blank experiment — and have since been repeatedly confirmed. The outstanding general compatibility was emphasised in every case. Supplementary investigations have shown that this preparation, with its original mode of action, represents one of the most important substances in modern cardiology. Segontin was released to the medical profession in August 1960.

The final word — the pharmaceutical commission

Once the clinical tests have been successfully concluded, the pharmaceutical commission at Hoechst has to make a most important decision. Should the new preparation be released for general clinical testing or not? In this general testing, both in German and foreign clinics, a comprehensive picture of the new medicament is obtained. Only when this has been done, usually after one to two years, does the pharmaceutical commission decide whether a new preparation will be marketed. This commission comprises representatives from the research and clinical testing departments and also from

244

production and sales. Once production has started, quality control has to be carried out. This control is responsible for the quality and reliability of Hoechst pharmaceuticals. It involves something like a quarter of a million tests a year.

Every preparation that Hoechst releases, in all its forms, is subjected to a stringent test of purity and efficacy. And even when the preparation has finally reached the doctor or the clinic, Hoechst does not regard its responsibilities as completed. A large number of people in the sales offices and in the various branches of the company ensures that any fact or observation of relevance to the preparation is transmitted to Hoechst. It may well be that such information indicates other fields of application for the product. Or it may be that the chemists are given a clue which induces them to start on the first syntheses for a new and perhaps even more effective preparation. Thus the fertile cycle between research and practical application is closed.

Anyone who has ever followed the long story of a new pharmaceutical will be filled with respect for the research effort that preceded it. The total pharmaceutical manufacturing range at Hoechst, including the Behringwerke preparations, comprises some 800 products.

After the second world war, the German pharmaceutical industry returned to its tasks solely on the basis of its own resources without any state aid. As always, it is in the forefront of the eternal fight between men and disease.

An industrial community

In autumn 1960, the number of Hoechst shareholders increased by 12,000. These 12,000 new shareholders were, however, not to be found among the many people from all walks of life who had already decided in the past to acquire some shares nor were they smart stock exchange operators who hoped to land a worthwhile profit on the strength of special inside information. These 12,000 new shareholders represented in fact an entirely new class of shareholder — employees of the company who had overnight become co-owners of the organisation for which they worked.

And although the amount involved was only a fraction of the share capital of Farbwerke Hoechst, the operation strikingly illustrated the changes in the social structure of society over the last hundred years — the metamorphosis from the class-conscious salaried worker to co-ownership in industry and in the means of production. Some 29 per cent of all Hoechst employees — 69.6 per cent staff and 30.4 per cent workers — acknowledged in this way their bonds with the company and in addition expressed their readiness to translate the idea of co-ownership, propagated in the theories of the social reformers, into practical terms, and not rarely at considerable personal sacrifice.

The issue of employee shares did not represent a spontaneous act on the part of the management. Its history goes back for ten years. At that time the company was still under Allied control and the economic situation was far less favourable. Problems such as co-ownership and the accumulation of personal assets nonetheless remained an item on the agenda of the joint discussions between the works council and the management. These discussions were held as part of the work of the social committee on which equal numbers of representatives from the board of management and from the general works council sit. This committee is in fact responsible for the personnel policy of the Hoechst group.

A start with investment certificates

The discussions of the social committee were always lively. They were based on careful analysis of social developments and legal possibilities. The experience of other companies was also used. All these factors counselled only stepwise progress. A programme of planned information for employees was drawn up and executed over a number of years to familiarise employees with the manifold opportunities of saving by way of stock investment.

The first opportunity to do this were investment certificates which offer a lesser risk than that accepted by holders of company stock. Through a number of articles in the Farbenpost, the house journal of the Hoechst group, and through special advisory offices, every employee was given the maximum advice and help for the acquisition of investment certificates. Employees were able to acquire these at the stock exchange rate with a rebate of $2^1/2$ per cent.

The success of this action was very encouraging. Investment shares amounting to a total of 150,000 DM were subscribed. Nobody had really expected this ready response by the employees. Hoechst did therefore not fail to draw their attention to the opportunity of participating in a new share issue at the end of 1956. The same was done two years later with an issue of loan stock. Again, circulars were sent to every employee, articles were published in the Farbenpost and advisory centres were opened.

Share law amendment as starting signal

Following this beginning, the issue of employee shares was regarded as having been sufficiently prepared. The starting signal was a reform of the share laws. This permitted companies, under certain conditions, to offer to employees shares free of income tax. Hoechst decided to realise these plans even before the Federal Government had been able to issue all the necessary regulations for carrying out the new law.

In a personal letter, the board of management recommended every employee to acquire two shares to a nominal value of 100 DM each at a rate of issue of 250 per cent. The letter stated that once an employee had acquired these shares he would enjoy all the rights due to an ordinary shareholder of the company and subject only to a resale restriction.

Originally, no more than 3000 to 4000 applications were expected. But when the day expired up to which shares could be acquired by employees — 15th September 1960 —

the number had grown to 12,000 and most of these had asked for two shares. A later statistical analysis showed that amongst the employee shareholders there were many young people as well as a large number of long service employees, some of them with more than 25 years service to their credit. One of the most satisfying features was that many of those who had acquired shares were heads of families. On the other hand, married employees whose wife or husband was also working showed the least interest in the scheme.

Voting rights for employee shareholders

The shares were acquired at the rate prevailing at the stock exchange on the day of issue. This meant that the company had to spend some 16 million DM. 6 million of this amount were recovered when the shares were sold to the employees. Everyone of the new shareholders had full voting rights from the first day. They received every shareholders letter and other literature and, apart from the dividend, also enjoyed free issue rights in capital increases. The only restriction to which he was subject was that he was not allowed to sell the shares before the 1st January 1962. Also, the difference between the normal rate for the shares and the preferential rates at which employees had acquired them was free from income tax only if shares were retained by the employee for at least five years. The reason for these restrictions was first of all to prevent speculation and secondly to educate employees in the owning of shares.

Naturally, there was a great deal of speculation in Hoechst as to what would happen after 1st January 1962 when employee shareholders would be free to sell them. How many of them would in fact avail themselves of this right? The result was surprising. Only 200 of the 12,000 employee shareholders wished to sell their shares. And for many of these, it were personal factors rather than a deliberate attitude that determined their action.

Hoechst was therefore able to record that employee shares had been well received. During the preparations for the centenary celebrations, the board of management therefore decided to present employees with a present of a special kind: the issue of further shares to employees.

Annual bonus and profit sharing

The month of May has gained particular significance for the Hoechst shareholders. This is the month when Hoechst normally distributes its dividend. But the dividend rate is important not only for shareholders because upon it the annual bonus or profit sharing rate also depends. This has been distributed to all employees since 1953. In that year, the Christmas bonus, which was felt to allow for too little differentiation, had been superseded by a new uniform arrangement. Its essential advantage was that it suitably combined the interests of employees with those of shareholders.

As early as 1952, employee representatives had been granted seats on the supervisory board. Of equal status with the other members of the supervisory board, they passed the annual accounts and the profits. And when, a year later, board of management and works council agreed the annual bonus arrangement, the dividend was taken as a measure of the profit sharing of employees.

This bonus arrangement operates on a points scheme and takes into account two factors: the length of service as an indication of the loyalty to the company and the performance as reflected in salary or wages. The value of the points and thus the rate of the bonus depends on the profits of the company. To reduce this to a simple formula, a high profit is a high dividend and a high dividend means a high bonus. A point value of 10 DM was fixed even for years when no dividend is to be paid. This was done to ensure that the employee would never be worse off than he would have been under the previous scheme. The annual bonus is paid in two instalments, one part before Christmas and the main part after the Annual General Meeting and the fixing of the dividend in May.

To give a concrete example: in 1961, a worker with a monthly income of 650 DM and with ten years service would have got an annual bonus of 832 DM. For the same monthly income but with twenty five years of service, the figure would have been 1,152 DM. A skilled craftsman or a trained chemical worker with a monthly income of 810 DM would have got 960 DM after ten years of service and 1280 DM after twenty five years of service. Foremen with an income of 1000 DM per month would have got 1120 DM after ten years of service and 1440 DM after twenty five years of service.

Success and risk

All workers and staff paid according to the agreed tariffs are entitled to the annual bonus. Staff not subject to the agreed tariffs enjoy a special arrangement agreed in 1953. In their case, the length of service is without significance and the only decisive factor is their performance. The amount of profit sharing is calculated solely from the annual gross income. The higher the dividend, the higher the profit sharing. However, if the dividend is 3.8 per cent, the profit sharing is zero. For every per cent by which the dividend increases, the profit sharing increases by 1.95 per cent of the annual income.

If the dividend drops to below 3.8 per cent, those involved in this scheme are not likely to be very pleased for their annual income may be reduced by as much as 7.5 per cent. So far, however, this has not yet happened.

Everybody can apply his annual bonus as he wishes. The law enacted in 1961 to promote the acquisition of personal property however induced the management to take a special measure. In agreement with the works council, employees were provided with facilities for investing part of the annual bonus. Up to 312 DM could be invested in this way free of tax. To eliminate all misunderstandings, a special information sheet was circulated to all employees which made absolutely clear that every employee was free to decide whether he wished to have his bonus paid in full or whether he wished to invest part of it. Some 26.8 per cent of staff and 5.2 per cent of workers availed themselves of the latter opportunity. They invested an amount of 1,549,000 DM in various projects. Half of this sum went into savings accounts which, as a result of the bonus law, bring additional fiscal advantages. Three quarters of a million were applied to the building of owner-occupied homes.

From the barracks to the owner-occupied home

The promotion of owner-occupied homes has long been a particular aim of the company. In the first minutes of the social committee for 1952 and 1953, there is again and again reference to the problem of how to meet the catastrophic shortage of houses and accommodation. This shortage of course had its origin in the destruction resulting from the war, in requisitioning and the large number of refugees amongst employees amounting to some 20 per cent. To provide adequate living accommodation had therefore become a vital problem for the company. And although the company finances were not at their best, rapid help was essential, particularly in order to terminate the unedifying barracks existence that many employees still had to put up with. The problem was to house as many employees as possible with the available means. To achieve this, large blocks of flats were built which were dominated by functional simplicity. In spring 1953, the social committee decided upon a programme specifically devoted to the building of owner-occupied houses. This met the wishes of many employees whose funds were insufficient to pay for the building of their own house. This company help supported personal initiative, promoted the acquisition of personal wealth and met the shortage of accomodation in a way that fitted best into the social programme of that day. All the fiscal and financial assistance that the laws of the state permitted were fully utilised.

In this way, it was possible to construct some 3,000 owner-occupied houses up to 1962. During the same time, some 11,000 flats for rent were made available.

The programme of building owner-occupied houses appeared to Hoechst important enough to warrant the setting up of a special commission. This commission disposes over company funds for this project and also examines the incomes of those who propose to build a house. This is not for reasons of curiosity but in order to make sure that nobody enters upon this project without being able to sustain it. Those employees who receive a building loan from the company enter into a life insurance to the amount of the money lent so that no liability is likely to devolve upon their families.

Shortage of houses during the early period

The building of owner-occupied houses has been systematically promoted since 1934. Indeed, the real origin of this policy goes back to 1875 when, some fifteen years after the foundation of Farbwerke Hoechst, the first houses for the Hoechst workers were built in an area near the factory. Each one of these houses was to become the home for generations of Hoechst workers. They each had a small garden for whose keeping the company presented special prizes. As early as 1895, these company houses were provided with running water and gas.

At the turn of the century, every tenth Hoechst employee lived in a house owned by the company. Most of these houses were located in rural settlements which were growing up around the steadily expanding plant. When one of the founders of the company — Wilhelm Meister — retired and on this occasion made a gift of 100,000 marks, this sum was used as the starting capital for an old people's home. Originally, this comprised twenty houses, in which workers with twenty or more years of service were able to spend their retirement without having to pay rent.

This generous housing programme, at any rate for those days, was based not only on social considerations. The company also had more direct interests at heart. Even if the labour reserve in and around Hoechst appeared inexhaustible in 1863, the rate of growth of the company soon upset even the most optimistic calculations. The factory's need for people was insatiable. In 1863, the company had begun operations with a crew of seven. In 1875, these had risen to 400 workers. When the company celebrated its 25th anniversary in 1888, there were 1860 workers. At the turn of the century, some 4000 names figured on the salary lists.

The company began to draw its labour from areas further and further away from Hoechst. Some people travelled ten or even twenty kilometres to get to Hoechst. Most

FARBWERKE
VORM. MEISTER LUCIUS UND BRÜNI
HÖCHST A.M.

BADEANSTALT
FÜR
DIE SÜDLICHE FABRIKHÄLFTE

ENTW. U. AUSGEF. V. H. KUTT.   GEZ. V. I.R.

of these in addition ran a smallholding where they lived. Of the 1200 workers that each year entered into the company's employ in the nineties, only few, however, remained. This fluctuation in fact was so violent that it was impossible for a core of trained workers to be established — an indispensable condition for a successful company. Hoechst therefore tried everything in order to settle people that had come to work for it from places away from Hoechst. One way of achieving this was through the construction of flats or housing estates.

Reminiscences from the good old days

But the working man of that time spent the larger part of his waking life not at home but in the factories. The men and women who came from afar had to travel long hours in addition to their already long working day. Most of them had to get up at four or five o'clock in the morning. Punctuality was an absolute condition at Hoechst. Sharp at six, a little bell would sound on the roof of the main workshop. When the bell finished ringing, everyone had to be in his place. The working day was from six in the morning until five in the afternoon from Monday to Saturday. The only interruptions were half an hour for breakfast and an hour for lunch. To us, a working week of sixty and eventually fifty seven hours may seem pretty tough. But it was nothing compared to the number of hours worked by other factories. In a social report from these "good old days", there appears the following passage: "The working week of 57 hours therefore is a very short one compared with most other factories. The board of management of the company takes the view that this shortened working week increases output so that the working hours lost are more than made good by increased productivity. In addition, the long distance that many workers have to cover between their home and the factory dictates that the working hours should be as short as possible."

This "shortest possible" working day was reduced in the case of most workers by 25 minutes by the "very popular" decision to regard the time used for bathing as part of the working day. A bath house had been erected as early as 1869. It was the forerunner of a series of modern baths. The hygiene-conscious works management was no less proud of these baths than it was of the canteen whose almost clinical cleanliness became a byword at Hoechst. The management were very strict about this canteen. They declared: "Workers are not allowed, under threat of penalty, to bring food into the factory. The factory has its own canteen. Food is provided for all workers and will be eaten in a special dining room". It appears that the cooking was not bad for a report of 1867 says: "These facilities are excellent and do not give rise to any kind of complaint".

Co-partnership in the canteen

The Hoechst works canteen was administered entirely by the workers themselves. Every worker had to pay 20 Pfennigs per meal. The company added 10 Pfennigs. For this amount of money, the workers received half a litre of coffee twice daily and a nourishing soup which had to contain 170 grams of meat. A special commission saw to it that the butcher did not violate this regulation and that the kitchen did not utilize the rations for any other purpose. Anyone found guilty in this respect was dealt with mercilessly.

Wages

The workers in the chemical industry received some 2 to 4 marks per day at the beginning of the nineties. Young people in the kitchens and in despatch as well as trainees received rather less than 2 marks. Almost 57 per cent of all the workers had to be content with amounts between 2 and 3 marks. 33 per cent received more than 3 marks. The average daily wage was 2.86 marks.

When looking at these figures, one must of course not lose sight of the fact that the cost of living was also very low. A bottle of beer in the nineties cost 10 Pfennigs and a complete lunch in a public house 30 or 40 Pfennigs. But still, it seems, that there is really little cause for garlanding this period with heavy curtains of sentimentality.

Normal salaries were supplemented by annual bonuses. Hardworking and reliable employees might get as much as 175 marks or more. If these bonuses are added to the wages, then the average annual income of a Hoechst worker was around 1000 marks. This, a factory notice said at the time, is a payment, in relation to the short working week, that is offered by only few factories.

Holidays was a foreign word during this period of industrialisation. Statutory holidays such as Christmas and Easter was all that the workers could look forward to. But progress was just around the corner. As from 1899, workers with more than 25 years of service were granted a week's leave. Starting in 1906, employees with 2 years service were granted 3 days leave and after six years service they were granted 6 days leave. In 1913, the maximum period of leave after 30 years service was increased to ten days. The eight-hour day and paid leave for everybody proclaimed after the first world war were Utopia indeed in those days.

Aid for the aged and the sick

The activities of many chemical companies were ahead of the general trend also in many

The trainees received their "school reports"

other social fields. Care for the sick and the aged was the concern of the founders of the chemical companies in the area of Frankfurt right from the very start. Even before Bismarck's sickness, accident, disablement and old age insurance scheme had been passed by the German Parliament, these companies were already trying to help any of their workers who found themselves in distress. In 1860, Griesheim founded a sickness and benefit society. In Offenbach, a sickness fund was established in 1876 and a similar fund was created by Kalle in Biebrich in 1882. In the latter case, this had been preceded by a fund that dealt specifically with expenses for doctors and drugs.

In the year of its foundation, in 1863, Hoechst had concluded an accident insurance for its first workers. Every employee paid 1.5 per cent of his wages towards this insurance, the company contributing 50 per cent of the total of all the contributions.

Even in these early days, it was accepted that prevention was better than cure. After all, chemistry was a young science and it concerned itself with substances about which little was known. What would be their influence on the people that had to handle them? Part of the raw materials used was known to be dangerous. This applied, for example, to fuchsine production in the early period. In 1867, no less than 4,300 hundredweight of 70 per cent arsenic acid were processed. It was not until 1871 that the toxic arsenic acid was replaced by another oxidant. The special festival brochure on the occasion of the 25th anniversary of the company stated: "Since then, Farbwerke Hoechst does not use arsenic acid in any of its operations and the elimination of this toxic material can be regarded as a significant progress."

Frankfurt physician as works doctor

Hoechst has always tried to gain systematic experience in industrial hygiene. A man who pursued this almost with passion was the Frankfurt physician Dr. Wilhelm Grandhomme. He had been engaged as works doctor in 1874.

This doctor, who had close ties with the founders of Farbwerke Hoechst, did not confine himself to the conventional tasks of a works doctor, to treating accidents and to undertaking continuous control of the health of the employees. He took a far more comprehensive view of his tasks. In 1880, he recorded his experiences in a book that was published in several editions.

In the preface to this book, Grandhomme outlined his functions. They consisted, so he wrote, of the sanitary evaluation of the raw materials used and the close control of all the procedures to which these raw materials were subjected until the finished product was obtained. This meant in the narrower sense a discussion of the measures taken both inside and outside the factory to prevent disease and in the wider sense in the medical evaluation of all facilities whose aim was the bodily well-being of the workers. Almost all the raw materials, intermediates and end-products of the factory were tested by Grandhomme in an intensive series of experiments. Grandhomme also examined, from the medical point of view, all the new production processes and new equipment. He recorded all cases of illness, usually classified by factory, plant and vocation. In 1875, a well-equipped sick-bay was established which was managed by Grandhomme.

Anyone applying for a job at Hoechst had to present himself at the doctor. No person under 14 was considered and in general no person older than 40. The most important question was whether the applicant was suitable, from a medical point of view, for the production plant in which he was to be engaged. Between 1883 and 1892, 12 046 workers were examined in this respect. Practically 1000 were found to be unfit. It has been a long way from this first sick-bay to the present-day medical department but now as then the Hoechst works doctors are concerned mainly with preventive medicine. Medical examinations upon engagement and continuous checks or special suitability tests for staff who wish to change their job form only part of the activities of the Hoechst medical department. Their many other tasks include radiation, vaccination against tetanus and poliomyelitis, mass X-ray investigations and convalescent stays.

Sickness was the exception

The low incidence of occupational disease during the early years of Hoechst, Griesheim, Offenbach and Kalle was no doubt due to large extent to the excellent work of the works doctors. During the first two months after the institution of the sick fund there were 11 cases of sickness at Kalle. This out of a total of 124 workers and 29 staff. An examining board reported that the patients suffered from diseases normally prevalent during the time of the year and that they were in most cases away from work for no longer than 4 days.

On the other hand, little mercy was extended to those who broke the rules. For example, a report of 1901 read: "The board of management has learned that Johann König from Schierstein, who went sick on 14th May, travelled to Cologne during Whitsun without first informing the board of management. Since König has thus violated paragraph 10 of our statutes, he will have to pay a fine of 5 marks".

During this period, sick people received 60 per cent of their wages payable from the third day of their illness. This was paid thirteen weeks but in special cases, payment was continued for a year. The original sum was however reduced from 60 per cent of the salary to 50 after a further 13 weeks, then to 40 and finally to 30 per cent. A year before Bismarck's dismissal in 1889, the disability and old age law of Germany was passed. It set a world-wide trend in respect of social legislation.

This was the first time that the state guaranteed to working people a minimum of protection against the vagaries of life. The foundation stone for further social progress had been laid.

Profit-sharing a la 1871

Many other social services however continued to be left to the initiative of the companies. It depended upon them whether they wished to tackle the social problem with purely charitable efforts, or, and this happened far more rarely, whether they sought to develop organised self-aid amongst the workers. Fritz Kalle, a brother of the founder of the company, was one of the latter group of progressive factory owners.

In 1871, Fritz Kalle had founded a savings bank in Biebrich which was a prototype of the modern profit-sharing schemes. The company paid into the savings bank a given sum every year in respect of each worker. This sum was calculated from the net profit of the company, the amount of wages and length of service. On the initiative of this great reformer, Kalle also formed a works council whose five members were elected by the workers of the company.

This works council was by no means a rubber stamp for the decisions of the company management. On the contrary, it was its job to help administer the social services and to act as mediator in disputes between employer and employees. It had the additional task of ensuring "order, honour and decency".

Two years previously, Griesheim had founded a pension fund. A similar fund was created in Hoechst in 1879. Its original capital was 150,000 marks. The intention was to pay pensions to disabled workers, widows and waifs from the interest that accrued on this capital. Members of the fund were all workers and foremen of the factory who earned less than 2,000 marks per annum and who had been employed by the company for no less than five years.

Totally disabled members of the fund received an annual pension of 525 marks after 30 years of service and one of 750 marks after 45 years of service. Widows received 50 per cent of the man's sum and each child ten per cent. Anyone who was continuously unable to follow his occupation as a result of an ailment or general physical debility was regarded as totally incapacitated. At that time, there was no such thing as a pensionable age. Everyone worked for as long as he could.

The state and its social conscience

A pensionable age was mentioned for the first time in the disablement law of 1889. An old age pension was made subject to completion of the seventieth year and membership in a pension fund of at least thirty years. Only people with a disability of at least 66.2 per cent enjoyed the payment of an earlier pension. This state pension was only a very modest contribution to the cost of living of these people. The state assumed that the people concerned would have savings and that they would be looked after by their children or other members of the family. But in many cases these assumptions were incorrect.

The pension funds of the private companies were therefore becoming increasingly important. In 1892, the Hoechst pension fund included almost 1000 members out of a total of 2,300 employees. Its funds had increased to 440,000 marks. When, in 1913, the company celebrated its fiftieth anniversary and made available some $2^{1}/_{4}$ million marks for social services, the pension fund capital was increased once more.

The first world war fundamentally changed the social climate in the factories. Shortly before the war ended, the state made an attempt to come to terms with the workers and their organisations. Both workers and staff were permitted to form committees in the factories. These committees were formed by the employees in secret elections. But it was already too late. The workers reacted with distrust and with barely concealed disdain. At Hoechst, only 2,270 workers out of a total number of 6,400 took part in the election of these works councils. The end of the war on 11th November 1918 put an end to this belated conciliation attempt by imperial Germany.

The Republic and its unhappy debut

The Weimar Republic began with sharp political fights, attempts at overthrow, strikes and lock-outs. Nor was that the whole catalogue of its difficulties. The shortages of raw materials and other commodities became more and more serious. Soon, a gradual inflation set in. And yet, at the same time, revolutionary social changes were brought about.

Perhaps the most important event took place on 1st December 1918, — the introduction of the eight-hour day and of the new tariff law. Collaboration in the internal social services was expressly approved by the first works council laws. The social services of Hoechst were also completely reorganised. A special social department was formed which was answerable to a social commission.

However welcome these reforms might have been — they had little effect at first on the Hoechst employees. Inflation was rampant and even 28 increases in salary in 1923 alone could not convince the workers that they were being suitably rewarded for their labours. The currency did not become stabilised until November 1923. 1 billion marks corresponds to 1 new Rentenmark. Only now was it fully realised just how impoverished the war had left the German people. Nor was German economy any better off. Especially in the chemical industry, the order books are empty: foreign competition has conquered a large part of the world market formerly held by Germany.

They get their cards

At Bayer, BASF and Hoechst, the management is forced to take the final remedy in times of shrinking production and turnover figures: dismissal. Dismissal notices were sent to thousands of workers. And although the impression is given that this is only temporary and would be revoked in a matter of weeks or months, it proved in the end to be practically permanent. The temporary crisis became a continuous crisis. Dismissals continued for many years.

The solution adopted by the large-scale chemical industry in Germany was the fusion in 1925 of those companies that, under the pressure of war, had joined in 1916 to form an association of German coal-tar dyestuffs manufacturers.

The first social director in Hoechst

The beginnings of a joint social policy of the I.G. companies goes back, however, to the years before fusion. The many joint commissions that attempted to co-ordinate after the first world war the policies of the individual companies also discussed and decided social questions. In 1921, a recommendation was made at an I.G. meeting to appoint social directors in all the works. Hoechst took up this suggestion in 1923 and appointed the first social director in the history of the company.

This was more than just a new title in the firm's hierarchy. The new laws and the growing influence of organised workers' associations during the first years of the Weimar Republic dictated this step.

We realise today that it was at this point in history that the patriarchical era had irrevocably come to its end. In 1907, a man like Gustav von Brüning, son of one of the founders of the company and the creator of many social facilities was still able to declare with sovereign diffidence: "We emphasise that in all the measures to improve the standard of living of our workers, we are in no way influenced by the demands of the organisation (by this he meant the trade unions). We have always rejected and we shall continue to reject any attempt at interference from outside and we would like to recall that we have always met the justified claims of our workers, where these were submitted to us directly, and that we shall continue to meet these claims".

In other words, Brüning took the view that as manufacturer, no one had the right to relieve him of his obligations to his workers. Just how seriously he took these obligations is shown by the long list of welfare measures that he initiated, ranging from a maternity home to domestic classes at the works library. Every detail of these enterprises was of major significance to Brüning. He concerned himself with the composition of the works orchestra, he examined with immense thoroughness all travelling expenses and he personally inspected the company flats whenever there was a suggestion that moral standards were being endangered. Brüning, the father figure, stopped the sale of hard liquor in the canteen, provided letter boxes for complaints and was available, at certain hours, for personal interviews with his workers.

Social policy in the I.G. era

Fifteen years later, during the first year of the I.G., the tete-a-tete between worker and employer had been replaced by factual negotiation. The chief of the large-scale undertaking was faced by the elected representatives of the thousands of workers and by the functionaries of the trade unions. A whole host of social laws and factory regulations controlled the relationships between employer and worker.

While therefore the staff intervened more and more in the social development of factories, the I.G. did all within its power to continue its independent social development. Features of certain works that had proved particularly successful became obligatory for the entire group. For example, in 1926, an I.G. savings bank, the Walther-vom-Rath Travelling fund and a year later the A. L. Häuser fund were instituted. Even more important, in 1926, an annual bonus was paid for the first time. This bonus depended on the success of the company during the preceding year. All the threads of the overall social policy of the I.G. were joined in the newly formed social commission. It formulated uniform directives for all the works, at the same time allowing the individual sites a free hand in their social expenditure.

This phase of social evolution did, however, not proceed without its upsets. The programme of rationalisation that had become necessary threatened to increase social tension in the company. Particularly in dyestuffs manufacture, various production units had to be joined, transferred or stopped. There were in addition a number of

Factory band around 1890

savings measures in order to improve the competitive position of the company. Each one of these measures had a direct effect on a large number of the employees. This effect was particularly marked in the case of Kalle. The employees at Biebrich had to change, almost overnight, from dyestuffs manufacture to cellophane production. For many employees, the fate was particularly hard. Several hundred workers and even more staff had to be dismissed or retired prematurely. To find full understanding for these unavoidable measures was an almost insoluble task for management and works council alike.

No more appointments in the I.G.

The group had hardly recovered from these radical measures, when the world depression also gripped German industry. During 1932/33, the large German companies faced the most serious prospects. Every third worker was without wages and the salaries of the staff had to be drastically reduced in accordance with an edict by the Chancellor of Germany Heinrich Brüning. At the same time, unemployment benefits and other welfare payments had to be reduced to the absolute minimum. Within twelve months, the number of employees at Hoechst dropped by 38 per cent. On 21st June 1929, the I.G. decreed that no further appointments should be made throughout the company. The working week was reduced to less than 40 hours in order to avoid further dismissals. For the same reason, the I.G. decided in 1932 to adopt the five-day week. The recovery of the I.G. did not start until 1935. And even then it was by no means spectacular.

In addition, the consequences of Germany's new dictatorship now began to imprint themselves on the social policy of the company. The operations of the plant were "streamlined" in accordance with the Führer's principles and the philosophy of the Nazi party. The trade unions and the freely elected works councils were replaced by the German Workers' Front. The works manager became the 'Führer' of the factory and his opposite numbers were similar creations with similar high-sounding titles. The Nazi party dictated the professional, social and cultural happenings in the plant. But even so, the social policies of the various works of the I.G. managed to retain a semblance of independence.

Strength through joy — a short-lived dream

The "strength through joy" Utopia ended abruptly with the beginning of the second world war, with mobilisation, wage freezes and ration cards. The next five years to follow terminate with workers, chemists, salesmen and even women and children building useless tank ditches and tank obstacles on the Rhine. And when the war was finally over, 713 members of the Hoechst staff did not return. The fate of a further 249 remains unknown.

The future of the works was equally doubtful. Hordes of plunderers decimated the stocks of the company that the bombs had not destroyed and it was only with difficulty that they could be prevented from stealing the experimental animals infected with various pathogens. The occupation forces requisitioned a large part of the works and of the flats and houses. They dismissed all employees that were members of the party. The management was fired and the financial funds were confiscated. Pensioners lost their pensions. The works manager appointed by the Americans had to consult the Control Officer before taking any decision. That any production at all should have been possible under these circumstances will forever remain a miracle.

The big attraction: baked potatoes in the canteen

During these hard times, the fate of the company was borne by its hard core of loyal workers and staff. For them, working for Hoechst had become a duty that you did not desert. Michael Erlenbach, Hoechst trustee and later a member of the board of manage-that they could be prevented from stealing the experimental animals infected with that will no longer remember that its fathers were sent by their mothers to work at Hoechst because there they could get a warm soup, the I.G. soup. Several thousand people looked forward for a whole week to Friday when they got a herring and three potatoes. People came to work on foot, in buses filled to capacity, in trams and trains without windows, both in summer and winter. It was the hour of glory for the men and women of the works council where they not only looked after the most elementary interests of the people they represented but where they also played their part in formulating the measures that were to be so decisive for the future".

Part of the Hoechst site became agricultural land. Fertiliser was distributed to peasants, salt to bakers and butchers in exchange for food. Wages or salaries were supplemented to a modest extent by cash in kind. Saccharine, washing powder and fertilizer were the most sought-after goods.

Pensioners, too, whose pensions were not paid until 1947, were provided with these highly desirable extras. But however much Hoechst tried to get additional food, it did not prove possible to stop all employees from being hungry. To hope for an increase in production under these circumstances was a forlorn hope.

But thanks to the untiring effort of everbody, the first signs of recovery did eventually appear. The Marshall Plan in 1947, the currency reform, the end of the infamous state control and of the price freeze, the birth of the trizone as an economic unit and above all the foundation of the Federal Republic were the milestones on the road to a return to normal conditions. And although during this period, the dismembered I.G. works are still subject to many limitations, in the social field human dynamism proves stronger than any theories.

The social background of the group

However close the Hoechst works grew together in the grave years after 1945, one factor could not be foreseen. The comparative independence of many works since the end of the war gave rise to numerous problems when the company was reconstituted in 1952. It was, therefore, important to establish uniformity not only in the technical and economical field but also in the social sphere.

Not that this was equivalent to a simple levelling-out. The real aim was to adapt the social conditions in the various works to one another. This mammoth task had to be solved by the social committee of the board of management together with the representatives of the staff. At the beginning of this work, there was a thorough inventory of all the social services that were being offered throughout the works at that time.

Modern requirements were fulfilled and well-tried institutions were retained with the same non-sentimental decisiveness with which many other traditions had been thrown overboard whose usefulness was no longer apparent. The co-operative shop, for example, that is to say the food department and the bakery of the Hoechst-owned store which had been founded in 1885 in order to provide employees with household goods at moderate prices and in top quality, was a victim of this cleaning-up process. The supermarket and the large store had replaced it. The domestic school, founded in 1895 for the daughters of workers, was closed. Modern educational and training facilities had made it superfluous. Choirs, works orchestra, sports club were also dissolved. Instead, Hoechst offered generous support to private organisations of this type. The sports clubs, for example, were given the use of the company's sports field without charge. This was done because the company took the view that its employees should not feel that their leisure time was controlled and supervised by the company.

The maternity and convalescence home which had formed a prominent part of Hoechst's social programme were also abandoned. When these homes were first founded, they were a remarkable event in the German industrial social history. But sixty years later, there was a sufficient number of public sanitoria and maternity homes to make it

266

unnecessary for Hoechst to maintain one of its own. The funds set free as a result of these measures were used for other social tasks.

Old age pensions

Great strides were, however, made with those institutions that are today grouped together under the collective term social security. The main item in this field is old age pensions. Many investigations have shown that apart from the amount of salary or wages, as security of employment, the German worker is most deeply concerned with old age pensions as a decisive criterion of his professional contentment.

In spite of pension reform which must be adapted to the requirements of all those insured, the company remains faced with the big problem of individual adaptation. The legal old age pension is governed primarily by the amount of contributions and the period during which the employee was insured. Loyalty to the individual companies cannot be rewarded and productivity only to the extent to which it is expressed in salary or wage subject to contribution.

Regard for these essential factors led to the introduction of annual bonuses. The same considerations became the basis for the present-day old age pension by the company. The staff pension fund numbers some 15,000 people. It goes back to 1886 and is obligatory for all staff. The contribution by the employee is between 2.5 and 5 per cent of income, depending whether and to what extent the employee contributes to the legal old age pension fund. The maximum contribution per month is at present around 62.50 DM. If an employee on the staff payroll is retired he receives an annual pension of 40 per cent of the total contributions he has paid. This can be done only because of the considerable subsidies provided by the company. The workers are taken care of by a different scheme operated by Farbwerke Hoechst. The basis for this scheme was provided by the Kaiser Wilhelm and Augusta funds. Workers do not have to pay contributions to these funds. They are financed entirely by the company. The amount of pension paid depends entirely upon length of service and position in the factory. Together with a company supplement, it can amount to a maximum of 160 DM per month. Looking after next-of-kin, contractual pensions and a death fund also form part of the Hoechst social programme. There is additional aid in case of death. Widows of employees are paid the full wage or salary of their husband for the month of death and three months thereafter. In 1961, the company paid some 30 million DM for the old age and widows pension fund. The legal social payments required from the company are even higher, namely 45.4 million DM.

The new apprentices school

Excursion into social statistics

Where there is a balanced age structure amongst the staff of a company, such expenditure may be justifiable. In 1952, however, the company was facing alarming figures. Only 29 per cent of all employees were below the age of thirty. The average age was forty. Twenty eight per cent of the employees were older than fifty.

Since then, however, the picture has become a little brighter. Those under thirty now account for 37.2 per cent of all employees and those over fifty account for 18 per cent. The average age of the people at Hoechst is now 36. Normally, an employee has worked for the company for some ten years. On average, the company pays him, including social payments, some 12,000 DM. For this amount of money, he worked in 1961 a total of 1965 hours and achieved a per head turnover of 56,000 DM.

This result could not be achieved overnight. It was due to many efforts made by the company during the last ten years, especially so far as the younger generation is concerned. It was realised to what extent career prospects offered by large-scale chemistry influenced the choice of job and indeed the social climate as a whole. But advancement presupposes training. This was, of course, not new and indeed Hoechst had set up a training school for 120 trainees as early as 1921. This was followed in 1938 by a works school for young chemists. In view of the increasing mechanisation and automation in the chemical industry, these people were becoming more and more important and they were prepared by the company for special problems. The outside training facilities simply were inadequate for the special demands.

"New blood is vital"

This applies even more to the years following 1945. The lead of world chemistry in technical, scientific and economic respects appeared in part overwhelming. If it was to be reduced, the intensive training of apprentices was not enough. Those already at their jobs had to return to school as well and gain new laboratory experience. This has been done since 1962 in the new Hoechst works school. It has 13 classrooms, 270 laboratory places and woodworking and metalworking shops. It deserves the attribute "modern" in every respect. A special training establishment was provided for measurement and control chemists for which there is a great need in the increasingly automated chemical industry. Some 200 craft trainees are at present instructed in the old training school. The local vocational school is also giving part of the lessons in factory-owned schoolrooms due to lack of accommodation in the city.

In addition to the 2000 apprentices which are continuously being trained by the company, some 1000 adults per year participate in various further education activities arranged by Hoechst. This involves a certain amount of sacrifice, for these courses take place almost exclusively in the evening. They are intended not only to increase the vocational standards of Hoechst employees and to enable them to keep up with modern progress in technology which the company will have to apply to its own operations if it is to remain in the forefront of German chemical industry. Management also hope that these evening activities will have a beneficial influence on the mental outlook of its staff. The less physical strain a worker has to endure due to modern production methods, the greater will be the intellectual and nervous stress. As a counter-weight to the unavoidable specialisation, employees require a broader intellectual basis. This makes it easier for them to view their work as part of the whole. Only people who know the part they play do their work gladly. This is a fact that has been known for as long as it has been neglected. Millions of D-Marks are now spent annually on training at Hoechst. The figure for 1961 was 4.7 million. In view of this expenditure, it is not surprising that the most modern means are employed in order to select the most promising trainees. This involves an obligatory medical examination as well as an intelligence test. The company's psychologist seeks to help youngsters and parents in the selection of job so that the best possible compromise between personal preference and talent is achieved. The whole apparatus of modern industrial psychology is brought into play before a final decision is made. This is not equivalent to a selection of the fittest but a sensible combination of talents in relation to the promotional prospects within the company.

Remuneration and working hours

Although social questions have become a major preoccupation of the company, the predominating theme remains remuneration and working hours. In the past ten years, wage negotiations and increases in tariffs have taken place practically every year. The company has had to absorb additional expenditure in this field which was made good only partially by increases in productivity, rationalisation and other economies. The investments necessary to achieve this have meant that in the last ten years the capital expenditure per head within the company has more than doubled.

What does an average worker in Hoechst earn today? An unskilled worker over 21 years of age starts at about 500 DM per month. After an initial introductory period, he joins a higher group where he earns between 600 and 750 DM per month.

A skilled worker who has completed a suitable vocational training course or has the equivalent in practical experience can look forward to an income between 650 and 850 DM. Trained chemical workers and craftsmen who have completed their apprenticeship have a monthly income of up to 850 DM.

These figures represent, of course, only average values. The annual bonus, social payments, and children's allowances are not included.

Of the 13,000 workers engaged by Hoechst in 1962, almost 50 per cent belonged to the category of skilled workers and craftsmen. In conformity with the character of the chemical industry, women are engaged only to a limited extent. In Hoechst, they account for 20 per cent of all workers. They are employed mainly in the laboratories and in the packaging plants. For the same output, their salaries are equivalent to those of their male colleagues.

Hoechst works a five-day week of 42.5 paid working hours. The first step towards the five-day week was taken in 1955 when Hoechst voluntarily introduced a 45 hour week and an extended weekend. Depending on age and length of service, every employee enjoys three to four weeks paid leave per year. Leave in Germany will soon be made uniform by a special Federal law.

The Hoechst cultural programme

In the early years of Hoechst, when a worker spent more than half of his life in the factory, it would have been a waste of time to discuss recreation. Nevertheless, even then the company made some modest attempts at providing a basis for cultural activities. The first institution that comes under this heading, if we ignore educational societies, works orchestras and choirs, was the library founded in 1904. Most of its volumes were of an educational character. Today, the shelves of the Hoechst library house some 18,000 volumes, of which 7,400 are technical books and 7,600 are literature. There are some 3,000 volumes for the younger readers. Some 20 per cent of the workers, 33 per cent of the staff and more than 80 per cent of the apprentices are permanent users of the library. Some 120,000 volumes are lent per year, a figure that has given a great deal of satisfaction to the social department. Of this figure, a third concerns technical books, another third detective and adventure stories and the remaining third literature.

Book reviews in the Farbenpost and poetry readings support the work of the librarians. The ambitious Hoechst cultural programme includes concerts, lectures, theatre evenings and art exhibitions. Frequently, these are joint events between the social department of Hoechst and the Hoechst Society for Popular Education. The new Hoechst centenary hall, an imposing building with its 4,000 seats, has greatly facilitated the execution of both these ambitious cultural and other sporting programmes.

Quo vadis?

Technical and economic progress within the company is proceeding at a hectic pace — without absolute perfection being achieved. Social life is proceeding at the same pace, hovering between wish and fulfillment. Of course, social policy, like all policy, is the art of the possible. But the last few years provide sufficient examples of how the common effort of both employer and employee has succeeded in overcoming even the most formidable obstacles. Of course, many an ideal, looked at closely, lost something of the lustre that it originally displayed. The final result proved often only a further stage on the path to a new social order whose outer face is changing continuously.

Prof. Dr. Gustav Ehrhart

**One Hundred Years
of Research**

One hundred years ago the founding of Farbwerke Hoechst coincided with the beginning of a new era in which many important events were to bring considerable changes in our way of life. Technical development and the scientific method gained more and more influence in our order of society, though this also made them responsible for maintaining and promoting this order of society with its higher standard of living.

More than any other branch of industry, the chemical industry depends for its development on active research. This attempt to describe the progress of research during the one hundred years at Farbwerke Hoechst cannot claim to be comprehensive. It is practically impossible to keep track of everything going forward in a concern as vast as Hoechst is today. But we shall take some major examples from that great span of time and show how the tremendous progress made in the chemical industry has only been possible through great discoveries, inventions or new theories to show the way. The growth of the whole chemical industry owes a great deal to the scientific research carried out at the universities, especially during the last decades of the 19th century, and to the industry's own research which soon after became greatly intensified.

It is not possible to give the names of all who have carried out important research work at the universities and in industry, and it is also the policy not to mention the names of those still actively working for the concern.

In 1845 the young chemist A. W. Hofmann from Bonn was appointed to the College of Chemistry in London. This caused quite a stir in academic circles in Germany, for one did not like losing a promising young scientist to another country. Hofmann worked and taught in London for 20 years. He devoted much of his work in England to the synthesis of aniline dyes which in those days attracted considerable attention among experts because of their brilliance and clear shades.

It was decided to recall Hofmann to Germany and he was offered the Chair of Chemistry in Berlin which had just become vacant, a very honourable position. Hofmann accepted and brought a new renaissance to the Berlin institute. It became a cradle for young scientists who were to help chemistry achieve its world reputation.

Emil Fischer was later to say that Hofmann's return from England had given a great new impetus to the chemical industry in Germany. It was at this time that big chemical concerns were being founded.

The development of the chemical industry is fundamentally different from that of other types of industry. The first manufactured chemical products were based on work done at the universities. The industry itself had the task of finding suitable methods for their large-scale production and application. Then the requirements of the industry grew in so many directions that it became necessary for the industrial concerns to have their own laboratories. These had to cope with all the problems brought up by a new field of research. Many new ideas came from the universities and from the industry and in the end a specific field of research developed. The tremendous rise of the chemical industry is based on close cooperation between academic science and technology.

———————

In 1863, after intensive laboratory investigations, E. Lucius discovered a better method for producing ALDEHYDE GREEN, so that large scale manufacture of the dye became possible. In 1869 one of Hoechst's chemists, F. Riese, described a technical ALIZARIN synthesis. One after the other, new dyes were rapidly going into production at Hoechst, though one still had to rely upon the established methods. In 1878 Hoechst was granted its first German State Patent. This protects the PONCEAU DYES, which are produced from two β-naphthol-disulfonic acids, R-acid and G-acid, a process developed by H. Baum of Hoechst.

Soon after this followed the first red TETRAZO DYES, BIEBRICH SCARLET RED and others, which had been discovered in the laboratories of Kalle & Co. Ten years later, A. Hermann of Hoechst made an important contribution in the field of dyestuffs. Through the condensation of m-hydroxybenzaldehyde with a dialkylaniline he obtained leuco bases. By sulphonation and subsequent oxidation these were converted into most valuable dyes, among them PATENT BLUE which has achieved great importance.

In the same year, 1888, a very important discovery was made at the Bayer works in Elberfeld and at the same time at the Badische Anilin- & Soda-Fabrik in Ludwigshafen.

This was to have tremendous influence on the further development of the chemical dyes. R. E. Schmidt in Elberfeld and R. Bohn in Ludwigshafen found that several hydroxyl groups can be introduced into anthraquinone and its derivatives by using oleum; the reaction becomes easier and more specific if boric acid is added as a catalyst (E. R. Schmidt). This reaction played a decisive role in the subsequent development of the whole range of ANTHRAQUINONE DYES and gave a tremendous boost to the work on chemical dyes.

In 1883, L. Knorr of Erlangen applied for a patent for the production of hydroxymethyl quinizine from phenylhydrazine and acetoacetic ester; this was to be used for the production of dyestuffs and drugs. Phenylhydrazine — which E. Fischer had discovered in 1875 — had shown itself to be a most interesting substance. At the same time Knorr described the production of a dimethylhydroxyquinicine which was obtained by heating methylhydroxyquinicine with methyl iodide. W. Filehne got excellent results when he tested this substance pharmacologically, and it showed an outstanding antipyretic action.

They were soon to find however that the new compound was not a quinoline derivative — as originally assumed — but phenyldimethylpyrazolone.

$$
\begin{array}{c}
C_6H_5 \\
| \\
N \\
OC \qquad N-CH_3 \\
| \qquad | \\
HC == C-CH_3
\end{array}
$$

Hoechst undertook the manufacture of the new compound which Knorr had called ANTIPYRINE because of its antipyretic action. Further work on this new group of compounds laid the foundation for systematic research in pharmaceuticals at Hoechst.

F. Stolz, a student of A. v. Baeyer, carried Knorr's work further. At that time, the pharmacologist Filehne approached Hoechst. He wanted to introduce another basic radical into the phenyl group of antipyrine. This idea was based on his concept of the chemical structure of quinine. Stolz was able to do this for him, though he chose to do the substitution on the actual pyrazolone ring and not the phenyl group. Nitrozation,

Hoechst's chemists at the turn of the century.
F. Stolz, discoverer of Pyramidon refuses to part with the
bicycle.

reduction and subsequent dimethylation produced a dimethylaminophenyldimethyl pyrazolone:

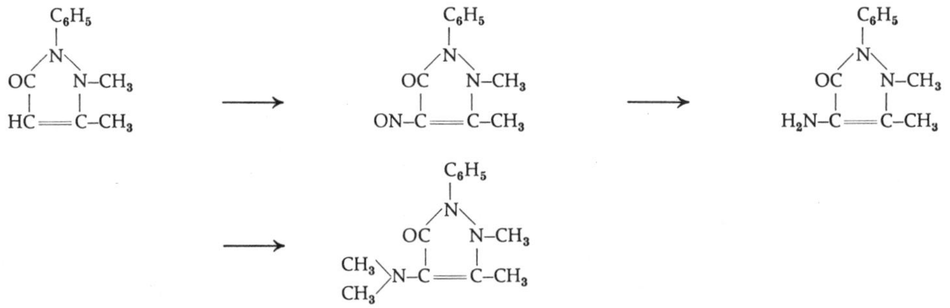

Very soon Filehne was to discover that this substance was superior to antipyrine. It was three times as powerful, and its action was gentler and more easily controlled. The new product was named PYRAMIDON and attracted considerable attention in medical circles. In Germany and abroad Pyramidon was studied intensively and soon hundreds of papers had been published in all sorts of medical journals, so that the name Hoechst became universally known.

No further research was done on the pyrazolones for some years, but at a much later date the work was taken up again.

1883 saw the first appointment of a university professor to Hoechst. This was A. Laubenheimer. It was probably intended at first that he should work in general research, but Laubenheimer soon became interested in bacteriological and serological problems. In these fields, his work with E. v. Behring, R. Koch and P. Ehrlich proved extremely fruitful.

E. v. Behring had published reports on his work on antitoxin production in 1890. Hoechst realised the significance of his discovery and invited Behring to continue his researches in Hoechst.

In this way they were able to produce a DIPHTHERIA ANTITOXIN within 4 years and bring it on the market in August 1894. A completely new sphere of work opened up, for now the therapeutic agents coming from the chemist's retort were joined by those developed from the living organism. The new sera did not entirely come up to expectations, yet it was soon to become evident that the antitoxins were the only means

of coping with certain diseases. In 1896 TETANUS ANTITOXIN HOECHST became available. This was followed by a serum against foot-and-mouth disease, by dysentery serum in 1908, anthrax serum in 1912, and other sera.

Laubenheimer was turning more and more towards general management. It therefore became necessary to find someone capable of organizing the whole of research on a uniform basis. The man chosen was Professor W. Roser of Marburg. He became the head of the newly founded central laboratories in 1893 and held this position until his death in 1923. The central laboratories had two main tasks. New chemists joining the staff, most of them straight from university, had to be trained for the needs of a chemical factory. They had to become familiar with the work on dyestuffs and pharmaceuticals and learn the methods used in the chemical industry. At the same time they had to be encouraged right from the beginning to solve problems arising on the factory floor, improve existing processes and develop new ones, and deal with patent problems.

Roser proved extremely competent in all aspects of this multifarious task. He had a remarkable memory, often the envy of his colleagues. Roser made many suggestions and greatly influenced those working with him.

From 1895 onwards, K. Schirmacher worked in Roser's laboratories. With his great knowledge and wide vision he wrote a number of important scientific publications. Schirmacher became the valued and honoured adviser to a whole generation of chemists.

Schirmacher's attention had been drawn quite early to the azo dyes. In 1900, — in hot competition with work going on at the Badische Anilin- & Soda-Fabrik — he successfully developed a black wool dye with excellent properties, ACID ALIZARIN BLACK. This dye, a combination of tetrazotized 2,6-diaminophenol-4-sulphonic acid and β-naphthol or β-naphthol-6-sulpho acid, achieved considerable importance in the dyeing of wools in those days.

Shortly afterwards came the problem of finding light-fast pigments for wallpaper and signal colours etc. Again Schirmacher and his colleagues provided the answer. They produced PIGMENT SCARLET G and LAKE RED C, an extremely fast colour combining 2-chloro-5-aminotoluene-5-sulphonic acid and β-naphthol. A number of other azo dyes are also linked with Schirmacher's name.

In 1880 A. v. Baeyer in Munich achieved the first indigo synthesis from o-nitrophenyl-propiolic acid, after first establishing the exact chemical structure of indigo. BASF and Hoechst acquired the patent. Both companies were trying to attain successfull commercial production of this «King of Dyestuffs»; but at first they made little headway. No economical method was found using o-nitrophenyl-propiolic acid as starting material. Finally, in 1890, when K. Heumann published his process for producing indigo from phenylglycine or phenylglycine-o-carboxylic acid, promising routes opened up for large-scale synthesis of indigo. Heumann used caustic fusion to convert phenylglycine or phenylglycine-o-carboxylic acid to indoxyl from which indigo is obtained directly. Phenylglycine gave poor yields, but phenylglycine-o-carboxylic acid proved satisfactory. BASF and Hoechst adopted Heumann's process and now concentrated their efforts on the production of phenylglycine-o-carboxylic acid. This is easily obtained as follows:

$$\text{phthalic anhydride} \xrightarrow{+ \text{ NH}_3} \text{phthalimide} \xrightarrow{+ \text{ NaOCl}} \text{anthranilic acid}$$
$$\xrightarrow{+ \text{ chloroacetic acid}} \text{phenylglycine-o-carboxylic acid}$$

The problem was how to produce phthalic anhydride cheaply. Hoechst oxidized naphthalene with bichromate and tried to find a method of processing the resulting chromium.

It did not take BASF long to find a simple method of preparing phthalic acid: it oxidized naphthalene with sulphuric acid in the presence of mercury as a catalyst. This put BASF in a position to market synthetic indigo in 1897. Hoechst was able to let its customers have a synthetic indigo that same year, but only in small quantities. These came from a pilot plant in which Hoechst was testing a second process discovered by A. v. Baeyer for synthesizing indigo from o-nitrobenzaldehyde and acetone. When Hoechst had succeeded in electrolytically oxidizing the chromium solutions, obtained by naphthalene oxidation, to chromic acid, the Heumann process using phenylglycine-o-carboxylic acid was tackled with renewed vigour.

In 1900 work started on building an indigo works at Gersthofen, where water power provided cheap electricity. Then in the middle of 1901, before the plant was finished, events took a new turn. Hoechst acquired a process from DEGUSSA in Frankfurt, discovered by J. Pfleger and O. Liebknecht, which made it possible to cyclize phenylglycine with good yields using sodamide. It was now possible to use aniline as the starting material for indigo synthesis on an economical basis:

$$\text{aniline} \xrightarrow{\text{+ chloroacetic acid}} \text{phenylglycine}$$

Indigo was manufactured in Hoechst while Gersthofen produced the preliminary and auxiliary chloroacetic acid and sodium.

In the pharmaceutical field, two Hoechst chemists, F. Stolz and A. Flächer, made an epoch-making discovery at the turn of the century. The chemical structure of adrenaline, a hormone from the adrenal gland, had just been established by J. Takamine, H. Pauly and F. Stolz. The substance was extremely expensive and very difficult to extract from the gland.

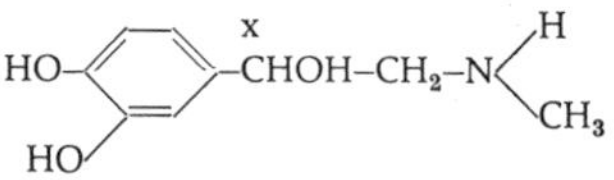

x = opt. active centre

Its complete synthesis appeared to be greatly worth while.

Stolz achieved this as follows:

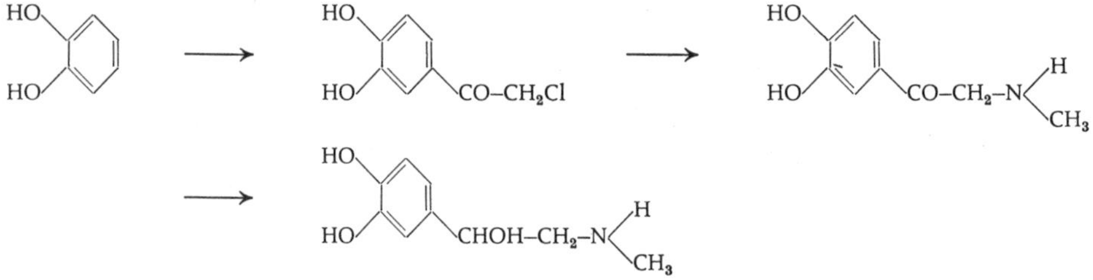

The synthetic product was only half as effective as the natural hormone since it was the racemate of adrenaline and still had to be separated into its optical isomers. This was achieved by one of Stolz's colleagues. By appropriate crystallization of the bitartrates from methanol Flächer obtained l-adrenaline. This proved in every way to be identical with the natural substance from the suprarenal gland. This was the first time that a hormone had been synthesized.

282

The management of Hoechst always considered it most important that a close link be maintained with the universities; this was certainly done by Laubenheimer, Roser and later on also by A. Ammelburg and particularly C. L. Lautenschläger. In Munich, A. Einhorn had been trying to find substitutes for cocaine. He had come across simple basic esters of p-amino-benzoic acid and finally p-amino-benzoic acid-diethylamino-ethyl ester which proved ideal as a local anaesthetic. He proposed that Hoechst undertake its large scale production. Hoechst carried out the necessary laboratory work and was able to manufacture the new preparation by 1905. It was given the trade name NOVOCAINE. Novocaine became a major product and even today, after almost 60 years, it remains one of the most important anaesthetics. With PYRAMIDONE, ADRENALINE (SUPRARENIN) and NOVOCAINE the Hoechst laboratories had established their name in the field of synthetic drugs.

In 1905 Friedländer discovered thioindigo and offered Hoechst the process.

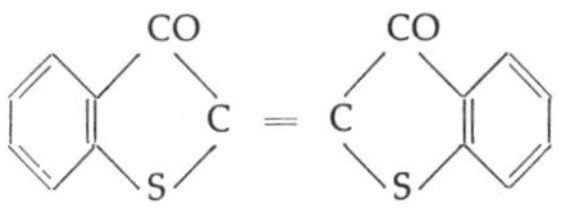

However, the importance of this new dye was not recognised at the time and Hoechst declined the offer.

Then Kalle & Co. in Biebrich acquired the process and brought the dye on the market under the name THIOINDIGO RED. The production of thioindigo is basically analogous to that of indigo; the starting material is thiosalicylic acid. This new group of dyes elicited a lively response in the research laboratories of the big firms. Numerous syntheses were made, among them the condensation of 3-oxy-1-thionaphthene with α-isatinanilide to form 2-thionaphthene-2′-indole indigo:

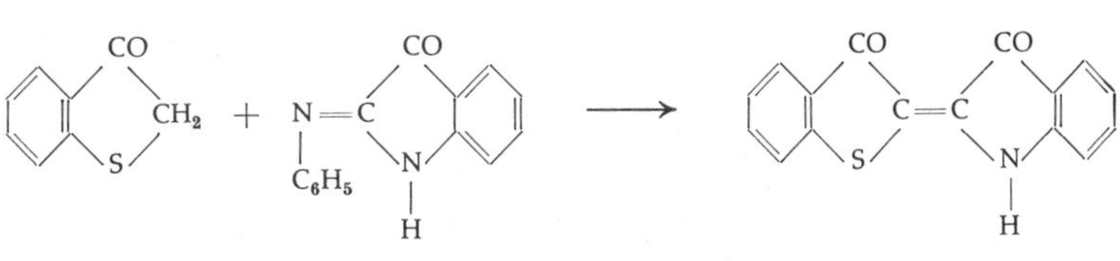

Now the aim was to widen the range of the indigo derivatives, which so far extended from blue-red to red-violet colours, to derivatives with brown, blue- and black colours.

E. Wiss, discoverer of autogenous welding

This job was tackled at Hoechst and brought great success. Two of those dyes, HELIN-DON ROSE (4,4'-dimethyl-6,6'-dichlorothioindigo) and HELINDON ORANGE (6,6'-diethoxythioindigo) became very important not only because their colours were beautiful but also remarkably fast. As indanthrene dyes they made their mark in the dyeing trade. In following years an active interest in indigoid dyes was maintained and we shall return to this later.

––––––––

Shortly after the turn of the century, E. Wiss, an engineer in Griesheim, was working with compressed hydrogen. This was delivered in steel cylinders and the gas was used to fill balloons and airships. Wiss wanted to find other uses for compressed hydrogen. He saw how the soldering shop in Griesheim laboriously produced hydrogen from zinc and sulphuric acid and then used it to solder the lead chambers for manufacturing sulphuric acid and calcium hypochlorite. It occurred to him that compressed hydrogen might be used. He constructed a torch which at first used air. Later he replaced the air with oxygen, making suitable adjustments to the torch. It was possible also to weld pieces of steel together with it. The first AUTOGENOUS WELDING TORCH had been developed.

After a patent was obtained from E. Menne, the field of autogenous cutting was developed. Unlike welding this does not involve a purely physical process (creating very high temperatures), but also a chemical reaction (oxidation of the metal).

Meanwhile a new welding process had been developed in France, using acetylene instead of hydrogen. Wiss experimented in this direction and the result was the oxyacetylene torch. The methods of welding and cutting which he developed have revolutionized metal working. The possibility of joining metals with a simple torch, using no rivets, and the striking simplicity with which it was possible to cut through steel blocks up to 1 metre thick were bound to make a considerable impact in the heavy industries.

In 1905, at a meeting of the Society of German Engineers in Frankfurt/Main, Wiss was able to present his complete process. In this lecture he also coined the term 'autogenous cutting'; he gave a demonstration in which, as he put it, «I am, so to speak, using oxygen to cut off a piece of steel plate».

Until about 1904 it was only possible to cut steel plate mechanically, a laborious and expensive process. The invention of autogenous cutting made it possible to cut the

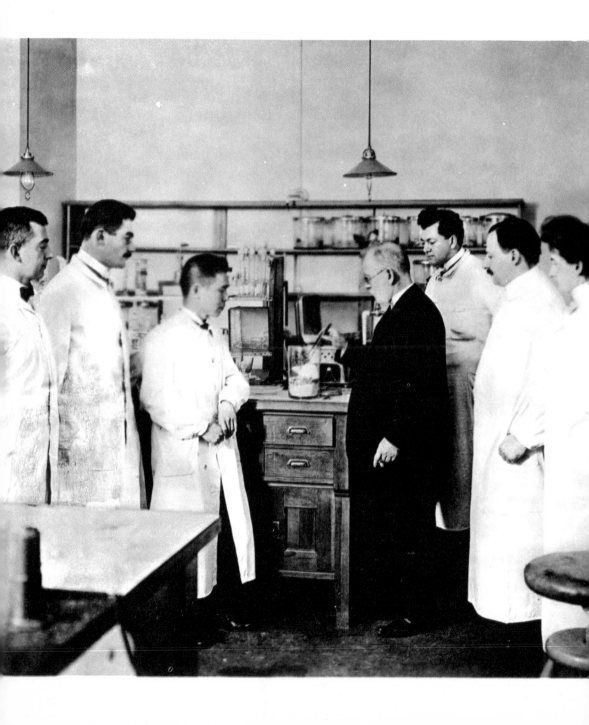

Paul Ehrlich and his collaborators

metal very quickly and right on the spot. In the early years the cutting torches were made at the Dräger works in Lübeck. At first they were experimental, but finally a practical devise was developed. By 1916 the demand had risen to such an extent that it was decided to build a special factory. Thus was the factory for welding and cutting torches etc. established in Griesheim. A laboratory was added in which the many problems arising in connection with the autogenous methods were studied. Production of commercial pure gases and the carbide industry made important progress through the impetus of the new methods.

Since 1899, P. Ehrlich had been working in Frankfurt/Main. His work laid the foundations of experimental chemotherapy. His views influenced the direction taken at the methods used in pharmacological research, and his statement «corpora non agunt, nisi fixata» became a concept which still governs scientific thinking today.

At the time, Ehrlich was chiefly working on the chemotherapy of infectious diseases caused by spirella and trypanosomes.

He found that these could be therapeutically influenced by arsenic compounds. With his colleagues, among whom L. Benda, A. Bertheim and S. Hata deserve particular mention, he synthesized a great number of arsenic compounds. The trivalent arsenic compounds were better than the pentavalent arsenic compounds, as they combined greater efficacy with fewer harmful side effects. The final result of this research effort was «Salvarsan», 3,3'-diamino-4,4'-dihydroxyarsenobenzene. Thereby Ehrlich had achieved his aim, the therapia magna sterilans. A mouse with a heretofore lethal infection could be saved with one single injection of Salvarsan.

When the experimental work at Ehrlich's laboratories had been concluded, the problem of producing the new compound on a large scale became acute. Ehrlich asked Hoechst to join him in this work.

SALVARSAN went into production in 1910. It was only five years since F. Schaudinn and E. Hoffmann had discovered the organism which caused syphilis and now this disease could be cured with Salvarsan. Shortly afterwards NEOSALVARSAN was developed, a water soluble product which made Salvarsan therapy very much simpler.

It was soon found, however, that in the production of Salvarsan it was difficult to obtain a preparation that was consistent in efficacy and toxicity. It was necessary to check each batch in animal experiments and this «government control» was carried out under Ehrlich's personal supervision at the Georg Speyer House in Frankfurt.

In addition to the danger of toxic by-products developing during various stages in the chemical process, the difficulties were mainly due to the fact that arsenobenzene solutions are colloids*).

Hoechst had to work out the most detailed procedures for every stage of production, from the quality of the starting materials to the precipitation of the final products. Only if these were precisely followed could one get preparations which Ehrlich himself might pass as «more than perfect».

To continue and extend the work on arsenic compounds, Hoechst established a special research department, the «Salvarsan laboratory». After delays due to the war, work started in 1922.

---

* Because of their colloidal properties, the structure of the arsenobenzenes is now assumed to be one of the following:

1) cyclic:

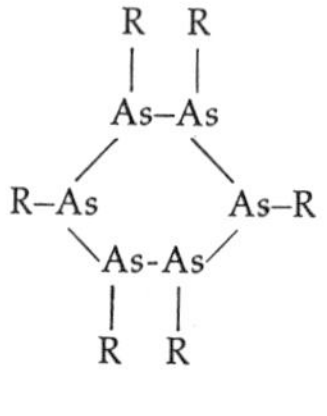

$$\begin{array}{cc} R & R \\ | & | \\ As & -As \\ \end{array}$$

R–As \qquad As–R

As-As

$$\begin{array}{cc} | & | \\ R & R \end{array}$$

2) linear:

$$HO-As-[As]_x-As-OH$$

$$\begin{array}{ccc} | & | & | \\ R & R & R \end{array}$$

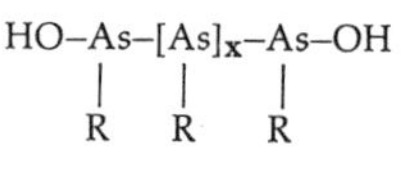

It is very probable that a mixture of the two forms in addition to monomolecular particles exists.

In addition to further development of production processes, it also became necessary to find new and better products as a result of the old patents having been lost through the Versailles Treaty.

The «Salvarsan laboratory» developed among others SOLUSALVARSAN, a stable aqueous solution for intramuscular injection with the following structure:

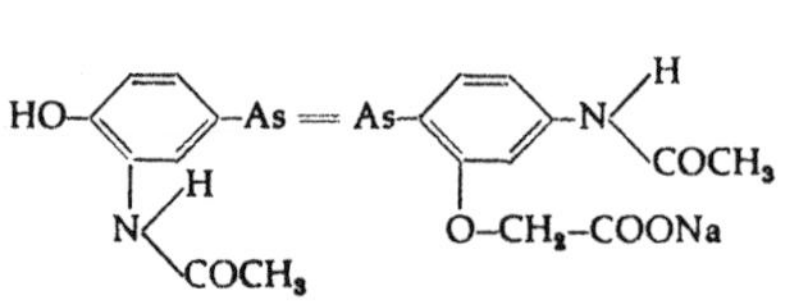

$$HO-\langle \rangle -As = As-\langle \rangle -N\begin{array}{c}H\\COCH_3\end{array}$$

$$\begin{array}{c}|\\N\\COCH_3\end{array}\begin{array}{c}H\end{array}$$

$$O-CH_2-COONa$$

and SPIROTRYPAN with the structure:

$$(CH_2OH-CHOH-CH_2)_2N$$

This too is stable in aqueous solution and suitable for intravenous administration. It has a great avidity for trypanosomes and is effective against anaplasmosis.

Finally we should mention HAEMOSEPT:

a prophylactic agent added to preserved blood, chiefly to prevent transfusion syphilis. It is effective against both gram positive and gram negative bacteria.

Work at the Salvarsan laboratory yielded interesting information on the symmetrical arsenobenzenes. If two different arylarsonic acids are reduced together, three different arsenobenzenes can be produced. Based on the equation

$$R — As = As — R + R' — As = As — R' \rightleftharpoons 2\, R — As = As — R'$$

these are in an equilibrium dependent on the temperature and the solvent used. Therefore asymmetrical arsenobenzenes are a mixture of three components whose proportions vary with the reduction process used.

The arsenic compounds have lost considerable significance with the advent of antibiotics, and research in that field has practically ceased. Nevertheless over 6,000 preparations were developed and tested chemotherapeutically, and about 250 patents were applied for to protect the results. The first director of the Salvarsan laboratory, K. Streitwolf, died in 1934 and his place was taken by W. Herrmann.

1912 also saw the production of MELUBRIN. M. Bockmühl, a pharmacist and chemist who had been working at Hoechst since 1910, had been asked to develop a pyrazolone which could be given by injection. PYRAMIDON was not suitable for parenteral use. It took 40 years until this problem was solved with the aid of special solubilizing agents.

Bockmühl then followed another route. In the production of Pyramidon, he used one of the intermediary compounds, aminoantipyrine, together with formaldehyde and sodium bisulphite to produce sodium-1-phenyl-2,3-dimethyl-5-pyrazolone-4-aminomethane-sulfonate:

$$CH_3-N \quad \overset{N}{\underset{}{\quad}} \quad CO$$

The new compound was given the trade name MELUBRIN. For many years it played an important role in the treatment of rheumatic disorders.

Interestingly enough, it was at the same time that work started on obtaining from the pancreas a preparation for the treatment of diabetes mellitus. Experiments by J. v. Mering and O. Minkowski in Breslau had laid the groundwork for this research. These two scientists had shown that it is possible to cause diabetes in animals by removing the pancreas. Because of the first world war the work had to be postponed, and it was only in 1923, after many experiments, that Hoechst were able to produce INSULIN. We shall return to this in another context.

P. Duden had been working at Hoechst since 1905. Before his appointment as head of a research department he had studied under E. Fischer and L. Knorr and for some years had been a reader at Jena university. At Hoechst he worked for a considerable time on dyestuffs and then returned to aliphatic chemistry, a subject already familiar to him from his university days. In 1912 he set two of his colleagues, O. Ernst and G. Peters, the task of producing acetaldehyde from acetylene. Acetic acid was more and more in demand as an intermediary product and Duden himself had been trying to achieve its synthesis since 1906. It was found that the use of acetaldehyde as an intermediate was the only really promising method. The solution of the problem is given in the German Patent 292 818. Acetylene gas was stirred vigorously together with a ferric sulphate solution and mercury in an aldehyde generator at 70—80 °C. The resulting gas, containing the aldehyde and water vapor, was pumped through a knock-out drum and reflux cooler, where the water was removed, and into a cooler in which the aldehyde condensed at − 15 °C. Additional acetylene was added to the remaining gas and recycled to the generator. In this way the aldehyde was removed as produced and did not have much chance to act on the mercury sulphate.

A patent dispute arose with N. Grünstein who was then working for Griesheim. This dispute was only settled when the various firms amalgamated to form the I. G. Farben company. The first pilot plant producing acetaldehyde in Hoechst started in 1914. Acquisition of a nitrogen fertilizer plant in Knapsack provided the source for the great quantities of calcium carbide needed to manufacture large amounts of acetylene. To produce acetic acid, acetaldehyde was placed in an aluminium-lined kettle fitted with an agitator, and oxygen was introduced under pressure. Lead acetate was first used as a catalyst, but later this was changed to manganese acetate. The yield was over 90% of the theoretical amount in both processes.

Acetone was initially produced using the old method of dry distillation of calcium acetate. The starting materials were crude synthetic acetic acid and the lime sludge resulting from acetylene generation. R. Leopold was in charge of the group working on these experiments.

Work also proceeded on the catalytic conversion of acetic acid to acetone. Impure cerium acetate proved to be the best catalyst. The catalytic process offered great advantages over dry distillation, and so this method was adopted. To assure production, a plant for acetaldehyde, acetic acid and acetone was built at Knapsack. During the first world war acetone was very much in demand as a gelatinizing agent for explosives and as the starting material for the production of synthetic rubber in Leverkusen. This speeded up technical development. In 1918 the journal Angewandte Chemie (Applied Chemistry) asked Duden to discuss the scheduling for the first acetic acid production. Duden's reply makes interesting reading:

«The basic fact that acetylene is converted into aldehyde via mercury compounds as intermediary products had been reported by Kutscheroff in 1884. Since then various authors had drawn attention to the problem of commercial production of alcohol and acetic acid using this reaction. H. Erdmann, for instance, had on several occasions spoken and written about this. The first patent applications on the subject appeared in 1908 (Dr. H. Wunderlich, Patent Application W. 27 177 and W. 29 233, Friedländer, vol. 9, page 55). The fact that neither this work nor that of N. Grünstein under Patent Application G. 31 034 (later, German Patent 250 356), led to large-scale production in spite of the lively interest shown by the chemical industry indicates the magnitude of the difficulties which stood in the way of finding a technically and economically satisfactory solution to the problem. It was finally achieved simultaneously and independently by Hoechst and the Dr. Wacker-Gesellschaft (the latter under licence from the Consortium für elektrochemische Industrie in Nuremberg). Both started large-scale manufacture of carbide acetic acid in 1916. The preparatory work is described in the patent specifications of Hoechst and of the Consortium. The latter have granted both the Dr. Wacker-Gesellschaft and Lonza a licence to use their process.»

About 1909 a very important invention in the field of dyestuffs was made by H. Wagner and J. Erber. A new range of pigments was discovered, giving Hoechst a leading position in this field; these were called the HANSA DYES. They are azo dyestuffs which use acetoacetanilides or pyrazolone derivatives as coupling components. For HANSA YELLOW®, for instance, 2,5-dichloroaniline is coupled with 1-phenyl-3-methylpyrazolone, and for HANSA YELLOW G 3-nitro-4-amino-toluene with acetoacetanilide. The colours in the group are generally noted for their high fastness, and their manufacture has developed on a large scale. Chemists, physicists and experts in the application of dyes worked in close co-operation and as a result it was realised that for practical use of these pigments not only their fastness, but also their physical form and the actual production process were of importance.

Brief mention should be made of another sphere of dyestuff chemistry, the sensitization of colours. This goes back as far as 1873, when H. W. Vogel used quinoline blue and other substances to sensitize photographic emulsions, optically and spectrally. The use of such cyanine dyes was limited to special cases until 1900 when E. König started a systematic study of this field and produced a whole range of sensitizers, e.g. PINA-CHROME and PINACYANOL

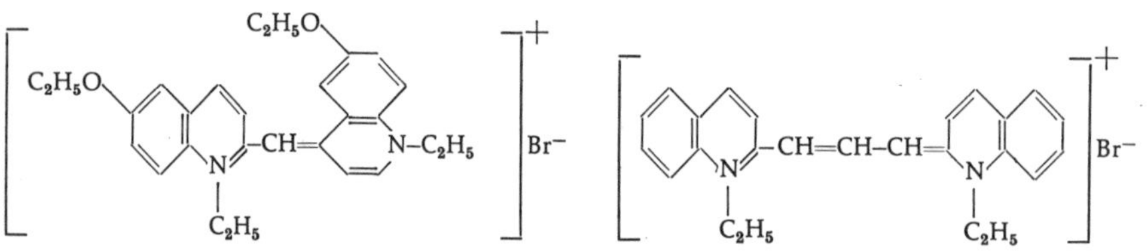

These products unquestionably enjoyed a leading position in the world market. Even in 1932 it was stated that most of the sensitizers then in use had been developed by König. Although he started mainly from quinoline and pyridine bases, various firms and institutes later extended research in this field to include many other heterocyclic compounds. Hoechst (A. Sieglitz and L. Berlin) developed sensitizers from pyrroline and tetrazole bases which achieved commercial importance, e.g.

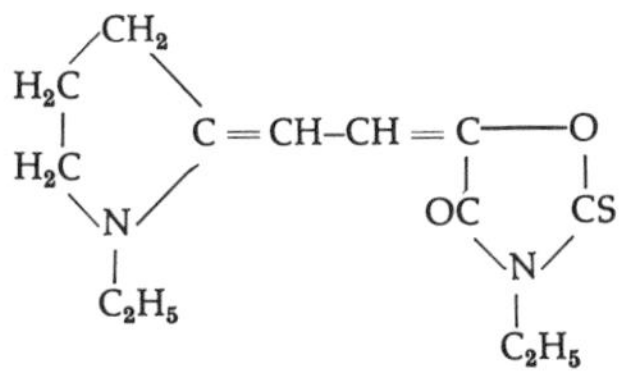

$$
\begin{array}{ccc}
H_2C\diagdown & & CH_3 \\
\quad\ \ C=CH-CH=C-O & \text{and} & N \\
H_2C\diagup & & \ \ N\ \ C=CH-CH=C-S \\
\quad N & & N \\
\quad C_2H_5 & & C_2H_5 \quad CH_3
\end{array}
$$

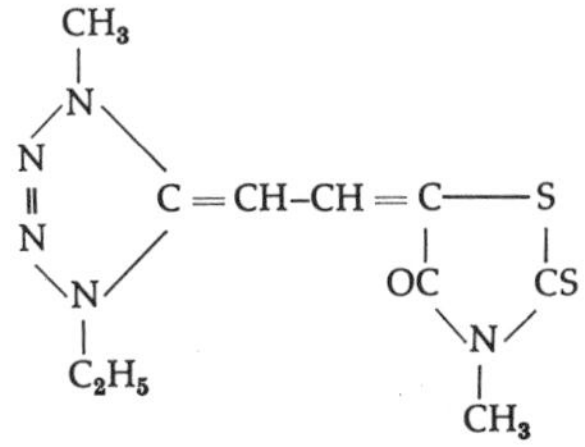

König was in contact with Lüppo-Cramer in Munich, who discovered in 1920 the phenomenon of desensitization and the fact that phenosafranine is particularly suitable for this purpose. The investigations were continued at Hoechst and led to PINAKRYPTOL GREEN, which has a similar chemical structure, and to PINAKRYPTOL YELLOW,

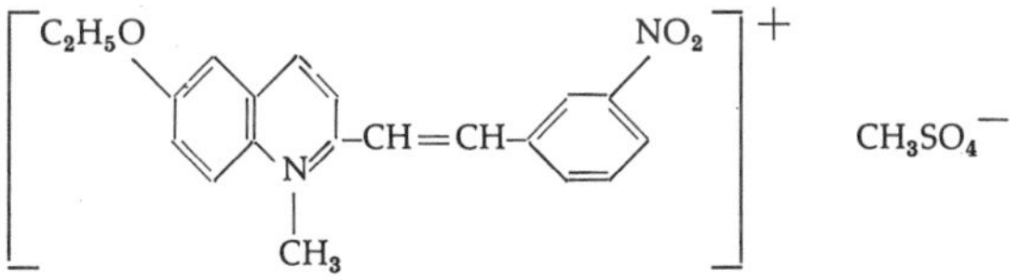

$$
\left[C_2H_5O\ \ \diagup\diagdown \ \ -CH=CH-\diagup\diagdown-NO_2 \right]^+ \quad CH_3SO_4^-
$$

which today are still two of the most important desensitizers.

Another field in colour photography involves the PINATYPE PROCESS. This was industrially developed by Hoechst chemists, particularly E. König, in collaboration with its inventor, the Frenchman Didier (1903). For many decades it was one of the best methods for producing colour prints and transparencies.

———

Hoechst also worked on the anthraquinone dyes, a field in which Elberfeld and Ludwigshafen had achieved great success. A. Schmidt and G. Kränzlein made the first major contribution with HELINDON 3 GN, the β-amino-anthraquinone derivative of urea. One very important discovery made at Hoechst (Uhlenhut, 1908) was that excellent vat dyes can be produced from α-anthrimides by caustic fusion or — as was shortly afterwards discovered — even better by fusion with aluminium chloride. These are the anthraquinone carbazoles. This knowledge was applied to differently substituted anthrimides and produced the very fast vat dyes which achieved considerable importance, among them INDANTHREN YELLOW 3 R, INDANTHREN BROWN GR, and INDANTHREN KHAKI GG which are still major products in the world market today.

Experimental dye shop at around 1900

Management realised quite early that coloristics play an important role in the application of the various dyestuff types and expanded the Coloristic Department. In 1910 A. Beil was appointed head of this department.

It is also worth mentioning that B. Homolka had found in 1902 that sodium benzylsulphanilate was a substance which would give a good dispersion of water-insoluble compounds. Known as DISSOLVING SALT B, this achieved great importance in the production of colour pastes.

Everything was done to further research in the pharmaceutical section after 1918. It was realised that a systematic search for new drugs would only be successful if pharmacological tests of the new compounds were done in close collaboration with the chemists. Even the smallest change in the molecule will often alter the mode of action of a substance. Continual discussion between medical and chemical experts was therefore absolutely essential. A pharmacological laboratory was established under K. Fromherz, and this was later followed by chemotherapeutic laboratories under R. Schnitzer and finally the parasitological laboratory under O. Wagner. Now all the conditions were met to make research really successful and also to turn towards problems of a purely biochemical nature. An excellent method was developed for obtaining protein-free extracts from the posterior lobe of the hypophysis. These were produced under the name HYPOPHYSIN. Later it became possible to split hypophysin into ORASTHIN and TONEPHIN. Orasthin proved most valuable in obstetrics, as an ecbolic, for postpartum haemorrhages and placental retention. Tonephin, the second component, is particularly indicated for diabetes insipidus.

Considerable research by many scientists was needed until 2-ethoxy-6,9-diaminoacridine could be developed by Roser. It went into production under the trade name RIVANOL. This drug has found a wide field of application, i.e. septic wounds, intestinal infections, mastitis, peritonitis, sore throats, etc.

NOVALGIN went into production in 1921. «Melubrin» was a formaldehyde bisulphite of aminoantipyrine. In Novalgin, a single methyl group was attached to the nitrogen atom. This was tremendously difficult and at first the team working under M. Bockmühl was only able to produce small quantities of the new substance:

The clinical results were so encouraging that work continued in this field, and K. Windisch worked out a simple method of producing Novalgin. Aminoantipyrine is condensed with benzaldehyde to form Schiff base, dimethylsulphate is added on, benzaldehyde split off, and the resulting methylamino-antipyrine converted with formaldehyde bisulphite. Novalgin has excellent spasmolytic and analgesic properties. It has found a wide range of uses and still plays a major role today — 40 years after its discovery — particularly in biliary and renal colic, angina pectoris, asthma etc.

At the same time F. G. Banting and Ch. H. Best in Toronto were following up an observation made by the German scientists J. v. Mering and O. Minkowski, that the pancreas played a role in diabetes mellitus. They succeeded in isolating an effective high-molecular weight protein compound from the pancreas — INSULIN. It was found to be successfull in the treatment of diabetes. At Hoechst work started on the large-scale production of insulin. In charge was C. L. Lautenschläger, who had joined Hoechst in 1920. By 1923 the laboratories had developed a process for commercial scale production of pure insulin. Year by year further improvements were made in the preparation of insulin; production continued to increase and remains one of the major activities in the pharmaceutical section today.

The work on insulin was the main occupation of the biochemical laboratories. Its preparation had been beset with difficulties and demanded considerable organisational requirements. Insulin is obtained from the pancreas of slaughtered animals. The pancreas must be deep frozen as soon as the animal is killed or the proteolytic enzymes of the gland will break down the insulin, which is a protein compound, and its activity will be lost. This is quite a difficult problem, for each individual slaughterhouse will only have a few of the glands at a time. They are collected from all the large slaughterhouses in Germany, deep frozen, and taken to Hoechst by the fastest possible route. In 1925 J. Abel and E. M. K. Geiling in Baltimore succeeded in crystallizing insulin, which previously had only been available in amorphous form. It now became essential to change production to this pure crystalline form.

Only forty years ago, diabetes was still a much dreaded disease. In some cases a balance could be maintained with a very strict diet, but diabetes did not really lose its terror until insulin was discovered. With a properly adjusted diet and regular shots of insulin the life expectancy of a diabetes patient is now almost normal.

Since insulin is a protein it can only be given parenterally, i.e. it has to be injected. Given orally, insulin is digested like any other protein and is not absorbed, so that it has no effect. In the early days of insulin a diabetic needed three injections a day on

the average; now we have delayed-action preparations so that usually one injection per day is sufficient.

Systematic research continued at Hoechst and in addition to the OLD INSULIN a number of delayed-action preparations have been developed.

In 1937 a special insulin complex was produced using SURFEN to give a clear solution without buffers. It is marketed as HOECHST DEPOT INSULIN CLEAR and satisfies all the demands which may be made upon a delayed-action insulin. It is still a major product. One year later, an INSULIN which obviously represents a precursor of natural insulin was obtained from some particularly fresh and deep frozen glands. In suspension with low molecular weight proteins of the histone class this NATIVE INSULIN has aroused considerable interest. After 1945 two further insulin preparations were added to the pharmacopoeia. To give insulin sufficient immediate effect, ordinary insulin and delayed-action insulin were combined in a proportion of 1 : 2 and the product was registered as COMB-INSULIN. Later LONG INSULIN, a suspension of ordinary insulin in amorphous and crystalline form and SURFEN salts of insulin in neutral 0.9% saline solution, achieved even greater prolongation of action.

Many attempts had been made to isolate a specific active substance, also called «heart hormone», from the hearts of mammals. Long and painstaking investigations» started in 1926 and it was found that this active substance is found not only in the heart, but in muscle tissue generally. This nucleoside preparation, containing adenosine, exhibited excellent circulatory properties and resulted in the development of our special preparation LACARNOL which is still well-regarded, particularly for angina pectoris, circulatory disturbances etc.

Apart from this biochemical research progress was also made in the development of synthetic drugs. One project which seemed particularly worth while was to study the relationships between structure and pharmacological action and find out what laws governed the mechanism of action of certain groups or radicals in a compound. These investigations have hardly brought any measurable success, and now as before the pharmacologist has to depend largely on experience. One particular approach however, which will be given in detail, led to remarkable results. If one puts the structural formula of adrenaline, the hormone from the adrenal gland, side by side with that of ephedrine, which is synthesized by plants only, two things strike one at once: the characteristic position of the methylamino group and the specific differences in the two structures.

HO—[benzene ring]—CHOH–CH$_2$
HO—   HNCH$_3$

and

[benzene ring]—CHOH–CH–CH$_3$
                HNCH$_3$

Here was an intriguing problem for the synthetic chemist: to try to achieve something which nature does not do — build a bridge between the two substances.

This train of thought led to the production of a number of substances in the thirties, some changing ephedrine in the direction of adrenaline and some vice versa. Without going into details about their synthesis, we shall just mention a number of products which were developed at that time and proved to be of pharmacological interest.

p-hydroxyephedrine was marketed as SUPRIFEN, a circulatory tonic, and later in combination with Lacarnol as CARNIGEN; m-hydroxyephedrine gained some importance as ICORAL.

3,4-dihydroxynorephedrine, CORBASIL, has excellent properties, so that it can replace adrenaline, chiefly in dentistry.

3,4-dihydroxynorephedrine has properties similar to adrenaline but is much longer acting. It has therefore become a valuable component in preparations like ASPASAN. Hoechst therefore became not only the birthplace of the first synthetic hormone, ADRENALINE, but also the producer of other compounds which formed a valuable addition to the group of circulatory remedies.

In the twenties, two Englishmen, O. Rosenheim and H. King, established a new formula for the steroids. Now the relationships between the many steroids, like vitamin D, sex hormones, adrenocortical hormones, cardiac glycosides and others, became extraordinarily clear and simple. A. Butenandt, a student of A. Windaus, demonstrated that the follicular hormone, also called the primary female hormone, is one of the steroids and can be formulated accordingly.

The second female hormone, progesterone, also belongs to this group.

CH$_3$
CH$_3$—[steroid ring structure]—CO–CH$_3$
O=

These structural formulae were so simple and clear that synthesis was the obvious next step, especially since it was very difficult to produce these substances from the hormone, or the corpora lutea. Many laboratories, in industry as well as at the universities, were working hard at this task. Teams were formed so that the goal might be reached more quickly. Workers at the pharmaceutical research laboratories in Hoechst first tried to achieve the partial synthesis of progesterone. One team, working under G. Erhardt, discovered a very neat new process which permits the production of progesterone in any amount desired. This was called LUTREN. The hormones of the adrenal cortex also belong to the large class of steroids. At that time, 4-pregnene-21-ol-3,20-dione, or desoxycorticosterone, aroused particular interest. This is important for the treatment of Addison's disease, orthostatic hypotonia etc. Here again, the Hoechst group succeeded in evolving a semi-synthetic method of production, independent of other laboratories. Later it was possible to simplify the method further. Desoxycorticosterone acetate, briefly called «Doca» in the literature, was registered as CORTENIL and made a very successful addition to the Hoechst range of steroids.

Research in the field of analgesics, the pain-killing substances, is traditional at Hoechst. Among the mild to medium analgesics produced were PYRAMIDON, MELUBRIN, NOVALGIN and others. But Hoechst also particularly desired to enter the field of what are called the heavy analgesics, with an action as powerful as that of morphine. Many reports were available in the literature which concerned attempts to imitate the structure of morphine using the phenanthrene skeleton. But none had been successful. Shorly before world war II two teams working at Hoechst solved the problem. O. Eisleb produced a compound, 1-methyl-4-phenylpiperidine-4-carboxylic acid ethyl ester, which was called DOLANTIN. O. Schaumann carried out the pharmacological tests and found that in addition to its powerful analgesic action the drug was also an excellent spasmolytic.

Dolantin has many advantages over morphine; it has become indispensable, particularly for the alleviation of spasmic pain.

At the same time, research went on in another direction, as mentioned above. This will be reported later.

In 1909, the laboratories at the Oehler Works of Chemische Fabrik Griesheim Elektron, now the Offenbach works of Farbwerke Hoechst AG., started on a line of research which led to the discovery of compounds now world famous as the NAPHTOL AS products. At the time, the scientists were investigating azo dyes which contained 2-hydroxy-3-naphthoic acid as one coupling component. Unfortunately these dyes changed shade if they were mixed with varnish in the presence of aluminium hydroxide. They were therefore of no commercial use. L. Laska and A. Zitscher discovered the reason for this: the free carboxyl group of 2-hydroxy-3-naphthoic acid prevents the formation of stable aluminium laquers. Therefore functional derivatives of 2-hydroxy-3-naphthoic acid were evolved, and the anilide, «Naphtol AS», was found particularly suitable for the production of brilliant pigments which were very fast indeed:

Naphtol AS

The tests showed that NAPHTOL AS had a certain affinity for cotton, in contrast to β-naphthol which had so far been used for the Para colours. Dyes produced by the same method as the Para dyes were outstanding in their fastness. This laid the foundations for «Naphtol AS» dyeing. The invention brought a tremendous new impetus to both printing and dyeing.

Fibres treated with Naphtol AS and developed with various diazonium compounds give strong, bright colours very fast to light and washing. In the course of time the number of naphtols and diazonium salts was increased, and stable diazo compounds which were safe to handle were developed. Hoechst played a considerable role in this field with the discovery of the FAST RED TR BASE, NAPHTOL AS-TR and the VARIAMINE BLUE range which made Variamine blue resist printing possible.

After the first world war pure research on dyes was gradually transferred to the alizarine laboratories which were directed by G. Kränzlein. First of all, A. Schmidt and his team made another intensive study of the thioindigo derivatives, both symmetrical and asymmetrical types (see page 283). Some of these dyes were so that they were included in the Indanthren range which had been developed in the meantime. The name HELINDON dyes was used only for wool vat dyes. By the end of the twenties, it appeared that the whole indigo field had been thoroughly covered; and work in this field was considered concluded. One major step forward came in 1924. Two Alsacian chemists, M. Bader and Ch. Sunder, made an invention which was acquired by Durand and Huguenin in Basle. This process changed the leuco vat dyes into the water soluble salts of their disulphates. Originally called INDIGOSOL dyes — and now ANTHRASOL dyes — these had tremendous advantages for printing applications. A contract with Durand and Huguenin brought in Hoechst, and the process was fully developed for large-scale production and application.

At that time a green was developed in England which surprised dyestuff chemistry (green always being the biggest problem in that field). This was CALEDON JADE GREEN. K. Schirmacher and K. Zahn were able to clarify the structure of this green vat dye by synthesis and found it to be benzene-2,2'-dimethoxy-dibenzanthrone. They developed a new process for producing benzene-2-methoxy-benzanthrone and converting this to the green vat dye by caustic fusion. This evoked tremendous interest in the whole field of dibenzanthrones. R. Scholl in Dresden had succeeded in fusing 1,4-dibenzoyl-naphthalene with aluminium chloride and producing 4,5,8,9-dibenzpyrene-3,10-quinone. But he could not achieve ring closure of 1,5-dibenzoyl-naphthalene which would have led to 3,4,8,9-dibenzpyrene-5,10-quinone.

In 1922, G. Kränzlein, M. Corell and R. Sedlmayer found that the fusion of benzene-1-benzoyl-benzanthrone with aluminium chloride produced a golden yellow vat dye which does have the 5,10-quinone structure:

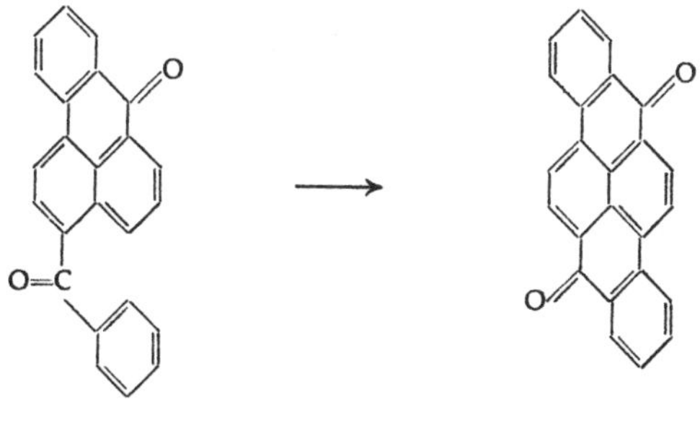

At first this reaction yielded only traces of the dye. It is a tribute to R. Sedlmayer's perseverance and ability that he finally managed to develop it on an industrial scale. The dye was marketed as INDANTHREN GOLDEN YELLOW GK. Shortly afterwards, F. Maier and A. Wolfram achieved the ring closure of 1,5-dibenzoyl naphthalene and thus showed a very simple and economical method of producing the vat dye.

303

Halogenation of the basic substance produced further commercial dyes in this series. The dibromo compound, INDANTHREN GOLDEN YELLOW RK, became the most valuable of the dibenzpyrenequinones and achieved considerable importance.

In 1924, W. Eckert and H. Greune developed a new type of vat dyes. Condensation of 1,4,5,8-naphthalene-tetracarboxylic acid with aromatic o-diamines produces imidazole derivatives, exceptionally bright vat dyes which are very fast.

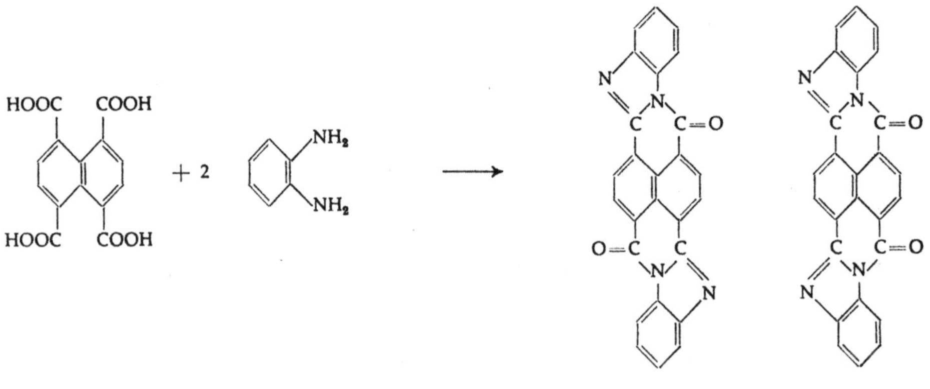

trans   cis

The naphthalene tetracarbonic acid needed for this reaction was soon obtained by a simple method from acenaphthene. This meant that the first commercial dyes of the series could go into production:

INDANTHREN SCARLET GG

INDANTHREN PRINTING BROWN B

INDANTHREN PRINTING BROWN 5R.

Later it became possible to obtain the pure cis- and trans-forms shown in the above formula by separating the isomers. This method produced the most beautiful and important colour in the series, IDANTHREN BRILLIANT ORANGE GR (trans-form), and INDANTHREN BORDO RR.

Trying to find a use for by-product carbazole, H. Greune found that if 3-amino-N-ethyl-carbazole was condensed with chloranil and the product of this reaction heated in nitrobenzene, one obtained a compound which was later discovered to be dioxazine:

304

Autogenous cutting,
photoelectrically controlled

Laboratory-scale dyeing of polyester fibres with Samaron dyestuffs

Dioxazine is a valuable violet pigment of great brilliance, very fast to light and to solvents. At first its dispersion presented difficulties and commercial production only became possible at a later stage. These dyes were then marketed as PERMANENT VIOLET RL and PV FAST VIOLET BL.

Sulphonated products of this dioxazine are valuable dyes. In aqueous solution these dye not only wool and silk a very fast blue but also cellulose and viscose. Successful results stimulated further research and other aromatic bases were used to form the corresponding dioxazines. 3-aminocarbazole, 2-aminofluorene, 3-aminopyrene, 4-amino-diphenyl-amino-2-sulphonic acid and 4-amino-4'-chlorodiphenyl-amino-2-sulphonic acid were used to develop a series of dyes which were marketed as SIRIUS SUPRA dyestuffs and are still well known today as REMASTRAL dyestuffs.

At this time, A. Wolfram discovered the INDANTHREN wet process and no effort was spared to develop this fully. The process consists in converting acetylaminoanthraquinone, for instance, into the disulphate of the leuco compound, saponification of the acetyl group, and subsequent alkaline oxidation. Two amines combine to form the tetrasulphuric acid ester of leuco indanthrenazine:

From this, INDANTHREN BLUE RS is easily produced in water at room temperature.

This process was later to achieve considerable importance in the production of ANTHRASOL BLUE IBC.

Another discovery made between 1926 and 1929 was that of the benzanthrone pyrazol-anthrone dyes by K. Wilke and his team. Condensation of benzene 1-bromobenzan-throne with pyrazolanthrone and subsequent caustic fusion produced the simplest compound in this series, INDANTHREN MARINE BLUE R. This was followed by INDANTHREN GREY M and MG, colours which were so outstandingly fast to light as well as to other influences that they found extensive application. They are still of commercial importance today.

At that time, the tar industry was beginning to produce larger quantities of pyrene. In-tensive research on this substance yielded valuable results. The chemistry of pyrene and its derivatives were fully established. And these studies, chiefly the work of H. Voll-mann and his team, also brought new knowledge applicable in the synthesis of dyes, and we shall quote just a few of the results.

Halogenated pyrenequinones can be converted with aromatic bases to produce green vat dyes. One of these, the leuco sulphuric acid ester, has been marketed as ANTHRA-SOL GREEN 13 G. The condensation of pyrene with benzoylchloride in the presence of a Friedel-Crafts catalyst is a very simple method of producing pyranthrone.

A method was also found of obtaining a very pure form of 1,4,5,8-naphthalene-tetracar-boxylic acid through the oxidation of halogenated pyrenes.

In the field of acid wool dyes, Hoechst made an important contribution through work on the products obtained by converting 1-amino-4-bromo-anthraquinone-2-sulphonic acid, the so-called bromaminic acid, with aromatic bases. Agfa had succeeded in 1913 in producing a blue wool dye by converting bromaminic acid with aniline, but this dye had attracted no attention. But the studies at Hoechst showed that a very pure, cornflower blue dye can be obtained by this method, which was even faster than the famous ALIZARIN SAPPHIROL B, and particularly fast to perspiration. By arrangement with Agfa, Hoechst adopted the process and marketed the dye as ALIZARIN SAPPHIROL A. This and other products, of which we shall only mention ALIZARIN DIRECT BLUE A2G, ANTHRALAN BLUE FR and SUPRANOL BRILLIANT BLUE G, provided the wool dyeing industry with colours which had considerable appeal because of their clear shades and excellent general fastness, above all great fastness to light.

In 1930, a line of research started which had the aim of introducing the trifluoromethyl side chain in Naphtol AS dyes. The experimental difficulties were tremendous. The conversion reaction with hydrofluoric acid presented major problems. The trifluoromethyl group shifts the colour toward yellow and at the same time brightens the shade, improves fastness to light and dischargeability. For instance, the base 1-amino-5-trifluoromethyl-2-ethylsulphonyl-benzene

coupled with Naphtol AS gives shades which are rather more yellow. As FAST GOLDEN ORANGE GR BASE, it still is of commercial importance today. Brightening of the shade through the CF_3 constituent is also exhibited by the anthraquinone dyes. One example is INDANTHREN PRINTING BLUE HFG. These two examples may suffice to show the importance of the CF_3 group in dyestuffs chemistry.

Considerable other research work was carried out at the former Alizarin Laboratory, which was renamed Central Laboratory in 1938. With the approach of 1939 and the second world war, research had to take second place to production problems and was only resumed after 1945.

What went on in the Catalytic Laboratory after the end of the first world war? At that time it was directed by O. Ernst, very much a pure scientist, who was working on aliphatic chemistry, particularly with acetylene. However another subject claimed prime attention, namely the chlorination of methane. The intention was to produce methanol, which was in very short supply, from methyl chloride. This approach was abandoned when it became known that BASF had succeeded in getting very good yields of methanol by hydrogenation of carbon monoxide under pressure. All that remained which was of value was direct chlorination. The methane used for chlorination had originally been obtained from water gas. Then Ernst used coal gas and this made the process much cheaper. O. Ernst, O. Nicodemus, W. Pfaffendorf and later K. Möller advanced the methane chlorination so greatly that all the products of chlorination — methyl chloride (chloromethane), methylene chloride, chloroform and carbon tetrachloride — were obtained in high yields and could be separated by destillation at low temperatures.

The products of methane chlorination have become very important as the starting materials for fluorinated hydrocarbons under our FRIGEN trademark. Using hydrogen fluoride and catalysts, 1 to 3 chlorine atoms can be replaced by fluorine in both chloroform and carbon tetrachloride. These fluorinated hydrocarbons are non-irritant, non-toxic and non-flammable and do not explode when mixed with air in any proportion. They were used as safety refrigerants. A licence was obtained from Kinetic Chemicals. The production process is our own. After 1945 the various Frigen products enjoyed a wider field of application. Their chemical and physiological properties make them particularly suitable propellants for aerosols.

After the end of the first world war, a considerable surplus of acetic acid was available. For this a use had to be found. Acetic acid could of course be used directly in production of vinegar and sodium acetate and for latex coagulation etc. But these did not use up the huge quantities available. The building trade and the manufacture of consumer goods began to flourish. There was great demand for nitrocellulose lacquers but their production was held up for lack of a solvent with medium boiling point. Using a mixture of butyl acetate and butanol, it was possible to develop a product which equalled amyl acetate for use in lacquer.

This consumed large quantities of acetaldehyde and acetic acid. Processes were also developed for the production of crotonaldehyde, methyl acetate and ethyl acetate so that the lacquer industry was offered a whole range of solvents. The depression was now giving way to a steady upward trend and the Catalytic Laboratory was fully occupied with production processes. Only in 1931 did the developing economic crisis make itself felt, and solvent production, one of the major projects, was heavily affected. When O. Ernst left in 1931, O. Nicodemus became the director of the Catalytic Laboratory.

Towards the end of the twenties I.G. Farbenindustrie started with production of synthetic rubber. Butadiene was the starting material for this and Hoechst used two processes to obtain it:

Starting from acetaldehyde, through aldol and 1,3-butylene glycol, butadiene was obtained by the elimination of water. Together with the commercial processes developed in Ludwigshafen, this method formed the basis for the production of Buna, the synthetic rubber made by I.G. Farbenindustrie.

The other method of producing butadiene by partial hydrogenation of vinylacetylene obtained by dimerization of acetylene did not reach the production stage. But Nieuwland had discovered that chloroprene is formed on addition of hydrochloric acid to vinylacetylene, and this method gave good results. The addition of water on vinylacetylene produced vinyl methyl ketone, which is capable of polymerization and co-polymerization. For a time this was of interest in the production of Buna K.N.P.

A process of economic importance was developed by J. Lösch and his colleagues in Knapsack in 1933. This was the production of acetic anhydride as a co-product with acetic acid in the presence of copper- and cobalt acetate as catalysts. The process was based on the observation that the crude acetic acid produced by the conventional catalytic oxidation of acetaldehyde always contained some acetic anhydride as well as water. This is now one of the most commonly used anhydride processes.

The great shortage of fats and oils and therefore of glycerol as well made its synthesis a worth while project. In 1927, G. Ehrhart and W. Krohs had hydrogenated carbohydrates and split the six-carbon chain into three-carbon chains to obtain a mixture of glycerol, propylene glycol and propanediol. W. Gädke very quickly converted this into a continuous process, particularly for use with invert sugar, and added calcium carbonate to neutralize the acids to obtain a mixture of the above-mentioned higher alcohols together with 25% of hexatol. This mixture could be used instead of glycerol for most purposes, e.g. as an additive to hydraulic fluids, for cosmetics, dressing media, printer's ink, marking ink and so on. Called GLYCEROGEN, this product became very important in the years up to 1939 and during the second world war.

One of the major research projects carried out in the Catalytic Laboratory was the production of vinyl acetate which was already planned in the twenties. Hoechst adopted a process from Griesheim and developed it into a recycle process using a reaction tower in which acetylene gas was passed into acetic acid to which mercuric oxide had been added. In the early thirties, Hoechst had made various improvements. Then large scale production became urgent and it had to be decided whether the Hoechst process or one developed by the Wacker GmbH should be used. In the latter process, acetic acid was added to acetylene in a catalytic reactor. The Hoechst process used mercury and its regeneration was complicated. It was therefore decided to take out a licence from Wacker. An important step forward came with the discovery that the reaction proceeded much faster with suitable heat absorption (e.g. in a Fischer reactor).

Following a suggestion made by P. Duden and utilizing the work which F. Klatte had accomplished on vinyl chloride and vinyl chloroacetate around 1913 in Griesheim, A. Voss took up the polymerization of vinyl compounds in 1926 while working in the laboratory directed by G. Kränzlein and in close collaboration with H. Staudinger in Freiburg. At first he concentrated on the homo- and copolymerization of vinyl acetate, the saponification of polyvinyl acetate to form polyvinyl alcohol and reactions involving polyvinyl alcohol and vinyl chloride polymerization.

The Griesheim process for polymerization of organic vinyl esters — initial polymerization in a stirred vessel by heating in the presence of peroxides as activators and subsequent completion of polymerization through exposure to light in glass tubes — was not very satisfactory from the practical point of view and had to be limited to small charges because dissipation of the heat of polymerization was poor. A. Voss and his team introduced a new process in 1928 which permitted production on an industrial scale. The monomer-peroxide solution was fed into a heated cylindrical vessel, more was added in accordance with the rate of polymerization, and the polymerization heat was removed by autoevaporation of the monomer which then condensed in a reflux condenser. By control of operating variables, such as the concentration of activators, modifiers and chain-transfer agents which affect the rate of polymerization, it became possible to develop a broad range of rigid MOWILITH products. The use of specific peroxides greatly broadened the range of product types.

Finaly a continuous process for the large scale polymerization of vinyl acetate was worked out and production started.

The new experience which had been gained could also be applied to the polymerization of vinyl chloride.

While Voss' team was working on copolymerization, they made the interesting discovery that individually non-polymerisable unsaturated compounds are capable of forming mixed polymers.

For instance, mixed polymerization of vinyl compounds with maleic anhydride or crotonic acid produced polymers soluble in aqueous alkaline solutions. These special-purpose products were marketed as POVIMAL and MOWILITH CT5.

Following some work done by Wacker GmbH, a method of producing polyvinyl alcohol by transesterification of Mowilith with methanol in the presence of acidic or alkaline catalysts was developed. This polyvinyl alcohol, known as VINAROL and MOWIOL, has many uses, e.g. for sizing rayon, in the production of hydrocarbon-resistant tubing and water-soluble films, and as a protective colloid for emulsion use, etc.

Polyvinyl alcohol reacts with aldehydes to form acetals which have a ring structure:

$$-CH_2-CH-CH_2-CH-CH_2- \quad + CH_3-CHO \longrightarrow \quad -CH_2-CH-CH_2-CH-CH_2-$$

These acetals, marketed as the MOWITAL series, are used in lacquers, and in combination with plasticizers for the intermediate layer in safety glass. Polyvinyl acetate in the form of stable, highly concentrated aqueous dispersions, was widely used in paints and adhesives, with polyvinyl alcohol as a protective colloid. The copolymerization of vinyl acetate with vinyl chloride and acrylic ester produced new Mowilith dispersions for specific purposes. Polymerization with special compounds, such as vinyl sulphonic acid, gave some interesting dispersions.

A decisive step forward in the field of polymerization came when the possibilities of redox activation of unsaturated systems became known. Work carried out at Hoechst, but also at Leverkusen und Ludwigshafen, demonstrated that molecular oxygen inhibits the polymerization of vinyl compounds induced by peroxides, and that the addition of reducing agents will activate it. It was found that the alternate use of oxidation and reducing agents sped up polymerization enormously and that this effect was increased further in the presence of certain metal compounds.

This method of metal redox activation permitted speedy production, at low temperatures and with good yields, of materials with a high degree of polymerization and with improved applications properties. The process found large-scale use in the production of COLD RUBBER.

So far only pure research has been described and nothing has been said of the tremendous difficulties which arise when a product apparently well developed at the laboratory level is to be manufactured on a large scale. It became more and more obvious that the problems which arose required the help of specially trained engineers. At that time, F. Jähne was chief works engineer at Hoechst. He was aware of that situation and started a development group. S. Kiesskalt was appointed the director of this group which began work on developing a technical basis for the application of engineering to production processes. The research was extended into physical chemistry and physics and in 1936 Hoechst organised these efforts into a Process Engineering Department which is now recognised as a specific venture in the field of technology.

Hoechst worked closely with a process group which had at that time been formed within the Association of German Engineers and to which A. Eucken and his students made successful contributions in the field of physical chemistry. Together they systematically developed specialist training and emphasized the importance of this field in teaching and research. During the last decade the increased use of mathematics together with all its recent auxiliary developments has made process engineering an indispensable ally which now plays an important role in all technical developments at Hoechst.

————————

In the laboratories of the Kalle Co. intensive work had been done since 1923 on compounds used in reproduction processes. It had been known for a long time that the diazo compounds are light-sensitive and there had been many attempts to use them for reproduction.

G. Kögel of Karlsruhe University had suggested the use of stable, slow-reacting diazo compounds of the diazoanhydride group (quinone diazides), which fade when exposed to light, in combination with coupling compounds to develop positive copying papers. This process found its practical application in OZALID paper. The exposed copies are developed with ammonia gas.

The quality of the papers was considerable improved by selecting suitable diazoanhydrides of the naphthalene series, the use of appropriate coupling compounds and discovery of stabilizers and agents to prevent fading. Further commercial success came with the design of suitable developing apparatus and combined exposing and developing machines.

The original Ozalid papers had reddish to maroon tones. The diazo anhydrides did not produce blue or black prints. These were achieved by using p-aminodiazo compounds and p-acylaminodiazo compounds of the benzene series. Much work was done to find the best diazo and coupling compounds. Apart from those with blue tones, coupling compounds giving yellow tones were very important. These are used to obtain black prints and for the production of ultra-violet light absorbing masters for further prints. The diazoanhydrides and p-aminodiazo compounds absorb light in the visible short-wave and ultra-violet long-wave regions of the spectrum. The o-aminodiazo compounds were found to absorb longer wave bands. They are used in combination with p-aminodiazo compounds to produce Kalle's TWO-COLOUR PAPER with which two-colour copies can be made. After the second world war, the light-sensitivity of aminodiazo compounds was considerably increased by introduction of new substituents.

Due to their light-sensitive properties the diazo compounds also found use in the production of pre-sensitized plates for the photomechanical production of printing blocks. Kalle's research laboratories found some diazo compounds which proved particularly suitable for this purpose. Older methods using bichromate as the light-sensitive substance were thus superseded.

Kalle's pre-coated OZASOL printing plates are getting more and more popular because their quality is good and they are simple to use.

The invention of electrophotography, which makes use of the photoconductivity of certain substances, seemed to open up a promising new field. Work was done with zinc oxide layers and organic photo semiconductors. Quite a number of these were synthesized. The first fruit of those labours is the ELFASOL electrophotographic offset printing plate. It is very much more light-sensitive than the Ozasol plates and therefore suitable for optical enlargement and reduction and for direct electrophotography of the original. Work in this field continues and is one of the major scientific research projects in the Kalle laboratories.

———————

When industry turned its attention to plant protection, only a few active agents were in practical use, such as blue vitriol, mercury chloride and formaldehyde against phytopathogenic fungi, Schweinfurt green, tobacco extract and Pyrethrum flowers to combat insects, and sulphur to combat mildew fungi and spider mites. The prime research goal was to relieve the user of the often inefficient and tedious job of preparing these media sometimes using poisonous materials, and instead to give him ready prepared and reliable commercially-available materials. Another aim was to find new active substances. A. Steindorff and K. Pfaff were put in charge of the laboratories which were to do this research. They had their first success in improving the chemical disinfection of grain seed using organic arsenic compounds. Large amounts of these compounds were available from the Salvarsan laboratory.

Bordeaux mixture was the only effective remedy against fungoid diseases in vineyards and orchards. The grower had to prepare this himself by mixing blue vitriol with milk of lime. Hoechst's efforts in this field produced a series of useful proprietary products and in the end it was possible to formulate powders bases on copper oxides or copper oxychlorides which could be mixed with water to give neutral solutions for spraying. NOSPRASIT (1923), which treats grapevines and fruit trees against both fungi and insect pests, contains calcium arsenate as an insecticide.

The use of arsenic and nicotine against insect pests had become absolutely essential if the German vineyards were to be saved from becoming uneconomic. There were objections from the health point of view and nontoxic substitutes were urgently needed. A great number of compounds, most of them organic, were synthesized and tested for their insecticidal action.

M. Erlenbach found that 1,3,6,8-tetranitrocarbazole was extremely effective against herbivorous insects. The new preparation was called NIROSAN. It superseded all the arsenic preparations so far used in German vineyards and since 1942 these have been officially banned in Germany. Nirosan is effective against all the major vineyard pests, has no adverse effect on human health, on domestic animals or bees, and no negative influence on grapes or wine.

At about the same time discovery was made of two contact insecticides based on phenyldiazopiperidine and phenyldiazopyrrolidine.

As Nirosan had shown, toxicity to insects and to warm-blooded animals do not necessarily go hand in hand. This gave new impetus to research.

In their search for safe substances to be used in agriculture Hoechst also developed synthetic fungicides. A group of benzene chlorination and nitration products (BRASSICOL, BRASSISAN, BULBOSAN) proved outstanding in the treatment of certain vegetable diseases and produced TRITISAN, a mercury-free protective agent for wheat. Rhodandinitrobenzene (NIRIT) became a medium for spraying fruit trees, replacing the copper compounds previously used which were apt to damage the trees. It is used for treating scab and is not toxic to bees so that it may also be used during the blossom period.

After the second world war, hexachloro-bicyclohepetene-bihydroxide-methylene sulphite (THIODAN) was developed. This insecticide differs from the large group of insecticidal chlorinated hydrocarbons in one sulphur radical in the molecule. The preparation is effective against many plant-eating and sucking pests which effect widely different plants all over the world. For such a powerful insecticide it has the rare advantage that it does not harm bees or other useful insects.

One of the latest proprietary products against plant pests is dinitrobutylphenol-dimethylacrylic acid ester (ACRICID). This is effective against both spider mites and mildew fungi.

When the second world war had come to an end, research seemed in a hopeless position. It took years until systematic work became possible again. Pharmaceutical research was the first to be resumed.

There were problems which could only be solved by intensive research. Many slaughterhouses in the big cities had lost their cold storage facilities. This endangered Hoechst's supplies of pancreas glands for insulin production. But Hoechst discovered that if the glands are processed immediately at the slaughterhouse with dehydrating agents, e.g. anhydrous sodium sulphate, fermentation even at normal temperatures will be retarded for some time so that the pancreas can still be used for insulin production. This coped with the most immediate problem and diabetics could be given insulin, though it had to be strictly rationed.

M. Bockmühl died in 1949 and G. Ehrhart became the director of the whole pharmaceutical research section. There was far from sufficient space for the work that had to be carried out, and new research buildings were erected as circumstances permitted. The new Paul Ehrlich Laboratory was reserved for pharmacological and biochemical research and new extensions were built for synthetic chemicals and biologicals.

Towards the end of the war, C. L. Lautenschläger had asked the research department to work on the production of penicillin which had just then become known. L. Pasteur had said in 1877: «Among the lower organisms, more so than among the higher animals and plants, life is destroyed by life.» In 1928 A. Fleming in England was able to produce a very good illustration of this. He was growing staphylococcus aureus in Petri dishes and found that in a culture contaminated with moulds, a clear area had developed around the mould colony. This mould obviously inhibited the growth of the cocci and he managed to grow them in a pure culture and identify them. It is

Crystals of sodium penicillin, magnified about 300 times

a strain of penicillium which has been named «penicillium notatum Westling». A large team of leading English scientists worked at Oxford under E. B. Chain and H. W. Florey to isolate the active substance. They succeeded in obtaining this substance, «penicillin», and in establishing its structure.

At Hoechst, work was done with various moulds. Some of the substances were already quite effective. A painstaking search produced one strain of cocci, staphylococcus aureus, which always showed the same sensitivity to penicillin and this could be used to standardize penicillin preparations.

Production on a laboratory scale was now possible to give a preparation which was still not pure but of low toxicity. Work had to be interrupted for a time in 1945 when Hoechst was occupied by American troops. But this was only for a few months. The military government gave the penicillin laboratories a thorough inspection and then permitted production to continue.

The necessary raw materials, apparatus and particularly glassware became more and more difficult to get, but in 1946 the first proprietary product, a PENICILLIN POWDER, went on the market. Later Hoechst worked together with an American firm, Merck, in Rahway. They let Hoechst have a highly productive strain of the mould and furnished technical advice for modern large-scale manufacture. Large microbiological laboratories were also established to maintain production control.

The discovery that the metabolic products of lower organisms can be such effective agents opened up a whole new field of research. A separate department was now added to the biological laboratories, with the aim of discovering new strains from which antibiotics might be won. The biggest sources are streptomycetes, which are easily isolated from soil. About 1,500 antibiotic-producing streptomyces strains are isolated each year from about 15,000 soil samples. About 750 are studied in more detail. Interesting substances and groups of substances have been found. Mutation of known strains, e.g. with X-rays, produced different metabolic products or increased the yield.

One antibiotic which had a particularly interesting structure was chloramphenicol

$$O_2N-\langle\!=\!\rangle-\overset{\overset{\displaystyle H}{|}}{\underset{\underset{\displaystyle OH}{|}}{C}}-\overset{\overset{\displaystyle NHCOCHCl_2}{|}}{\underset{\underset{\displaystyle H}{|}}{C}}-CH_2OH$$

which was discovered by American scientists and which showed for the first time that nitro group as well as the dichloroacetic group exist in nature. No one had expected this.

The structure of chloramphenicol is relatively simple and shows certain similarities to ephedrine. This suggested that synthesis should be possible. To go into details would go too far. At Hoechst, G. Ehrhart and his colleagues found a method of producing chloramphenicol on a large scale with very good yields and this was given an American firm.

One group of antibiotics, the tetracyclines, have the following basic formula:

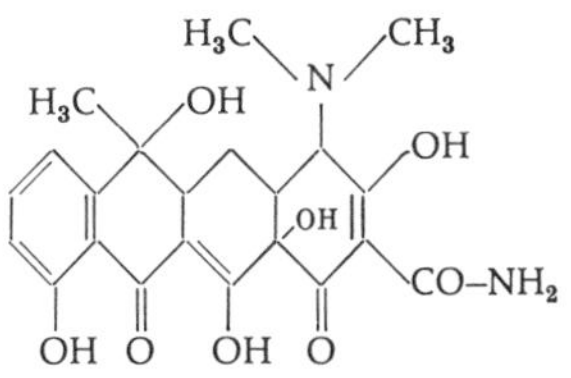

Since the antibiotic tetracyclines, due to their free basic radicals, are difficult to save in water in the physiological pH range, they were therefore mostly used in oral therapy. No satisfactory way of producing injectable preparations of the tetracyclines themselves could be found. It was therefore necessary to change the tetracycline molecule in such a way that it became more easily water soluble. An interesting problem. Aminomethylation (Mannich reaction) produced pyrrolidinomethyl tetracycline, a successful compound with the following structure:

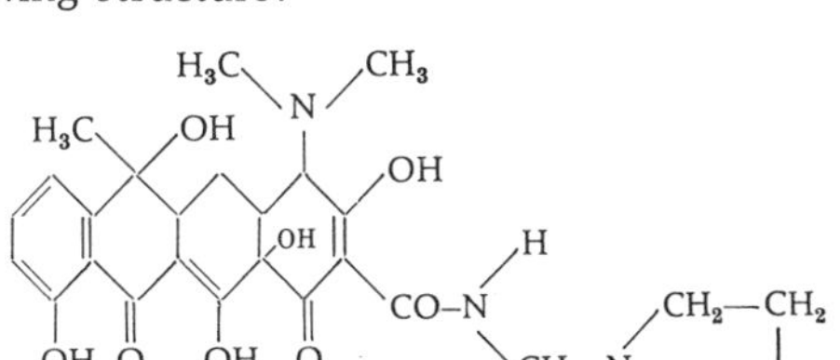

The salts which this compound forms with the most varied acids are readily water soluble and well suited for both intramuscular injection. This means that it is now possible to make full use of the excellent antibacterial action of the tetracyclines. Hoechst markets this substance under the name REVERIN.

Tremendous progress has been made — from as early as 1939 — with analgesics and spasmolytics. Pharmacologically substances were expected from amino-alkylation of

319

diphenylmethane and its derivatives in view of the similarity in structural formula to morphine. G. Ehrhart used a new method of amino-alkylation for this. The first substance produced, 1,1-diphenyl-3-piperidinopropane (ASPASAN), showed excellent spasmolytic properties. Other work on this series proved extraordinarily fruitful. Among the substances produced were 6-dimethylamino-4,4-diphenyl-3-hexanone, TICARDA, which has become known as a cough remedy; POLAMIDON, 6-dimethyl-amino-4,4-diphenyl-3-heptanone, and POLAMIDON C, a combination of Polamidon with diphenylpiperidino-ethyl acetamide; and the antihistamine AVIL, 1-phenyl-1-pyridyl-(2′)-3-dimethylaminopropane.

This was a completely new class of compounds. Their various pharmacological actions (O. Schaumann) aroused considerable interest, particularly among American scientists who studied them intently once they had become known. Interestingly enough, POLAMIDON

was the first compound with a painkilling action many times more effective than that of morphine, and with the additional advantage that it was also effective when given orally. After the war, Hoechst lost all patents covering this field and the new drugs were produced in nearly every civilized country. They were marketed under different names, and POLAMIDON, for instance, is known as « Adanon », « Dopridol », « Dolamid », «Dolophin», «Mecodin», «Methadon», «Physepton» and so on.

Further research in this field led to N-3′-phenyl-propyl-(2′)-1,1-diphenylpropyl-amine-(3)

This compound showed a surprising change in pharmacological action. The new property was that it increased the coronary circulation and also increased the oxygen

supply and oxygen reserves in cardiac muscle. Hoechst gave this substance the name SEGONTIN.

It has already been mentioned that INSULIN cannot be taken orally because it is a peptide. All attempts to produce a preparation with insulin activity which could be given orally have failed. For a time it seemed that some guanidines might be suitable for the treatment of diabetes. Hoechst, for example, investigated phenylethylguanidine and isoamyl-enylguanidine, GALEGIN. But there were side-effects so that the preparations could not be used clinically. Nevertheless as one particular goal of the pharmacological laboratories there still remained the search for substances which develop hypoglycemic activity when given orally. From about 1942 onwards, it was known that certain sulphanilamides can lower the blood sugar level. In 1955, H. Franke and J. Fuchs carried out a clinical trial with N-(4-aminobenzolsulphonyl-)-N'-butylurea, a compound produced by E. Haak and his team at C. F. Boehringer in Mannheim. This showed an excellent hypoglycemic action.

At about the same time, Hoechst found this surprising action in N-(4-methylbenzolsulphonyl)-N'-butylurea. The compounds produced by Hoechst differ from the sulphonylureas of C. F. Boehringer in that the amino group in the p-position on the benzene ring is absent. This is remarkable because the antibacterial activity of the sulphanilamides depends on the amino group in the p-position and the hypoglycemic action need not be coupled with the antibacterial effect.

C. F. Boehringer of Mannheim and Farbwerke Hoechst agreed to work together in the future on these interesting and important substances in order to make available the best and most effective substances for the treatment of diabetes. The preparations mentioned above were marketed as INVENOL (Hoechst) and «Nadisan» (Boehringer) and as RASTINON (Hoechst) and «Artosin» (Boehringer). They found rapid acceptance and are now produced on a very large scale. In this field research depends largely on the pharmacological testing of synthesized substances. By now over a thousand of these have been produced. All future progress demands close cooperation between chemists and medical staff.

Whereas the hormone « insulin » replaces the missing amounts of insulin, the lowering of blood sugar level which develops after oral doses of «Rastinon» requires a different interpretation. It was soon realised that the effective mechanism of the sulphonylureas is closely linked with the pancreas. Animals without a pancreas given sulphonylureas will no longer react with a lowering of the blood sugar level. There now seems to be hardly any doubt that the sulphonylureas liberate insulin which exists in sufficient quantity in the pancreas. For the diabetic, the physiological stimulus of increased blood sugar levels is not sufficient to free the amount of insulin required to bring the blood sugar back to normal, which is what happens in a healthy subject. The sulphonylureas appear to be able to break up excessive, pathological bonds of insulin, liberate it and let it act upon the blood sugar. However, the mechanism is still under discussion and other interpretations are possible.

Apart from this action on the β-cells in the islets of Langerhans, or on the insulin-protein bond, the sulphonylureas cause the release of adrenaline from the adrenal medulla. Adrenaline has a glycogenolytic action with the result that healthy animals or humans given sulphonylurea will rarely show hypoglycaemic shock. With very high doses there may even be a change to hyperglycaemia. This means that the sulphonyl-ureas are very safe to use, as there is no danger of severe hypoglycaemic shock. Another effect of the sulphonylureas is that new α- and β-cells are formed in the islets of Langerhans. The formation of β-cells is a possible explanation for remissions which are frequently observed in diabetics given sulphonylureas, though these are only of short duration (4—6 weeks).

In 1929 the then I.G. Farbenindustrie took over the «Behringwerke» at Marburg, founded by E. v. Behring, and incorporated them in the Mid-Rhine industrial complex. Research and production management of the Behring Works were taken over by Hoechst.

After the serum and vaccine productions of Hoechst and Marburg were combined in the Behring Works, intensive research was started in this field. Many new sera and vaccines against human and animal diseases were developed. Milestones along this road were the ERYSIPELAS PRODUCTS, DISTEMPER SERA and VACCINES, SWINEFEVER VACCINE, COMBINED VACCINE against diphtheria, tetanus and whooping cough, and finally MKS VACCINE against foot and mouth disease in cattle and pigs. Using the method of producing a poliomyelitis vaccine developed by J. E. Salk in the USA, Marburg developed a production process and marketed a poliomyelitis adsorbate vaccine under the trade name VIRELON. Recently oral poliovaccination with attenuated live virus has also been included in the Marburg research programme.

Work on biological products led to a special protein chemistry, immuno-chemistry. Particular attention was paid to the human blood fractions. These are obtained by separating the various proteins found in human serum. They include HUMAN SERUM

ALBUMIN and γ-GLOBULIN as well as numerous end products like FIBRINOGEN and ANTIHAEMOPHILIC GLOBULIN which can often save lives. Special methods were developed in protein chemistry to obtain sera and antigens in increasingly purer forms. This has greatly improved their tolerance.

The production of immunobiological preparations very much involves their standardization. This requires special reagents which have to be produced in the laboratories. Their further development has in the last decades produced a wide range of DIAGNOSTIC REAGENTS for the detection of diseases or pathological functions in the organism, a valuable addition to the physician's armory.

At Hoechst, research was mainly in the field of organic chemistry. Inorganic chemistry was only included where it played a role in the manufacture of organics or was needed for the preparation of preliminary products. Yet it was inevitable that work should also be done on improving the old production methods and developing new ones for these inorganic chemicals. Here are some typical examples:

Various processes for the production of oleum were studied, developed to the industrial level and evaluated from the economic point of view. The manufacture of sulphur trioxide from sulphurous acid proved too costly (1881), but it could be obtained directly from roaster gases using the contact process (1886/87).

Working on acid resistant materials, K. Dietz and K. Frank developed the Hoechst self-hardening ACID-PROOF CEMENTS based on water glass. These went into production in 1926. Later came the ASPLITS which use synthetic resins as binding agents. Progress in the field resulted not only from close collaboration between chemists and engineers, but also from the work of W. Matz who developed theoretical principles.

The oxidation of organic compounds with CHROMIC ACID, for instance the manufacture of anthraquinone and phthalic acid, became interesting when a method was found to electrolytically reconvert the resulting chromium sulphate solutions to chromic acid. In 1892 Hoechst regenerated chromic acid in a pilot plant and after further development, large-scale conversion started in Gersthofen. There it is still used today, because large quantities of chromium sulphate solutions are a by-product in the manufacture of waxes.

Hoechst became particularly interested in the manufacture of nitric acid from ammonia, a process originated by W. Ostwald in Leipzig. On the basis of research started by M. Rohmer in Gersthofen, the building of a production plant at Hoechst started in

G. Pistor

1914 and this became operative in 1915. In 1918, 3600 tons of ammonia a month were oxidized to produce 40% nitric acid, and part of this was used to produce about 5000 tons a month of concentrated nitric acid. After 1918 this could be used for the development and production of the following nitrogenous fertilizers: SODIUM NITRATE (1919), AMMONIUM SULPHATE NITRATE (1921), POTASSIUM SULPHATE NITRATE (1922), CALCIUM NITRATE (1924), POTASSIUM NITRATE (1927), AMMONIUM NITRATE-LIMESTONE (1949) and finally (1952) COMPLETE FERTILIZER and SPECIAL COMPLETE FERTILIZER WITH TRACE ELEMENTS.

To produce potassium and sodium nitrate, ammonium nitrate was reacted with alkali chlorides. Ph. Osswald of Hoechst developed a process of « elutriation » in which the potassium, or sodium, nitrate separates from the other product of the reaction, ammonium chloride, because of its higher specific gravity. The process was used at Hoechst and elsewhere after 1927 to produce saltpetre.

The manufacture of sulfamic acid from gaseous ammonia and sulphur trioxide was worked out at Hoechst, and production started in 1938.

The industrial development of electrochemical and electrothermal processes started at the Chemische Fabrik Griesheim, now part of Hoechst, where the first chlor-alkali electrolysis was developed by I. Stroof and put into production in 1890. For the sake of completeness, other electrochemical and electrothermal processes developed at Griesheim, Bitterfeld and Knapsack should be mentioned (carbon and graphite electrodes, aluminium, magnesium, carbide, phosphorus). Many problems were solved and in recent years there have been major improvements in these processes. When the concerns belonging to I.G. Farben started to switch from the diaphragm to the amalgam, Hoechst made contributions to the further improvement of the amalgam process. Development work continues and production units are built with larger and larger capacities. Higher power efficiency, increased current density and lower voltage are the practical results of these efforts.

At the inorganic laboratories of the I. G. works at Bitterfeld G. Pistor and his staff had evolved the principles for the electrothermal manufacture of PHOSPHORUS. A big production plant had been built in Piesteritz on the river Elbe. Changed conditions after the last war made it necessary to build a new production plant for phosphorus in the Federal Republic. Phosphorus in the form of polyphosphates was increasingly in demand for the production of detergents.

Based on the experience gained in Piesteritz and with many major improvements, F. Ritter built the first phosphorus furnace in Knapsack. After only a short time this proved too small to cope with the demand. A second furnace with a capacity of 49 MW was therefore erected and a third is now under construction. The manufacture of PHOSPHORUS requires large quantities of electric power, phosphate rock, coke and silica. Put in the form of a simple equation, the process of manufacturing elemental phosphorus is as follows:

$$2 \, Ca_3 \, (PO_4)_2 + 6 \, SiO_2 + 10 \, C = 4 \, P + 6 \, CaSiO_3 + 10 \, CO$$

The starting materials, especially the tricalcium phosphate, are never entirely pure. This presents considerable difficulties in operating the furnace and requires constant control and supervision. After the elemental phosphorus has been removed from the furnace effluent gas, about 90% of the remainder is carbon monoxide. This can be used as a source of energy for sintering phosphate.

About 10% of the elemental phosphorus is used as raw material for plasticizers, insecticides and plant protection agents. A small proportion of the white phosphorus is converted into red phosphorus. Most of the white phosphorus produced in Knapsack is burnt to form phosphoric acid. In the manufacture of the modern detergents, phosphoric acid and soda or caustic soda are used to produce primarily sodium tripolyphosphate and tetrasodiumpyrophosphate. These processes are based on methods developed in the research laboratories.

The technical production of the rare gases argon, helium and neon (1913), krypton and xenon (1935) and their practical application in the fields of illumination and welding were worked out by Ph. Siedler at the Griesheim Chemical Works.

The flushing process, phase separation of hydrophilic and hydrophobic materials, had been specially developed for one of the dye-producing plants. In the mid-thirties extensive research was successfully carried out at Hoechst to find similar methods for up-grading coal as a raw material most important to the national economy. Oils were added to aqueous coal suspensions and the mixture processed in kneading machines until the water and ash were largely separated from the coal and oil paste. This paste could then be used for the hydrogenation of coal or for fuel. If hydrochloric acid was added to crude lignite, this too could be up-graded by separating most of the water, ash and salt. The coal and oil pastes thus obtained could be converted to solid, low-ash coke suitable as raw material for carbide and electrode production. Instead of Werner Pfleiderer mixers operating on a similar principle, Hoechst developed double-screw kneaders — later in collaboration with the firm Leistritz of Nuremberg — thus obtaining a continuous process. These machines should have made it practical to operate on a large scale. With the loss of the central German lignite fields, for which these methods had been developed, this work was discontinued.

Many efforts to develop detergents which do not possess the disadvantages of soap resulted in Hoechst marketing in 1930 the first fatty acid condensation product of a chlorinated fatty acid and sodium oxethanesulphonate, IGEPON A. Today it is sold under the name HOSTAPON A. Another I.G. Farben group developed IGEPON T, a condensation product of chlorinated fatty acid and methyltaurine. Hoechst worked chiefly on the development and production of its intermediary products. This type is now marketed as HOSTAPON T.

Another basic development in this field were the IGEPAL brands which are water-soluble agents produced by reacting ethylene oxide with alkylphenols of a higher molecular weight. These were the first detergents produced without fatty acids as their base. They are now manufactured in all industrial countries and Hoechst market them unter the name of HOSTAPAL.

Intensive work in problems concerning the application of soapless detergents led to the discovery of the anti-greying properties of carboxymethylcellulose which is now an additive to all modern detergents. During the second world war the Leuna Works produced large quantities of mersol for the manufacture of crude detergents. This is an alkylsulphochloride produced by the reaction of SO_2 and Cl_2 on high molecular weight aliphatic hydrocarbons. Hoechst processed this compound further and by reaction with ammonia produced the sulphamide which was then reacted with sodium chlor-acetate to form an alkylsulphamido acetic acid. It went on the market in 1942 as BOHRMITTEL HOECHST (Hoechst Drilling Agent). In view of the great shortage of cutting oils, it was successfully and extensively used in all metal working processes. It is still sold today.

Chlorination of aliphatic hydrocarbons produced the DERMINOL OILS. Direct or in emulsion form, these were a perfect substitute for the greasing agents used in the leather industry.

One interesting product in the field of «textile softeners» deserves mention. Condensation of octadecylisocyanate with ethylenimine produces the corresponding ethylenimine urea.

This compound is a wash-fast softener with excellent properties used particularly in the processing of very fine cotton materials. It is sold under the name PRIMENIT VS.

After the second world war Hoechst also resumed research in the dyestuff field. Dissolution of the I.G. had created some problems, and there were gaps to be closed in the existing ranges. In the indanthrene dye and printing ranges, for example, clear blue and green tones were completely lacking. By making use of previous work, the missing products were developed in the anthraquinone, acridone, benzanthronepyrazolanthrone and pyrenequinone series and included as new dyes. A few years ago an asymmetrical dye, INDANTHRENE PRINTING BROWN HRR, was developed from naphthalene tetracarboxylic acid. As a result of its excellent properties it has become very well known. A new process of esterification was developed, using N-methylacetamide instead of pyridine bases for the production of anthrasol. Thus vat dyes of the anthrimide-carbazole series, which were difficult to esterify, could be included in the range, among them INDANTHRENE YELLOW 3R.

The field of organic pigments has grown increasingly important over the last twenty years. They are used for many purposes, some of them quite new, and increasing demand presented many research problems. The synthetics and laquer industries wanted dyes which were very fast to light and weather and resistant to solvents, top sprays and heat.

By introduction of suitable groups into azo dyes of the HANSA YELLOW and BENZIDINE YELLOW series and into the classical PERMANENT RED, products were developed which far exceeded the quality standards of the older products. But the real top quality products were found later in the DIOXAZINE, VAT and QUINACRIDON series. These, too, were included in the PERMANENT and PV FAST RANGES. Apart from the purely chemical aspect, a major problem was the development of suitable finishing processes to obtain finely granulated, brilliant pigments. One new development in the trichromatic field is a ROSANILINE BLUE process. It is now possible to manufacture this established class of dyes more simply and cheaply than on the old fuchsin basis.

A new research field had to be opened up to develop dyes for synthetic fibres, particularly for Hoechst's TREVIRA fibre. The development was made more difficult in that Hoechst did not have any background in the field of dispersion dyes for rayons. However, a number of suitable products were developed in a most varied classification of dyes and have been included in the SAMARON range.

The most important new development to result from Hoechst's dyestuff research are the reactive dyes. The discovery of the vinyl sulphone dyes by H. Heyna and his group was a pioneering effort of great technical importance. The basic patent, entitled «A Method for the Fixation of Water-soluble Organic Compounds on Substances with a Fibrous Structure», was described in 1949. Other patents followed. They show that dyes (and also colourless compounds) which contain vinyl sulphone groups ($- SO_2 - CH = CH_2$) or masked vinyl sulphone groups like β-oxethylsulphone sulfuric acid ester groups ($- SO_2 - CH_2 - CH_2 - OSO_3H$) or β-chloroethylsulphone groups ($- SO_2 - CH_2 - CH_2 - Cl$) can react with fibres to form a covalent bond. After the dyeing process these dyes became a chemical constituent of the fibre and were fixed so as to be fast to washing. This was a completely new principle in dyeing. As so often happens with new discoveries, the value and significance of the new principle were not at first fully realised. Intensive work was still required, particularly in application technology, until it could be put to practical use. The vinyl sulphone wool dyes were developed fairly quickly and the first of these were marketed in 1952 as REMALAN DYES. But a similar range for cellulose fibres, the REMAZOL DYES, did not come out until 1957, and just before that, two other firms (ICI and CIBA) had brought reactive dyes, developed on a different principle, on the market. There were six Remazol dyes to start with, but by now the range has been extended to more than twenty. The dyeing of cellulose fibres with Remazol dyes proceeds as follows:

$$F-SO_2-CH_2-CH_2-O-SO_3^{\ominus} \xrightarrow[-HSO_4^{\ominus}]{+ OH^{\ominus}} \begin{array}{l} F-SO_2-CH=CH_2 \\ \quad \left| \begin{array}{l} + \text{Cellulose} \\ + OH^{\ominus} \end{array} \right. \\ F-SO_2-CH_2-CH_2-O-Cell \end{array}$$

In dyeing in an alkaline medium, the sulphuric acid esters are converted to vinyl sulphones and sulphuric acid is split off. The vinyl sulphones then react with the hydroxyl groups of the cellulose, forming a coloured cellulose ether. F stands for any water-soluble dye constituent, in the commercial products usually azo, metal-complex azo and also anthraquinone and phthalocyanine dyes. The Remazol dyes are outstandingly reactive towards cellulose fibres. Apart from textile printing they are also particularly suited for the dyeing industry. They are highly soluble, give a good depth of colour and are very fast. Their fastness to washing is very much better than that of the direct colours.

Addition of the vinyl sulphone group into the dyes or their intermediates was achieved by well-known methods. But intensive work was required to adjust these methods to production. The vinyl sulphone principle is applicable in other fields as well. Polyfunctional, colourless vinyl sulphone products can be used in cross-linking reactions, e.g. for pigment fixation, to harden gelatine and in the production of high quality fibres.

The new developments, initiated through the chemistry of reactive dyes, are only at their beginning and the future should bring further success and progress.

One very recent development are the INTHION DYES which are characterized by thiosulphuric acid ester groups ($-S-SO_3Na$). A new method, a cross-linking and polycondensation reaction, is used to apply them to cotton fibres as fast dyes. The first dye of this range, which is still being developed, came on the market in 1960 as INTHION BRILLIANT BLUE I5G.

The NAPHTHOL AS dyes were also further developed in Offenbach. These are primarily cotton dyes. They had originally gained importance because of the brightness and fastness of the red shade as well as for economic reasons. Since then the range has been extended considerably. The importance of the Naphthol AS dyes is indicated, in part, by the fact that at present about 162 combinations bear the indanthrene label. After the second world war, further work was concentrated on navy blue, black, grey, brown and green.

A strong new impulse was felt through the development of the VARIOGEN BASES. These products are new dye bases. Combined with the usual naphthols they form metallizable dyes on the fibre. The metal complexes used (so far green, grey and brown shades have been produced) have remarkable qualities of fastness which quickly attracted attention. A number of the new synthetic fibres can also be dyed with Naphthol AS dyes by specially adapted methods. The dyeing of polyester fibres (INTRAMINE DYES) has achieved some importance.

In 1938 the coloristic department started experiments on the fixation of pigments in textile printing, which were fast to washing and to rubbing. This was prompted by development, in the United States, of the «Aridye» pigment printing process, using emulsified lacquer binding agents such as oil-modified glyptal resins, but this process did not prove satisfactory. After only a short time application for basic patents could be made on use of a combination of mixed polymer latexes like butadiene styrol or acrylic ester vinylchloride and urea formaldehyde precondensates as binding agents for pigment printing. The basic idea of using dispersions of synthetic substances, which would dry to a flexible film, as pigment-binding agents, and resins such as urea or melamine formaldehyde condensates to strengthen adhesion, is still employed today in pigment printing processes, an example of which is the Hoechst IMPERON TF process.

During the second world war, isocyanates and ethylenimine compounds began to be used for cross-linking pigment-binding agents in different classes of substances. This work led to a new pigment printing process based on synthetics containing carboxyl groups and polyfunctional ethylenimine derivatives. It was introduced into practice as the IMPERON FA process. The development of pigment preparations for the process was a parallel programme.

If one surveys the development of the dyestuff industry from its beginning to today, certain trends are noted which predominated during different periods. When A. Kekulé had formulated his benzene theory in 1865, the purely empirical search for dyes gave way to planned, purposeful investigation. But the development of new dyes was still an end in itself, with little regard for the needs of the dyeing industry. Only later did the need for close interrelation between production and the practical application of dyes begin to be realised and became an influence in the synthesis of dyes.

Today every new dye is tested for fastness, behavior during dyeing, etc. These tests have become so numerous and intensive that the synthesis of dyes has become a very difficult field in chemical research. If in spite of this more beautiful and improved dyes are produced, this can only be due to the devoted work of large and experienced staffs working in up-to-date laboratories and using all modern aids.

In the field of plastics and resins, research became very active after 1946.

Polyvinyl acetate dispersions were required for so many different purposes that the Mowilith range had to be extended. Apart from the co-polymers containing vinyl acetate and maleic or acrylic esters, valuable products such as MOWILITH DM 4 and MOWILITH DC were developed by using special protective colloids and emulsifying agents. Further progress was made when it became possible to graft vinyl esters in to polyalkylene oxides. This led to a series of new products.

In 1934 Hoechst were the first to discover that unsaturated compounds containing fluorine, like trifluorochlorethylene, could be polymerized to form products with very high melting points. With the processing methods then used, these substances were difficult to mould.

During the war the USA did intensive work in this field. Because of their high resistance to chemicals and temperature, these polymers were of particular interest to industry. During and after the war Hoechst continued experiments on the polymerization of olefins containing fluorine and developed the commercial products HOSTAFLON C (polytrifluorochlorethylene) and HOSTAFLON TF (polytetrafluoroethylene). For the latter Hoechst obtained a licence from Du Pont.

It was also decided after 1945 to resume work on polymerization of vinyl chloride. A continuous emulsion polymerization process had already been developed by the I.G. The products manufactured by this process contained admixtures, such as emulsifying agents, detrimental to their use for some purposes. Thus, as was the case with other firms at home and abroad, Hoechst developed a suspension polymerization process which produces purer polyvinyl chloride (HOSTALIT C). A special resin for lacquers (HOSTALIT CAM) was also developed from vinyl chloride as a basis.

Towards the end of 1953, K. Ziegler of Mülheim/Ruhr found a method of polymerizing ethylene at normal pressures. He used a new catalyst system, a combination of compounds of transitional elements like titanium, vanadium, and organometallic compounds of the first to third group of the periodic table. Hoechst already had an agreement with K. Ziegler and then entered into an option and licence contract with him. The polyethylene produced with Ziegler's catalysts has a higher crystallinity and softening temperature, greater hardness and dimensional stability, and is less flexible than the high pressure polyethylene produced by ICI for the previous 20 years. The differences in properties are due to the molecular structure. High pressure polyethylene shows some branching. The Ziegler polyethylene is not, or only slightly, branched.

Through the concentrated efforts of Hoechst's research and engineering staffs, Ziegler's laboratory work was relatively quickly developed into a large-scale process. This low-pressure polyethylene was given the trade name HOSTALEN G.

The scientific work of Hoechst contributed much toward explaining the mechanism of polymerization and led to selective catalysts and operating conditions resulting in a great number of Hostalen types for special purposes.

In addition to ethylene polymerization, co-polymerization with other α-olefins (propylene, butene-1) was developed. Thus, alternating polymerization of ethylene and propylene produces block (periodic) polymers with specific properties.

G. Natta in Milan extended the Ziegler polymerization to propylene. He obtained amorphous polymers and also the first crystalline polymers with a high melting point. Hoechst was successful in attaining very high yields of this highly crystalline, isotactic product, valuable as a plastic, and named HOSTALEN PP.

Pioneering work was done in a large range of commercial applications of these new products. Low pressure polyethylene is chiefly employed for domestic articles, shipping containers, vessels, bottles and pressure tubing. Polypropylene is used for technical parts, household goods and films. The chlorination of low pressure polyethylene in Hoechst resulted in products having very interesting properties. When mixed with polyvinyl chloride, they increase its tenacity even at low temperatures, without marked reduction in its resistance to heat. The product is increasingly used in the building industry. It is marketed as HOSTALIT Z.

About 30 years ago, H. Staudinger in Freiburg investigated the polymerization of formaldehyde. He realised that the polymer could only be thermally stabilized by deactivation of the end hydroxyl groups by acylation or conversion to an ether.

Subsequently, Du Pont developed a commercial process for production of polyformaldehyde («Delrin»), a polymer with blocked end groups. Hoechst also entered and embarked on its own course in this field. Trioxane, the cyclic trimer of formaldehyde, was chosen as the basis. It is used for co-polymerization with small quantities of cyclic acetals or epoxydes. Polymerization and appropriate auxiliary processing produce thermostable polymers which are easy to form. The Celanese group in the USA was working along the same lines independently of Hoechst. They were somewhat ahead with the technical development of the process. The two firms formed a company for the production of this polymer, HOSTAFORM.

At first there were difficulties in obtaining the quantities of lower olefins, chiefly ethylene and propylene, for large-scale production. Since 1952, work had already been under way in laboratories, specializing in solvents and plastics, on cracking petroleum hydrocarbons to obtain olefins, and this research was intensified. After a thorough investigation of the fundamental principles on a laboratory scale and in pilot plants, a large crude oil cracking unit, called a coker, was built at Hoechst. In addition to the more important steps involved in the cracking process, such as contacting the preheated crude oil with the spherical-shaped coke heat carrier, indirect heating of this heat carrier to supply the heat of cracking, separation of the cracked gas from the coke, and pneumatic transport of the coke to a height of 75 meters, the problem of separating the gas mixture into its individual components required solution. Finally, this process could produce up to 22 weight percent ethylene and 15 weight percent propylene from a selected crude oil cut.

Soon after this, in 1954, high temperature cracking of petroleum hydrocarbons came into consideration to produce acetylene, in addition to ethylene, since Hoechst needed large quantities of acetylene for production of vinyl acetate.

The first commercial process for the production of acetylene used calcium carbide as raw material. Calcium carbide is prepared by high-temperature reaction of coke with lime in an electric furnace. This requires a large amount of electric power, 9–10 kwh per kilogram of acetylene. The obvious way was to replace this electrical energy with a cheaper heat energy produced by burning hydrocarbons with oxygen. The cracking process requires high temperatures, above 1200 °C, which could not be attained by indirect heat transfer to the reaction system, therefore a direct method had to be used and a two-stage process was developed. In the first stage, tail gas, produced as a by-product in the cracking process, is burned with oxygen to produce a combustion gas at very high temperatures and high heat content. The flame temperature can be as high as 2700 °C, which is much too high even for high temperature resistant ceramic linings. A metal burner was therefore developed. Water, circulated through its jacket, provided intensive cooling. The furnace was constructed such that heat losses are very low. Its heat generation density is tremendously high and is about one billion kilocalories per cubic meter per hour.

The preheated hydrocarbon, e.g. light naphtha, is injected into the burner combustion gas under highly turbulent mixing conditions in a reactor section such that acetylene and ethylene are the chief products of cracking. Direct heat exchange makes extremely rapid transfer of large quantities of heat possible and this is required for acetylene and ethylene production. The residence time in the second stage of the reactor is very short and is in the order of about a thousandth of a second. Hydrocarbons containing more than 3 carbon atoms are then separated. A special absorption process removes the so-called higher unstable acetylenes which are returned to the reactor for further cracking. A selective absorption process had to be developed to obtain pure acetylene in smaller quantities relative to the larger quantities of ethylene. Optimum reaction conditions were developed such that a combined yield of acetylene and ethylene on light naphtha of 54 weight percent was attained. The first commercial plant of this type is now in operation at Hoechst. It produces 40,000 metric tons per year of acetylene and ethylene through this High Temperature Pyrolysis (HTP) Process.

The Consortium fuer Elektrochemische Industrie, a subsidiary of Wacker, in Munich, were the first to produce aldehydes and ketones by oxidation of olefins using a palladium chloride catalyst. In conjunction with Farbwerke Hoechst AG, this was the basis for development of a process used in large commercial plants for the production of acetaldehyde at home and abroad. The same basic reaction is now used for commercial production of acetone from propylene and methylethylketone from butylene.

Ketene is produced by catalytic cracking of acetic acid under a vacuum of 80—100 torr at 700 °C. Positive displacement compressors are used to maintain vacuum upstream to the compressor for cracking and to forward the ketene downstream under a positive pressure to the dimerization unit. The production of diketenes by dimerization does not require a catalyst but is best done at a higher ketene partial pressure. Diketene is used for various industrial reactions. It offers considerable advantages over acetoacetic esters. For example, diketenes and aromatic amines in an aqueous medium give an excellent yield of acetoacetic arylides. It was also found that diketene, via acetoacetic amide, in aqueous solution with salts of phenylhydrazine derivatives will give 5-pyrazolones. Diketene is also reacted with alcohols to produce acetoacetic esters on a commercial scale. The reaction of ketene with carbonyl compounds has so far achieved some significance in two applications. Acetone reacts with ketene to produce dimethylacrylic acid through β-lactone as an intermediary. Ketene and crotonaldehyde react to produce sorbic acid with β-lactone as an intermediate. Hoechst built the first industrial plant using this process for sorbic acid production. Sorbic acid is probably the best fungicidal preservative now available. Physiologically it is fully metabolized like a fatty acid.

The discovery of atomic fission in 1939 by O. Hahn opened up a field which still awaits full exploration. Radioactive substances have so many possible uses in research and industry that it became necessary to build a special laboratory in which all radiochemical work and radioactive determinations are carried out. Establishment of a radiochemical laboratory in Griesheim in 1958 made this modern speciality available to the Hoechst research workers on a very wide basis. In addition to using radioactive materials scientifically and in production problems, some radioactive preparations are made for sale. Other operations include: separation of yttrium from strontium, yielding ^{90}Y with a ^{90}Sr content of less than 10^{-5} %; exchange reactions to synthesize radiochemically pure radio-iodine-labelled compounds such as thyroxine, diiodothyronine, Bengal pink, 5-iodouracil; investigations into the stability of ^{131}I compounds of high specific activity; determining the behavior of very small amounts of ^{131}I proteins in paper electrophoresis; the preparation of radio ruthenocene (one of the metal-cyclopentadienyl complexes which have recently attracted considerable interest).

That same year Hoechst started operation of a plant for the liquefaction and distillation of hydrogen at temperatures of about $-250\ °C$. This was the first large-scale production of the hydrogen isotope deuterium on the basis of a single process principle using a hydrogen-nitrogen ammonia synthesis gas as the raw material and yielding a product deuterium over 99.8% pure. The pure deuterium is then burned with pure oxygen to produce heavy water for use as a moderator in nuclear reactors.

Griesheim had considerable experience in the production of the usual electrode graphite. First, it was necessary to catch up with the progress made in other countries. Purity, density and radiation resistance are of prime importance in a graphite moderator used for chain reactions. The carbonized material produced in Griesheim is then graphitized and further processed by Siemens-Plania. A number of German pilot and research reactors use it as a moderator, reflector or as a special graphite for reactor elements.

As particular problems arose throughout the years in chemistry, physics, biology, technology or industrial application, departmental laboratories were developed at Hoechst in which work was geared chiefly to the research problems of that particular department. Dynamic development of all departments made it necessary to combine the various individual laboratories into one new research center as well as to build a main laboratory where emphasis would be on research problems of the whole company and in new spheres of activity. The first buildings of this new research establishment, the Hoechst Main Laboratories, built on the south side of the Main river, became operational in 1960. It was now possible to take up new research and to continue others, all of which may be of tremendous importance to the company as a whole now and in the near future. Chemists in these laboratories are not obliged to work on specific immediate problems and research is conducted more along the lines of a university. Here they become familiar with modern methods of industrial research and are trained for specialized research and production problems. The new laboratories have already experienced initial successes, namely, adaptation of the production polymerization process to production of modified low pressure polyethylene; synthesis of the condensation dyes which are now on the market as Inthion dyes; the agriphile Acricid, and the narcotic Halothan. They have also developed β-lactams and raw materials for fibres of the nylon-3 type. Finally, new processes have been developed for some important organic intermediates. These are enough to demonstrate the versatility of the main laboratories.

If one surveys the various research problems of Hoechst, it becomes obvious that practically every branch of chemistry is covered through the large-scale production of inorganic chemicals, solvents, dyes, raw materials for plastics, lacquers and synthetic fibres, drugs, biological sera and the radiochemical specialities, as well as the necessary preliminary and intermediate products. This tremendous range demands research activity on a very broad basis. A commemorative volume, «Research at Hoechst» has been published separately. It contains 78 scientific papers in which Hoechst scientists have tried to convey a dynamic expression of their work in all spheres of modern research.

Participation in the almost phantastic rate of scientific development was and will only be possible in the future by making available all possible research resources. About 4—5⁰/₀ of the total annual sales volume is spent on research. Over 850 graduates and their assistants are employed in the research laboratories, always endeavoring to maintain and further technical progress.

This continuous advancement of scientific development in the laboratories and in production demands imagination, ideas and — lest we forget — human spirit at all levels of our endeavors.

Industrial research in the past and in the future can only be successful if it continues to receive the impulse of new discoveries from universities, engineering schools and scientific institutions and, above all, from new generations of scientists.

Research is the continuing struggle for new knowledge, research serves progress, for the research of today determines the production of tomorrow.

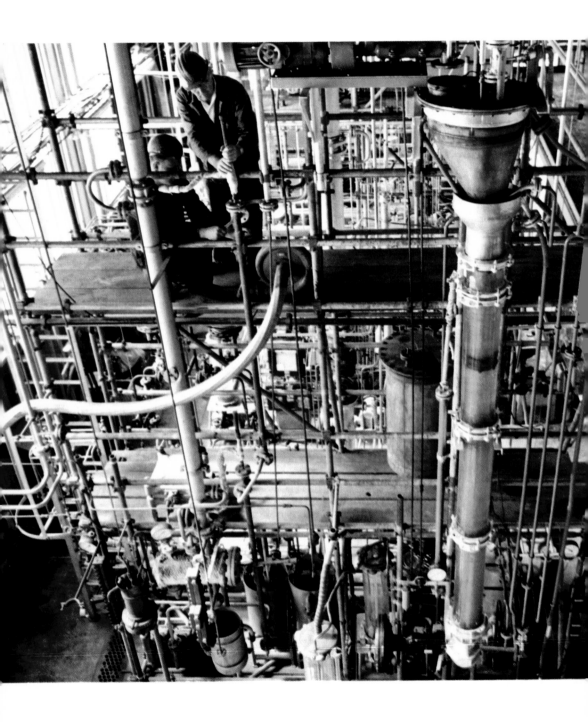

Dr. Volkmar Muthesius **From Florins to Deutschmarks**

When Wilhelm Meister, Dr. Eugen Lucius and August Müller founded the Farbwerke Hoechst, their starting capital was 66,450 florins. Now, a hundred years later, the firm's own capital is 1.5 thousand million DM, with a total balance of approximately 3.5 thousand million DM, making it one of the leading industrial concerns in the Federal Republic. If the Frankfurt florin of 1862 is reckoned at 1.71 of the present Mark, the money now invested in Farbwerke Hoechst is about thirty thousand times the original capital.

Nowadays economists and politicians talk a great deal about the growth of the national economy. It is considered one of the chief aims of political economics to ensure the highest possible rate of growth. Yet the discussions on the subject often seem somewhat abstract to those involved in practical economics. — Well, here we have a concrete, practical example: the growth of an enterprise which started from small beginnings (just as every business founded as a private firm has always had to start small) and has grown steadily with the tasks taken on by those at the helm. There are various standards by which this growth may be measured. One might study the increase in turnover or in the number of people employed, the area covered by the plant, the energy consumption or other numerical factors. But there is one element serving best as a common denominator and showing the development of the whole: the increase in working capital. The purely financial approach will be the simplest and most effective way of showing growth, since money is the instrument which enables us to add together apples and pears — to quote Wilhelm Röpke. We must remember that all these figures stand for reality and life itself. Money is merely the reflection of worldly goods, but money values are the only way we have of expressing the growth of these goods and this would seem to justify the addition of a chapter on financial development to this book.

It would of course be impossible to describe here every capital transaction of these hundred years in detail. That would need quite a volume of its own. A few aspects which may throw a light upon the whole financial development will be discussed. Then the financial decisions taken by the directors of Hoechst, their significance for the fate of the enterprise, and their relation to the national economy in general and to stock market developments in particular will be described. This will round off the picture given in the previous chapters concerning production, scientific achievements and other details. At the same time the example of Farbwerke Hoechst will serve to illuminate some topical questions of industrial and national economy and will perhaps stimulate even the layman to think more deeply about the problems and tasks of company finance, so often misunderstood.

Strains on family capital

By the end of 1863, the financial means of the then «Meister, Lucius & Co.» were probably the same as the capital originally invested by the partners. At the beginning, Wilhelm Meister and Eugen Lucius chose August Müller, a merchant from Antwerp and a relative of Lucius, as a partner. A few years later August Müller withdrew and Dr. Adolf Brüning took his place, the name of the firm changing to «Meister Lucius & Brüning». Brüning had worked for the enterprise from the very start; but he did not put in capital until 1864 and thus also became a financial partner.

Even today, these three names still remind us of the early days. In many of the other big chemical concerns the names of the founders or the founder families have vanished in the sea of anonymity of capital dealings, if one may be allowed to put it this way.

This should not imply that there is any fundamental difference in the financial development of the great chemical industries in Germany. At Hoechst just as in Elberfeld-Leverkusen and in Ludwigshafen, the companies grew into such dimensions that very soon the capital of individual families could not cope with the financial needs and it became necessary to apply to the stock market.

Farbwerke Hoechst was no exception to the rule. An industrial enterprise of such a size cannot forever remain in the possession of one family. By the end of 1870, the working capital of the firm Meister Lucius & Brüning had increased to nearly half a million Thalers (which would be about 1.45 million DM or even much more if one considers present-day buying power — at the time of the 1870/71 war between Germany and France, a labourer earned about 3 marks a day). This tremendous increase

340

Höchst am Main, im Januar 1863.
(bei Frankfurt a. M.)

Wir erlauben uns hiemit Ihnen anzuzeigen, dass wir am hiesigen Platze eine **Chemische Fabrik** unter der Firma

Meister, Lucius & C⁰.

errichtet haben.

Das Etablissement wird sich speciell mit der Darstellung der Anilinfarben und der in diese Branche einschlagenden Artikel beschäftigen.

Indem wir uns die Freiheit nehmen Sie auf unsere demnächst zu erlassenden Preislisten aufmerksam zu machen und Sie bitten von unseren Unterschriften am Fusse dieses Vormerkung zu nehmen, zeichnen wir mit

Achtung und Ergebenheit

Wilhelm Meister.

Dr. Eugen Lucius.

L. Aug. Müller.

Wilhelm Meister wird zeichnen:

Dr. Eugen Lucius . .

L. Aug. Müller . .

in capital in such a short time indicates an enormous rate of expansion in production, sales, investments and capital requirements. No wonder that in 1880, a mere seventeen years after the founding of the enterprise, Hoechst had to be changed into a shareholders company, thereby losing its character as a family undertaking.

Growth factors during the early decades

On 1st January 1880 the firm with all its assets and liabilities became the joint-stock company «Farbwerke vorm. Meister Lucius & Brüning» — the family firm became a company. Unfortunately the Hoechst archives contain nothing to give details of the stages in capital development from 1870 to 1880. For our purposes it is sufficient to know that at its founding the joint-stock company had a basic capital of 8.5 million marks. The seventies had therefore brought further expansion at a rate which in no way lagged behind that of the earliest years. From its beginning until the end of 1870 the company's capital had shown an average annual increase of what would now be approximately 165,000 marks. For the next nine years, until the joint-stock company was formed, calculations show the average annual increase to have been no less than approximately 800,000 marks. By then the total balance had reached 10.4 million marks. These are growth factors which have never been achieved by the national economy of a whole country, and probably never will be. But this incongruity merely reflects the exuberant growth of a new branch of industry. By way of substitution, its products replaced those which had previously satisfied the market. The synthetic dyes brought not only a technical revolution. In economic and financial areas too, this new development led to consequences which no doubt astonished many. It may well have given the people of those times the triumphant feeling of the human spirit overcoming material difficulties and at the same time the barriers to financial expansion. During that time of great industrial development men's faith in progress was creating its own impulses when it became apparent that increasing production with increasing profits would also continuously provide further capital resources.

Thus the solid foundations were steadily broadened, their long-term stability unaffected by occasional set-backs and crises on the market. Growth was based on two factors: firstly that part of the net profits was ploughed back into the business, and secondly that the resources of the stock market were opened up. A brief remark concerning the first of these factors: Without reinvesting and using part of the net profits to cover some of the capital expenditure, without this very old established precept, German industry as a whole and the chemical industry, then the dye industry, in particular could not possibly have achieved its development. This method is indeed an old and established precept. In spite of widely accepted notions, the ploughing back of profits is nothing new and has not been invented in the middle of the twentieth century, nor is it in any way unusual.

More about this later. For the moment it suffices to say that during the early years of Farbwerke Hoechst the company financed its own development, until 1880, the time when the capital sums required became so great that the enterprise obviously could not provide them from its own profits.

Family interests and company interests

Demands made by the technical and economic aspects of production and the whole structure of the undertaking led the company to change its legal basis at the beginning of its second great period of expansion and consider the issuing of shares. Until the late seventies the money put into the firm had been used for the production of dyes and the gradual expansion of this field. Now, in 1880, came the first step in the «vertical» direction, as one would now call it. The building of the company's own acid plant demanded greater financial resources. The founder families might perhaps have managed to provide these with some effort and by cutting down even further on an immediate return for their money. But the problem seemed to hint at even greater demands in the future and it was considered wise to adapt to the situation in good time. Looking ahead, the founders no doubt knew that this would mean an even more difficult renunciation — giving up the sole right of determining the firm's major policies.

If a family company admits public shareholders as its new «partners», then the family or families who originally were the only partners forgo the possibility of maintaining the company for all time as a truly «private» concern, the fate of which would be determined only by the policies of the founders and their heirs. So they know full well that in this respect at least the future is uncertain, but the sacrifice must be made if their company and its future is to be made secure. They are faced with the choice between the interests of the founders of the company and the interests of the company itself; personal and family interest has to be weighed against the interests of the enterprise. The history of industry has shown that even the type of man absolutely made to start and run his own firm, if faced with this decision, will always choose not to preserve his own and the family's interest, but to put the industrial plant, his creation, and its future well-being first. This is what happened in the case of Hoechst, and all the other founders and founder families of big industries have done the same. There was of course a difference in the time which it took until new, developing firms found themselves faced with such vital problems. With Hoechst it took barely one and a half dozen years, in other cases very much longer. As an example from quite a different branch of industry let us take the house of Siemens. The parent firm was founded by Werner Siemens and the Berlin mechanic Johann Georg Halske in 1847; it was not changed into a joint-stock company until 1897. The financial resources of the Siemens family and the firm's own earnings available for reinvestment were therefore able to back the growing concern for half a century.

It would take us too far if we were to carry the comparison further; but apart from the time factor the situation was fundamentally the same: the family renounces the right to sole control and accepts shareholders — the interests of the company are placed above those of its founders. The creation is greater than its creator.

The transition

This did not necessarily mean (and in most cases where the position was similar it also did not mean) that the men who founded the company would abruptly drop out of its affairs. It certainly was not the case with Farbwerke Hoechst. Wilhelm Meister, Eugen Lucius and Adolf Brüning were on the board of directors of the new joint-stock company and continued to guide it even in the years which followed, when new shareholders came in great numbers and with great sums of money.

When the joint-stock company was formed, the original stock was fixed at 10 million marks. 8.5 million were issued at once and secured on the existing plant and all other assets, plus about 1.8 million marks owing. The remaining 1.5 million marks stock was issued in 1881, except for a small remainder, giving a financial interest to two Frankfurt banking houses, Hauck & Son and J. I. Weiller Sons (eight years later these two banking firms introduced the Hoechst shares on the Frankfurt stock market). With the capital thus obtained, building of the company's own acid plant continued.

In 1882 the share capital was increased further, this time by 5 million marks. This was quite a strain on the money market in those days, as can be seen from the fact that at first only 40 per cent of the new shares were paid up; the rest was paid up in 1895. In the meantime money for capital expenditure was obtained by short-term loans whenever the share of the net profits reserved for the purpose was not sufficient. The balance

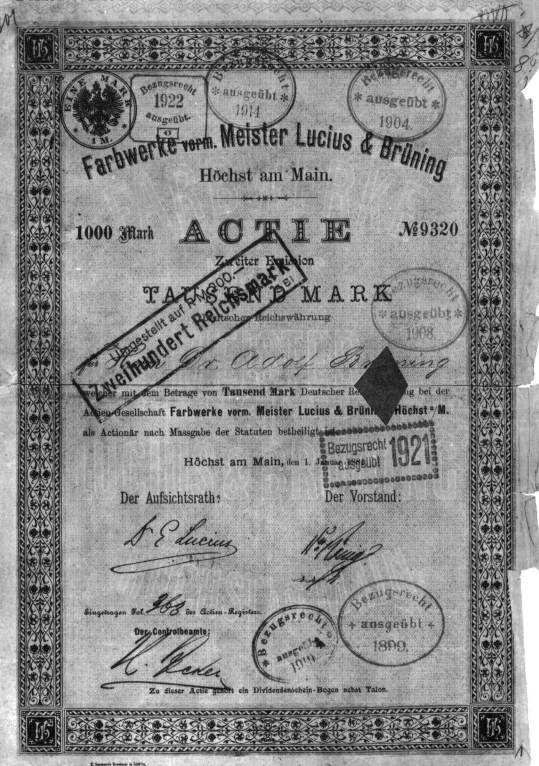

EINE MARK 1 M.

Bezugsrecht 1922 ausgeübt. 6

Bezugsrecht *ausgeübt* 1914

Bezugsrecht *ausgeübt* 1904.

Farbwerke vorm. Meister Lucius & Brüning

Höchst am Main.

1000 Mark | **ACTIE** | **№ 9320**

Zweiter Emission

TAUSEND MARK

Deutscher Reichswährung

Bezugsrecht *ausgeübt* 1908.

Umgestellt auf RM 200.— für Zweihundert Reichsmark DEI

Dr. Adolf Brüning

welcher mit dem Betrage von **Tausend Mark** Deutscher Reichswährung bei der

Actien-Gesellschaft **Farbwerke vorm. Meister Lucius & Brüning** Höchst a/M.

als Actionär nach Massgabe der Statuten betheiligt ist.

Bezugsrecht ausgeübt 1921

Höchst am Main, den 1. Januar 1898.

Der Aufsichtsrath: | Der Vorstand:

E. Lucius | *H. Brüning*

Eingetragen Fol. 963 des Actien-Registers.

Der Controlbeamte:

H. Becker

Bezugsrecht *ausgeübt* 1919

Bezugsrecht *ausgeübt* 1899.

Zu dieser Actie gehört ein Dividendenschein-Bogen nebst Talon.

C. Naumann's Druckerei in Frankfurt a/m.

sheet for 1881 showed 2.63 million marks owing to creditors. When the capital had increased from 10 to 12 million marks this went down to 1.64 million, but rose again, though there were fluctuations, until in 1895 it was almost 4.5 million marks. Then, with the further increase in capital, these short-term loans went down again. These figures reflect the methods of financing capital expansion which developed between industry and the banks in Germany during the second half of the last century.

Other times, other balance sheets

The relative proportion of the various items in the balance sheets of those days is very much different from what we see today, one hundred years later. Let us take the year 1895, for example. The share capital was 15 million marks and the reserves amounted to 3.77 million. Creditors were 4.47 million, but profit shown — including 994,000 marks carried forward — was 6.19 million marks. 200,000 marks were put in reserve, 904,000 marks paid out as a share in profits, 310,000 marks transferred to the social fund, and the remainder, about 3.8 million marks, paid out to shareholders as a 28% dividend. How enviable that seems to us today — a paradise lost to both company and shareholders, vanished through double taxation. Then industrial economy flourished, and the profit and loss accounts showed a considerable amount of elbow-room. A 28% dividend on shares issued a short time before at par — this meant that within four years the shareholders received more than their original stake in the form of profits, a most respectable rate of interest.

Thus Farbwerke Hoechst, like many other enterprises during this period of expansion at the turn of the century, had no difficulty in obtaining further financial backing when they approached the stock market from time to time.

In 1899, when the capital was increased by another 2 million to 17 million marks, and even more so in 1904, when new shares worth 8.5 million marks were issued and the firm's capital increased to 25.5 million marks, shares could sometimes be issued with an agio of 200 per cent and more: subsequently premiums became quite general. But until shortly before the turn of the century shares apparently still had to be issued at par. This meant that at times the total dividends paid would be higher than the new capital brought in.

People who kept their shares for a long time could therefore in those days reap astonishing financial benefits from the expansion of industry. But this bounty, which might seem somewhat surprising, has a very simple explanation: the tax system of those days and the way in which profit tax was applied. Before the first world war there was no corporation tax, it had not occurred to anyone to tax joint-stock companies and the government was satisfied with a tax on the shareholder's net profits. Nor did the tax have to be paid by the company then, the shareholder had to declare his own income from dividends. Nowadays about two fifths of the profits of those days would have to go straight to the fiscal office and only three fifths would remain for transfer to reserves and the paying of dividends, so that the shareholders would have received very much less. In 1900, Farbwerke Hoechst had to pay a total of 392,000 marks in taxes to the state and the community. In 1961 profits tax alone was 151 million marks.

These reflections reveal the contradictions which have developed in our tax system. After the first world war the income tax was considerably increased, and so it was felt necessary to invent an «income» tax for joint-stock companies, to prevent unfairness towards private firms. That was the beginning of double taxation of the sums paid to those providing the capital. The weaknesses of the system have recently become very apparent in the experiments with «allowances» — sometimes there are investment allowances and sometimes profit allowances, i.e. tax is reduced on one or the other.

Figures for the time before 1914

However that may be, at the turn of the century such considerations were entirely unknown, and this continued until the first world war. On the other hand the profits which could be made and the attitude of the state towards them left a good margin for capital investment from the company's own earnings. In 1908 the share capital of Hoechst had been increased to 36 million marks. Including premiums on the latest share issues and the original capital put in by Messrs. Meister, Lucius, Müller (and then Brüning), the capital for which the concern was then responsible amounted to about 40 million marks. Capital investment for the period from 1863 to 1907 on the other hand was about 65 million. Of course, by present-day standards 65 million, raised and invested in over forty years, so that the annual average would be about 1.5 million, does not seem exactly enormous. Now, a hundred years since Hoechst was founded, we are used to operating with much larger figures. The company now invests over 400 million DM per annum, in one single year six times as much as was then necessary and possible in half a century.

When the first world war started, the share capital was 50 million marks, with almost 25 million reserves; by the end of that war the share capital was 90 million marks.

Then began the crazy dance of figures that grew and grew. They were hollow numbers with no real meaning. At the end of 1922 the total capital (i.e. all the money involved in the works, including reserves and liabilities) was 23.5 thousand million paper marks, and by the end of 1923, when the first great inflation of our century had reached its zenith, it was around 9 trillion paper marks. But these figures were merely symptomatic of the destruction of all financial foundations.

It was a sign of those times that Hoechst paid no dividend in 1923; this was for the first and only time in the history of the company, if one discounts the exceptional circumstances of the years immediately after the second world war. But in those days following the break-down of the currency after the first world war the financial confusion was so abysmally great that no special importance was attached to the fact. When the dollar became worth billions, when a pound of bread cost thousands of paper marks, even a dividend of 30%, or 300 marks for a 1000 mark share, would have been a drop in the bucket. Nor could it surprise anyone that once this numerical madness was over, the inflated share capital had to be cut down to about one fifth. There was hardly any company which could avoid such measures. Hoechst was no exception; many had to cut down even more drastically.

But if we restrict our comparison of balance sheets again to the time before 1914, there is another striking difference from what we would regard as normal proportions today. This is the relationship between assets and liabilities. In 1899, for example, the total liabilities were only about one fifth of the firm's capital (share capital and reserves) and about 12 per cent of the total balance. Now if we look at the balance sheet for 1961, the structure is quite different. The total liabilities are almost as high as the capital and nearly 40 per cent of the total balance. This is partly due to the fact that long term loans are much more common now than they were in the last century — Hoechst issued its first debentures in 1901. In addition bank overdrafts are now used as financial backing. The changed ratio of assets to liabilities reflects a major change which has occurred in the economy as a whole. Through credit relations between customers and suppliers, companies are now financially much more interdependent than they were in the early days of the industry. On the one hand the number of trade debtors is much greater in relation to turnover, and longer production routes make it necessary to keep larger stocks. On the other hand it is neither possible nor necessary to finance the whole of this expansion with the firm's capital. Today bank overdrafts for current expenditure and to some extent even capital investment go up to nine figures. At the same time current assets (including sums temporarily invested in securities) may also amount to several hundred million DM. These astronomical figures are now a matter of course, indicating how the balance sheets of great concerns reflect modern financial trends.

There is another impression to be gained from a comparison of balance sheets then and now. Instead of a summary report, giving just a few big totals, we now get something akin to a very detailed photograph. The modern laws governing joint-stock companies demand the publication of reports which the shareholder at the turn of the century would probably have regarded as enforced indiscretions. In those days it was usual and permissible to give one single figure for the total liabilities, and the law did not even request a breakdown of accounts receivable. Any comparison between balance sheets then and now must therefore be restricted to very general terms.

The phases of big combines

With these reservations, let us return once more to the chronological order in financial history. The last balance sheet before the war, in 1913, shows that the total capital involved in Farbwerke Hoechst was 114 million marks, well into nine figures. The share capital was 36 million marks and the firm had considerable reserves, almost 20 million marks, built up in the new century not so much from retained profits than from the premiums on several new share issues. Since 1899 shares had hardly ever been issued at par. The practice of issuing at par was briefly returned to after the second world war, but do not let us get ahead of the story. During the first world war and in the years which followed, when all figures were subject to inflation (as has already been mentioned) the share capital was increased six times: in 1916 from 50 to 54 million, in 1917 to 90 million, in 1919 to 252 million, in 1921 to 430 million, in January 1922 to 470 million and finally in October of that same year to 940 million marks. The 40 million increase — in paper marks! — in January 1922 was in connection with an event which had occurred outside Hoechst's actual sphere of work, the catastrophic explosion at Oppau, still remembered by the older generation. On 21st September 1921, the Oppau plant of the Badische Anilin- & Soda-Fabrik went up in an explosion and Hoechst had to shoulder part of the enormous losses. Five years previously Farbwerke Hoechst had joined the «Interessengemeinschaft der deutschen Teerfarbenfabriken», a structure which had its early beginnings in 1904. At that time Hoechst and Cassella had combined to form «The Two», and Farbenfabriken Bayer (Leverkusen), Badische Anilin- & Soda-Fabrik (Ludwigshafen) and AGFA (Berlin-Wolfen) had become «The

Three». The intent and purpose of these combines was to replace competition with co-operation. One of the leaders of the chemical industry, Carl Duisberg, had studied the concentration of industries in the United States and on his return told German industry that a similar development in this direction would be inevitable.

Duisberg had foreseen this necessity, in spite of the fact that at that time, ten years before the outbreak of the first world war, the German coal tar dye industry was still producing at least four fifths of the synthetic dyes in the world.

Competition between German firms and the gradual appearance of foreign competitors did make it seem advisable to take the long view and consider the question of combines. A rational division of production lines between individual firms would have economic advantages. Subsequent developments after the second world war were to show that Duisberg had been right. But in 1903/1904, when he published a memorandum and presented the findings of his American tour to his colleagues (and competitors), the time for such far-reaching decisions had not yet come.

But these discussions did induce the firms to combine their interests in «The Two» and «The Three». The Two were later joined by Kalle of Biebrich. Ten years later, right in the middle of the first world war, the trend towards concentration entered a second, decisive phase. The two groups combined and were joined by «Chemische Fabrik Griesheim Elektron» and «Chemische Fabriken vormals Weiler-ter Meer» in Uerdingen. The new association called itself the «Interessengemeinschaft der deutschen Teerfarbenfabriken», with contracts which legally upheld the formal individuality of members, but introduced considerable uniformity in business policy, financial and all other arrangements. It was the first step towards total integration, as we would call it today. This 1916 development was completed by the acquisition of a number of smaller dye works which had not joined the combine. Their owners realised that with the changed world situation they would have no chance and therefore accepted the take-over bids of the «I. G.» combine.

I. G. — the name was accepted very quickly. The German coal tar dye industry had now become one unit. The war gave the final impetus towards amalgamation, a term used for the trend towards concentration which had appeared in the coal mining industry of the Ruhr district already in the nineties of the last century. The loss of German deliveries in the war had had catastrophic effects on the textile and other industries all over the world. A further direct result of the shortage of supplies was not only the sequestration of plants which the German chemical industry had built in many other countries, but also the establishment of new plants by the national industries. Germany's position in the world markets had definitely changed. After the war the situation would be entirely different and one would have to be prepared for strong competition and be ready for it by concentrating one's powers.

The I. G. Farbenindustrie AG

Concentration was all the more indicated because the coal tar dye industry had during its financial expansion also considerably broadened its spheres of activity. The coal tar dye factories were no longer producing only dyes; they had branched out into other products covering many other fields. Hoechst is an example of this. Other chapters in this book describe the course of events and the scientific and technical achievements which characterize the tremendous, world-wide progress of chemistry. At Hoechst this expansion began in the eighties with the production of pharmaceuticals and later led into the fields of plant protective agents, fertilizers, synthetic fibres and plastic products. Even before the first world war these developments intensified the need for large-scale financing; the capital transactions which have been described for the years preceding that war were to a large extent necessitated by the broadening activities of the chemical industry, in this case Farbwerke Hoechst which played a leading role in this development.

Hoechst had managed to remain on an equal footing with the other big concerns. This became obvious during the next stage of integration, the total merger of all firms joined in the I. G. since 1916. The merger to form the I. G. Farbenindustrie was carried out in 1925, about one year after the final stabilization of the currency in the spring of 1924. There had been an intermediate stage based on the Rentenmark, and then the new currency unit, the Reichsmark, was established. After the currency reform, all joint-stock companies had to prepare an initial statement based on the gold mark. All assets had to be revalued, balanced against existing liabilities, and the capital restated. For Farbwerke Hoechst, the share capital came to 177.2 million gold marks, a figure also reached by BASF and Bayer. The three were therefore on an equal footing for the merger which followed one year later. They could prove to each other that they had, so to speak, marched in step and were quantitatively and qualitatively entitled to equal rights. The three big firms were very much in the lead among the firms which merged in 1925. Having a share capital of 177.2 million RM each, they were well ahead of the other three partners, AGFA with 58 million, Griesheim with 44.3 million and Weiler-ter Meer with 12.1 million. The merger produced a total share capital of 646 million RM. Officially the merger was carried out as follows: BASF increased its share capital to that amount, the shareholders of the other companies received new shares in exchange for their old certificates, whereupon BASF changed its name and moved its headquarters to Frankfurt a. M. Together with Vereinigte Stahlwerke AG. which was formed at the same time, I. G. Farbenindustrie AG. moved into the forefront of German industry. In the history of Farbwerke Hoechst, the merger which had produced the I. G. meant the end of a phase, the end of independence. No one could know at the time that this was in fact not an end but only a temporary break. About two decades later higher powers, the victors of the second world war, stepped in and broke up the I. G. into its old components. In view of the ensuing decartelization it seems justifiable to treat the I. G. Farbenindustrie AG. as only an interlude in the financial history of Farbwerke Hoechst. Another chapter in this book described the events which led up to decartelization, the process itself, and the re-establishment of Farbwerke Hoechst.

I. G. Farbenindustrie AG. was not able to pay the high dividends which Hoechst as an independent concern had at times been able to present to its shareholders. This was a reflection of the totally changed world situation as far as the chemical industry was concerned, which situation had been the underlying reason for the merger.

During its best periods, before the first world war, Hoechst had paid 30% dividends. From 1918 to the year of inflation, 1923, the dividend varied between 30 and 14 per cent. Only once, in 1924, when the currency was being stabilized, was it as low as 8 per cent.

I. G. Farbenindustrie AG. started with 10 per cent. After a temporary increase to 12 per cent, it had to be reduced to 7 per cent. A few years later the dividend was increased to 8 per cent. During the second world war a fixed interest of 6 per cent was paid, which was the standard rate laid down by the national socialist government. During the two decades of the I. G.'s existence, its working capital had more than doubled. During this time the profits paid to shareholders were roughly twice the starting capital — quite a contrast again to the figures from before the first world war. This change was merely the numerical expression of the difficulties encountered on the way back to normal relations on the international economic scene — the good old days of 1913 were over. If one considers only the dividends paid it might almost be concluded that after the second world war — not immediately after, but about ten years later — greater progress was made towards establishing normal conditions.

View of the Hoechst plant

After decartelization

Now as we come to the financial history of Farbwerke Hoechst after the second world war, we can limit our consideration to the period after 1952. In the spring of 1953 the intermediary period of decartelization came to an end and the works, grouped in so-called successor companies and in part newly constituted, were freed from Allied control. The events which took place between 1945, the time of the sequestration of I. G., and 1953 are fully described in another part of this book. That description takes us to the year 1952 and it is at this point that we resume our financial history, with just a brief mention of the final stage of decartelization. This is best described by telling what former I. G. shareholders received for their certificates: For 1000 mark I. G. shares they were given 285 DM Bayer shares, 250 DM BASF, 210 DM Farbwerke Hoechst, 25 DM Cassella and 60 DM Chemie-Verwaltungs AG. (which holds 50 per cent of the capital of Chemische Werke Hüls AG.) plus 50 RM Rheinstahl shares (resulting from the winding-up of the affairs of the I. G. and the Rheinische Stahl-werke). The shareholders also received a form of betterment certificate, a liquidation share which was partially redeemed, but it would take us too far to discuss this here. All in all, the new shares and possible further expectations resulted in an exchange rate of about 10 : 9. It must be remembered that the old I. G. Farbenindustrie AG. had lost more than half its property in East Germany and abroad; the 1953 exchange rate was made possible only through the use of hidden reserves.

The exchange rate of about 10 : 9 was a compromise between the point of view held by the shareholders' representatives (and probably also some of the banks) and that of the managements. The directors of the successor companies had been thinking of a 10 : 8 ratio, to keep the share capital low. In spite of the fairly high value put on the assets (to allow for depreciation and thus strengthen the power of capital reinvestment), a way was found to keep the share capital low, namely, by having large open reserves. The three main successor companies, Farbenfabriken Bayer AG, Badische Anilin- & Soda-Fabrik AG and Farbwerke Hoechst AG, together had a total balance of 2,250 million DM in their initial statements, with assets of about 1,600 million DM composed of 1,010 million DM capital and almost 600 million DM in statutory and free reserves. This was at the same time an indication that there were no, or at least only very minor, hidden reserves.

This conclusion of decartelization was an event of tremendous importance to the Germany money market. The old I. G. share had been the most active on the stock market and had been held by many sections of the public. When the Allies had banned dealings in I. G. shares in 1945, a very important sector of the stock market was paralysed. Then the shares of the successor companies appeared on the market instead and at one stroke the situation was reversed and legal dealings again became possible. This event meant very much a return to normal conditions and it was only now that the successor companies were again able to use the stock market to raise investment capital.

And so, from the ashes of war damage and severe interference from the occupation authorities, rose the phoenix of the new joint-stock company. The old tradition was resumed. The name of the firm, «Farbwerke Hoechst AG, vormals Meister Lucius & Brüning», was very little changed from what it had been before 1925 and on the whole the company was constituted much as it had been before the I. G. period. Apart from everything that stands and stood in and around Hoechst itself, the complex includes «Knapsack-Griesheim AG», «Kalle & Co. AG», «Behringwerke AG» und «Bobingen AG für Textil-Faser». The latter merged with Hoechst in 1954. The other three companies, factually the property of Hoechst, retained their formal independence until 1959, though they were linked to Hoechst through contracts which made them for all practical purposes the members of one single concern.

What have been the financial developments of Farbwerke Hoechst during the last decade before the hundredth anniversary? The table below will give the reader a general outline. It gives the figures for the whole concern (in million DM), covering the last 10 years.

This table gives the main data for the economic and technical progress made by the firm in that time. A study of the totals shows that between 1952 and 1961, capital investment amounted to about 2.400 million DM. Of this, 56 per cent came from depreciations, the rest chiefly from the money market.

This picture, which is only a very general one, does show that the widely held notion that industry can provide its own capital is quite untenable, in any case as far as Hoechst is concerned. The method of increasing the company's assets by not paying out some of the net profits in dividends and reinvesting this money, thus financing oneself in the real sense of the term, has played no important role in the transactions of Farbwerke Hoechst since the second world war. This will be seen indirectly from the relation of the dividend paid to the profits tax paid. If a joint-stock company retains and reinvests considerable parts of its profit, the tax figures will inevitably be very much higher than the total dividends. Examples could be quoted where the tax is two or three times the dividend paid, and there are extreme cases where the difference is

| | Turnover | | Invested | | Depreciation of plant | Longterm finance | | Dividend | Interest paid | Taxes*) | Wages etc.**) | No. of employees | Spent on research |
	total	export	plant	holdings		own	outside						
1952	762	169	92	2	57		39	12	3	58	197	26189	37
1953	943	276	83	1	65		76	20	7	,67	243	28389	55
1954	1127	338	136	6	73		114	23	11	82	271	32489	60
1955	1270	380	241	53	104	126	103	32	19	91	312	36135	69
1956	1482	448	242	24	129	84	64	42	25	105	327	39615	81
1957	1761	569	232	23	152	3	146	51	35	123	355	42739	89
1958	1889	586	248	54	158	12	148	65	47	127	403	43328	93
1959	2222	720	254	20	175	175	85	86	54	202	438	45363	100
1960	2703	884	422	62	209	227	25	107	54	240	529	50332	113
1961	2876	911	446	34	230	219	52	126	58	239	595	52162	120
1952 to 1961	17035	5281	2396	279	1352	846	852	564	313	1334	3670	—	817

* Income, Profits, Property, Sales, Corporation and other taxes
** Wages and Salaries, plus statutory and voluntary social payments

No. of share holders end of 1961	— 180,000 (including 12,000 employees)
Energy consumption 1961	— 4,200 million kwh
Turnover of goods 1961	— 7.1 million tons

even greater. As for Hoechst, the ratio of income, profits and property tax to dividends for this whole decade is about 4 : 3 (745 million DM to 564 million DM).

Dividend policies and the raising of capital

Farbwerke Hoechst is one of the best companies in the Federal Republic for paying dividends. In ten years the total distribution of profits has been approximately twice the nominal starting capital with which the reawakened company had begun its new life after decartelization.

It should also be remembered that Hoechst's financial policies have granted shareholders rights on several occasions. In 1955 and 1956 the capital was increased by a nominal 99.3 and 77 million DM; the issue prices were at 125 and 120 per·cent. 94 million DM shares were issued at 150 per cent in 1959, although the market price had in the meantime risen to over 400 per cent. In 1960 the capital was increased by 56.2 million DM and shares issued at 250 per cent, and it was only in 1961 that it was decided to issue at 300 per cent when another nominal increase of 63 million DM was made. In view of the general situation it was felt that the company must not be deprived of the chance to increase its reserves, and thus its own strength, by issuing the shares at the current favourable prices. The last shares in 1962 were issued at 275 per cent to increase the capital by a nominal 70 million DM.

Such figures express the good standing of the company's shares on the stock market. They are the fruit of a definite dividend policy. The circulation of capital in its traditional sense is restored — shareholders like to put their money into a concern which can promise them a good return.

The public and experts with a particular interest in this field have widely discussed the trends in issue prices for new shares. In these discussions shares issued by the so-called Farben successor companies have had more than their fair share. To begin with it was not sufficiently taken into consideration that general statements on issue prices are not really admissible because there has to be differentiation as to the purpose in increasing the capital. New shares are generally used to get new secured capital for capital investment. But under some circumstances new shares may be used for another purpose, namely to restore the balance where the nominal capital is not in the right proportion to the volume of business and the profits. In that case an issue at par is indicated and useful. Or an issue might be made free, a transaction which became possible from the tax point of view through the law governing capital increase from company funds which was passed on 23rd December 1959.

If it is a matter of asking shareholders to invest more money in the company for the purpose of business expansion, to finance further growth, the directors must first consider what interest can be offered on the new capital. No one will blame the board if they propose an issue price which lies between the nominal value of the new shares and the market price, i.e. the value put upon them in the stock market. If companies whose shares are high in the market were to issue at par, they would in effect be squandering reserves. This fact is often not fully appreciated by shareholders interested in a low issue price.

Incidentally, any debates based on an intellectually assumed conflict of interest between the shareholder and the company are pointless and without basis in fact.

There is in reality no such «natural» conflict of interest, for one may assume that in making its decisions the board considers not only the present position, but also the future earning power of the concern, which of course can more readily be evaluated by the directors than by the majority of shareholders. The joint-stock company is an organisation for the reproduction of capital. The directors of the «association» of shareholders are responsible for seeing that the capital of the «members of the association» bears interest and at the same time grows; by giving away reserves they would commit a breach of their most important duty. In some of the disputes over issue prices, in which, as we have said, the Farben successor companies and their policies have at times figured large, reference has quite rightly been made to the American practice. In the USA, companies issuing new shares will usually issue as near the market price as possible — in Germany one generally tends towards a middle course. Issue at par for the purpose of increasing capital has become rare, and so the right view has won after all. The administrators of Farbwerke Hoechst have made their contribution to this, in word and deed, with all capital increases since 1959.

It has also become normal practice to finance capital investment not only by issuing shares but also by taking up long-term loans. Hoechst has twice since 1952 issued debentures, in 1957 and 1958, on each occasion for 100 million DM. This method had probably been considered before, but until 1955 the market was blocked in this direction. Tax policies had given privileges to share issues which helped the state finances and the financing of social building programmes. The so-called law for the promotion of the market, which remained in force until 1954, made the interest on such shares tax free. It was in fact a discrimination against the capital needs of industry and served to maintain the interest structure. At any rate the industry was unable to enter the debenture market until 1955/56.

Since 1957 use has been made of the possibility of covering long-term capital requirements by taking up bonded loans. Industrial debentures are more costly than bonded loans, especially because they carry a $2^{1}/_{2}{}^{0}/_{0}$ capital transaction tax which can be avoided with promissory note loans.

A discourse on financing out of one's own capital

Between 1952 and 1961 Hoechst issued stock worth 1,034 million DM. As a result the balance sheets of the company were kept in good order and such that they would to a high degree correspond to the kind of accurate and careful financial management which a sound business man who has studied economics would appreciate. The assets (fixed assets and trade investments) were always fully covered by the company's own capital (share capital and open reserves) and long-term liabilities. At the same time it must be taken into account that the remaining liabilities probably include considerable sums which should not be regarded as short-term. It is therefore not surprising that with the large sums required for capital investment the book-values of assets and holdings could no longer be entirely covered by the firm's own capital.

If the money invested in fixed assets, the acquisition of trade investments and the strengthening of those interests is added together, the total invested since 1952 is approximately 1,400 million DM. About 2,700 million of this came from depreciations, and 1,300 million from the stock market.

At certain periods in the early history of the company, the means for financing its own development appear to have been considerable. It is reported that one of the first leading products, aldehyde green, fetched 15 Thalers a pound when production started in the 1860s. A year later the price had gone down to 4 Thalers. The old books also tell us that synthetic indigo started its great career in the mid-nineties at a selling price of 16 marks per kilogramme, but a few years later the price was only 7 marks. This shows three things:

Firstly, the starting prices must have brought considerable profit and left a wide profit margin for the further development of production, so that existing production programmes could be expanded, new lines developed, and even entirely new fields opened up. If later on the profit and loss accounts were not upset by proceeds which were less than half the prices originally charged, the early profit margin must have been quite a respectable one.

Secondly, these figures illustrate the intense competition which must have existed in the dye market, with strong rivals both at home and abroad. This competition was positively murderous at times and the German coal tar dye industry gave battle so heroically, if one may use such war-like terms, that at the turn of the century it provided almost nine tenths of the synthetic dyes sold in the world market — a spectacular victory, particularly over the much older British industry, and this when Germany had for decades been very much behind the British in economic development in general and industrial progress in particular.

Thirdly, if we interpret these figures in relation to the general development of the chemical industry, they give us a glimpse of the industry's chameleon-like nature. Here one must never stand still, never rest on one's laurels. Intense and almost obsessional scientific endeavour is forever striving for the latest trend — to use a term from the world of fashion —, everything is always in a state of flux. Whilst one production line is in full spate its profits must immediately be used to finance new activities, and when the market is good and these new products are doing well, part of the profits must again be used for further new developments.

When the first world war started, 70 per cent of the turnover at Hoechst was in dyes. In 1961, dyestuffs, textile auxiliaries and organic intermediary products amounted to only about 16 per cent. Instead, other fields had developed strongly — pharmaceuticals and plant protection agents, fertilizers, synthetic fibres and films, plastics, resins and many other products are very much part of the programme. In a never ending stream of events and decisions the newly developing, stagnating and finally perhaps even dying branches follow one upon the other; «panta rhei», that old Greek saying, appears here in a new guise, more tangibly and convincingly than in any other branch of industry. In the chemical industry, it is indeed a question of survival that financial management must allow for this essential process of continuous renewal. This can only be done by combining the different methods of financing in the best possible way, and Hoechst gives an example of this in its use of money from the firm's own resources plus funds obtained on the money market, always with a concern for keeping careful balance between profits paid out and profits retained.

Let us for a moment look ahead at the last years preceding the hundredth anniversary. The balanced policy of profit allocation has been such that the amount put back into the concern certainly does not appear to be exceptionally high in comparison to the usage and possibilities of other industries and of earlier days.

The percentages paid out show that Farbwerke Hoechst can no longer afford to be quite as liberal in its dividend policy as it was during the two decades before and after the turn of the century. Since 1960, however, dividends paid have annually reached nine figures and this is telling proof that the ploughing back of profits can no longer be as intensive as it was in the early years of the industry. In those days it was taken as a matter of course. Now suspicion is thrown upon it with pseudo-social arguments, in spite of the fact that quantitatively it now plays a very minor role. Strange indeed are the ways of public opinion.

Aims and results of the investment policy

Since 1952, capital investment has served three main purposes: the expansion and modernisation of existing production lines, the development of new products, and last but not least the reconstruction of the export trade. Among the leading new products are plastics and fibres and their starting products which are chiefly the result of developments in petrochemistry. This field permits us to draw something of a contrary parallel to developments during the first world war and immediately afterwards. When Germany dropped out of the world market at that time, its former customers started to produce their own dyes. Hoechst therefore could not expect that it would ever become as successful in the world market for dyes as it had been during the early years of the twentieth century. After the second world war the situation was in some ways the reverse. Just before and during the period when Germany was again cut off from the world market, the American chemical industry had made tremendous progress in the field of petrochemistry. The German chemical industry therefore had to make great efforts to catch up with the Americans in this field. Many thousands of million DM invested by Hoechst reflect the determination of German chemistry to «catch up» to the others. As for export business in general, reentry into the international markets after 1952 has been successful beyond expectation. In 1952 Hoechst exported around 170 million DM worth of goods (then 22 per cent of the total turnover). By 1961, the total income from exports had increased to 911 million DM, almost a third of the total turnover. After the first world war, attempts at a return to normal were frustrated after a few years by the world-wide financial crisis of the late twenties which intensified in the early thirties. The development of these last ten years has been the result of a successful capital investment policy and sound financial management. A discussion of the social significance of capital investments also belongs in this chapter. At Hoechst, this is brought out very clearly by a comparison of the figures for 1952 to 1961 which are illustrated in the graph on the next page.

The divergence of the lines is very striking: Number of man-hours worked down by 11 per cent, wages per hour up 102 per cent, turnover per man up 90 per cent. Less labour yet higher production — how? Through increased capital investment. In 1952 the capital employed per man was approximately 28,000 DM. By 1961 this had risen to 59,000 DM. Rationalization, technical progress, can only be achieved through capital investment. Wages and salaries have risen accordingly, because the machine is increasing man's productivity. Here we have a concrete example of the combined effect of capital, labour and management: the worker's standard of living is rising because in «his» firm more capital is employed.

If the employees know this, their relations with the firm are very much strengthened. But there are also other ways of doing much in this respect, for instance by issuing worker's shares. This factor in the financial history of Hoechst must not be omitted. After the minor reform in the laws governing the operation of joint-stock companies, it became possible to issue worker's shares to the firm's employees which carried tax advantages. In the summer of 1960 this opportunity was first made available to the staff. Every employee was entitled to take up two shares at a nominal value of 100 DM each, issued at 250 per cent. The money saved on the issue price was free from income tax as long as those who bought the shares undertook not to sell them for a period of five years. Those who did not wish to benefit from the saving in income tax had to promise that they would not sell these shares before 1st January 1962. About 12,000 employees — 29⁰/o of those entitled to — made use of this opportunity to become shareholders in their own company. Of these, 30 per cent are wage earners, 70 per cent are salaried. The staff had thus subscribed for a total of 2.4 million DM Hoechst shares. More shares were bought by the older age group of employees than by the younger. Those who had been with the firm longer bought more, as was to be expected. It is worth mentioning that among those who had been with Hoechst for over 25 years, 42 per cent made use of the offer. The cost to the company, mainly the difference between the market price and the issue price of those shares, was 9.7 million DM.

Size does not mean «power»

Today, on the list of the big companies of the Federal Republic, Hoechst holds eleventh place among those whose turnover amounts to thousands of million DM. In the size of its share capital Hoechst ranks third. The list includes not only old established industries like iron and coal, but also some of the youngest branches like the automobile industry and the newest electrotechnical concerns. The chemical industry and the traditional sectors of the electrical industry hold a rather middle position between « young » and « old ». The big concerns in these two fields are not « young » in the sense that they did not even exist in the last century, but the great chemical and electrical concerns achieved their present significance within the whole industrial picture only fifty or sixty years ago. They may also be considered parallel because both, the chemical and electrical industries, cannot really age, since they are constantly faced with new tasks. This continuous renewal and rebirth from within is probably the underlying reason why the big chemical concerns are now playing such an important role.

Research and development on which Farbwerke Hoechst have spent a total of 817 million DM since 1952 — at least 4 per cent of the turnover for each year — can be undertaken only by financially strong concerns, by firms which can afford to spend millions a year on projects at a stage when it is quite impossible to say whether they will in the end pay. This in itself is justification enough for the existence of big industrial concerns, quite apart from the fact that mass production, which is and must be carried out in all branches of the chemical industry, can be done rationally only in big organisations. Technically, chemical production involves interrelated main and side products; here also a large-scale enterprise is both desirable and imperative.

In the author's opinion these facts made concentration inevitable, not only in the sense of quantitative growth, which is not really concentration, but also of «amalgamation», i.e. the merging, in aims, organisation and finances, of concerns which had been less successful operating in the new fields with their more inventive, go-ahead competitors. Such inventive firms become the crystallizing centres for concentration. Public opinion often has a tendency to disparage these crystallizing centres, to denigrate them and expose what is taken to be an economic power complex. Against this there is the simple truth that the growth, size and concentration of the industry is the result of competition. One cannot on one side uphold freedom of competition as part of one's political creed and on the other decry and avoid the results of competition. This lack of logic is the really weak spot in modern competitive policy as one of the most important factors in the whole political economy.

Twentieth century economics without big firms and organisations has in fact become inconceivable. It is entirely wrong to accuse these big concerns of striving for power. They developed through the need for technical and economic rationalization. They grew big because they did better in competition and served the consumer better than their rivals. Greatness in industry is the reward for performance. The customer is not forced to buy, but he wants to be served. It is up to him to choose his supplier, and he goes to the one who serves him best — now where does this involve power? Where, however, one could theoretically speak of «power» i.e. where one man alone owns one of the very big concerns, the history of economics has shown that such a theoretical proposition cannot stand: As a rule the very big firms are quite unable to exist as private property. They are only conceivable as the common property of many, as companies. This division of property automatically dissolves power.

Anyone who knows practical economics can only wonder why such simple factual relations are so seldom seen clearly and why there are so many serious misunderstandings — like those which find expression in the disputes over so-called concentration and sometimes over the question of the big combines. In the chemical industry we have here a particularly good example which confutes the critics of concentration. Why did Farb-werke Hoechst grow so big? How did they and the other two big complexes in this branch of industry achieve their leading position? Many other enterprises started during the last century with the same chances in the same fields. To paraphrase the Bible, one might say: Many felt called, but only few passed the test of the chosen — in the course of time, stringent selection left only the most capable. Those became the giants which now, in their present structure, attract the attention of public opinion — which pays no heed to historical development and contibutive factors. But these are things which may not be ignored, and no effort should be spared in endeavouring to enlighten public opinion on these matters. This has become yet another task for the modern industrial giants.